Edexcel GCSE

Design and Technology

Food Technology

Student Book

Anna Woodman
Sue Manser

A PEARSON COMPANY

Acknowledgements

Published by Pearson Education Limited, a company incorporated in England and Wales, having its registered office at Edinburgh Gate, Harlow, Essex, CM20 2JE. Registered company number: 872828

Edexcel is a registered trademark of Edexcel Limited

First published 2010

12 11 10
10 9 8 7 6 5 4 3 2 1

British Library Cataloguing in Publication Data
A catalogue record for this book is available from the British Library.

ISBN 978 1 846907 53 1

Edited by Kim Vernon
Designed by Juice Ltd
Original illustrations © Pearson Education Limited 2010
Illustrated by Juice Ltd
Printed and bound in the UK by Scotprint

Acknowledgements
The author and publisher would like to thank the following individuals and organisations for permission to reproduce photographs:

(Key: b-bottom; c-centre; l-left; r-right; t-top)

Alamy Images: 2010StockVS 95/4, Bon Appetit 48/4, GONDWANA PHOTO ART 130, Olaf Doering 97, 134/4, Food Features 117, HolgerBurmeister 37/2, mediablitzimages (uk) Limited 115, 144, mediablitzimages (uk) Limited 115, 144, Steven May 127, Nikreates 72/2, Oramstock 50, razorpix 102, Alex Segre 31, studiomode 48/3, Art Directors & TRIP 14, Libby Welch 115/2; **Corbis**: Monty Rakusen / cultura 73/2, Michael Rosenfeld / Science Faction 96/3, James Leynse 122, Gideon Mendel 30; **DK Images**: Andy Crawford 10/2, Steve Gorton 13/2, Ian O'Leary 86/3; **Getty Images**: Lisa Romerein / The Image Bank 112, Jean-Marc Giboux 15, Michael Rosenfeld 116, Ariel Skelley 107; **iStockphoto**: A-Digit 20-21, 10, 13/3, 13/4, 14/3, 24/3, 37, 45/3, 45/15, 51/3, 52, 55, 57, 63, 67, 68/4, 79/6, 81, 81/3, 84, 85/2, 87/3, 90, 90/2, 98, 106, 108, 124, 137, 149/2, 155/2, 159/2, 161, can akat 119, Luis Albuquerque 13, Scott Anderson 47/4, Dale Berman 158, Siniša Botaš 47/2, Anthony Boulton 58, 84/4, stuart burford 98/2, Gary Buttle 46, Doug Cannell 155/3, 159/3, Florea Marius Catalin 45/4, Jill Chen 101/2, davide chiarito 86, Kelly Cline 47, 148, Kelly Cline 47, 148, Alessio Cola 45/14, Paula Connelly 85, craftvision 81/2, Karl Dolenc 62/2, 68/5, Alexey Dudoladov 80, murat $en 134, enviromantic 35, Donald Erickson 79/3, Felipex 51, foodandwinephotography 57/2, FotografiaBasica 99/2, Eric Gevaert 167/2, Joe Gough 84/2, 122/2, 143, 144/2, 144/3, 153, Joe Gough 84/2, 122/2, 143, 144/2, 144/3, 153, Joe Gough 84/2, 122/2, 143, 144/2, 144/3, 153, Joe Gough 84/2, 122/2, 143, 144/2, 144/3, 153, Shelly Greer 58/2, Izabela Habur 87, Tom Hahn 36, 56, nicolas hansen 79/2, Steve Harmon 47/3, Birgit Reitz-Hofmann 101/3, Auke Holwerda 99, Justin Horrocks 45/6, Juha Huiskonen 78/2, Waltraud Ingerl 136, Marko Jamnik 163, Daria Kiseleva 81/4, Viktor Kitaykin 45/2, Viacheslav Krisanov 79, Olivier Lantzendörffer 24, Chris Leachman 79/4, Ye Liew 45/9, Dr. Heinz Linke 133, Sean Locke 84/3, Daniel Loiselle 157, 161/2, Vladimir Melnik 54/2, Minko Mihaylov 24/2, Vasko Miokovic 136/2, karam miri 137/2, Greg Nicholas 155/4, Sandra O'Claire 87/2, Regina Catharina Fernandi Paassen 54, John Peacock 30/2, Barbara Pheby 101, RedHelga 45/8, 45/16, RedHelga 45/8, 45/16, Celso Pupo Rodrigues 14/2, 62, Henryk Sadura 86/2, Pradeep Kumar Saxena 85/3, 133/3, Elena Schweitzer 22, Anna Sedneva 45/12, Andrea Skjold 57/3, Denis Sokolov 45/10, Irek Soloniewicz 25, Tarek El Sombati 35/2, Alexey Stiop 66, 122/3, StockStudios 43, Morgan Lane Studio 9, 16, 52/2, Alasdair Thomson 45/7, 51/2, 68/2, Alasdair Thomson 45/7, 51/2, 68/2, Kheng Guan Toh 109, 132, 157/2, 158/2, Kheng Guan Toh 109, 132, 157/2, 158/2, Kheng Ho Toh 102/4, Valentyn Volkov 45, Duncan Walker 48, Dave White 79/5, James Whittaker 95, 134/5, James Whittaker 95, 134/5, darren wise 145, Yasonya 45/11, YinYang 45/5, 45/13, YinYang 45/5, 45/13, Bridget Zawitoski 42, ZeNeece 48/2, Dušan Zidar 116/2, 163/2, ZoneCreative 34; **Paul Martin**: 29, 48/5, 70, 74, 81/5, 99/3, 101/4, 101/5, 101/6, 102/3, 128, 133/2; **Katharine Oakes**: 129; **Photolibrary.com**: JOFF LEE / Fresh Food Images 149, F1 Online 95/3, 134/3; **Shutterstock**: 64/3, 68/3, 71, 72, 73, 78, 79/7, 102/2, 103, 134/2, Anthony Berenyi 68, Yehuda Boltshauser 96/2, Gregory Gerber 41, Kris Jacobs 22/2, Alexander Kalina 64, Timothy Large 75, 75/2, Timothy Large 75, 75/2, Luis Santos 78/3, Elena Schweitzer 64/2, Mark Yuill 95/2, 96, 135, Mark Yuill 95/2, 96, 135; **Thinkstock**: 155, 159, Goodshoot 178/2, Hemera Technologies / Getty Images 167, Brand X Pictures 178, 180, Brand X Pictures 178, 180, Stockxpert 178/3, 183, Stockxpert 178/3, 183; **Anna Woodman**: 154, 154/2, 154/3, 155/5, 155/6, 155/7, 163/3, 163/4, 165, 167/3, 173, 175, 175/2, 175/3, 175/4, 175/5, 175/6, 177

All other images © Pearson Education

We are grateful to the following for permission to reproduce copyright material:

Logos
Logo on page 29 copyright Coeliac, from www.coeliac.org.uk; Logo on page 26 copyright Vegetarian Society, from www.vegsoc.org; Logo on page 28 copyright British Heart Foundation, from www.bhf.org.uk; Logo on page 41 copyright Assured Food Standards, from www.redtractor.org.uk; Logo on page 42 copyright Marine Stewardship Council, from www.msc.org; Logo on page 121 used with kind permission of the RSPCA, a charity registered in England & Wales, no. 219099, from http://www.rspcagoodbusinessawards.com; Logo on page 129 copyright Traidcraft, from www.traidcraft.co.uk; Logo on page 129 copyright Soil Association, from www.soilassociation.org; Logo on page 129 the FAIRTRADE Mark is reproduced with kind permission of the Fairtrade Foundation and FLO International

Screenshots
Screenshot on page 167 copyright Edexcel Ltd, from http://www.edexcel.com/migrationdocuments/GCSE%20New%20GCSE/SAM-D-T-5FT02-01-collated.pdf; Screenshot on page 144 copyright Edexcel Ltd, from http://www.edexcel.com/migrationdocuments/GCSE%20New%20GCSE/Edexcel%20GCSE%202009%20Design%20and%20Technology%20-%20Food%20Technology%20-%20SAM.pdf;

Screenshot on page 94 copyright Edexcel Ltd, from Edexcel GCSE Design and Technology: Food Technology (Full course - 1970) Paper 2F Foundation Tier 1970/2F; Screenshot on page 87 copyright Lakeland, from http://www.lakeland.co.uk/burger-maker/F/product/2647_3413; Screenshot on page 98 Crown copyright, from http://www.food.gov.uk/multimedia/pdfs/guidance.pdf; Screenshot on page 115, from http://www.benecol.co.uk/ccp/cms/html/benecol-uk/home, (c) Benecol, McNeil Nutritionals - Johnson & Johnson; Screenshot on page 115 copyright Unilever, from www.unilever.co.uk/brands/foodbrands/Flora; Screenshot on page 123 copyright Premier Foods, Mr Kipling, from http://www.premierfoods.co.uk/our-brands/grocery/mr-kipling/

With final thanks to Lavington School pupils for creating the selection of dishes for exemplar work featured in chapter 6.

Every effort has been made to trace the copyright holders and we apologise in advance for any unintentional omissions. We would be pleased to insert the appropriate acknowledgement in any subsequent edition of this publication that would enable us to do so.

The websites used in this book were correct and up to date at the time of publication. It is essential for tutors to preview each website before using it in class so as to ensure that the URL is still accurate, relevant and appropriate. We suggest that tutors bookmark useful websites and consider enabling students to access them through the school/college intranet.

Contents: delivering the EDEXCEL GCSE Design and Technology Specification Units 1–2

About this book

Objectives provide a **clear overview** of what you will learn in the section.

Engaging photos bring Food Technology to life.

Key terms are highlighted in the text and summarised at the end of the book to enable you to develop your understanding of Food Technology terminology.

Chapter 1: Nutrition

Fats

Objectives

- **Describe** the functions of saturated and unsaturated fats
- **Understand** the dietary sources of different types of fat

ResultsPlus
Watch out!

You need to know the difference between saturated and unsaturated fats and their effects on the body.

```
   H   H   H   H   H   H
   |   |   |   |   |   |
H— C — C — C — C — C — C — COOH
   |   |   |   |   |   |
   H   H   H   H   H   H
```

Diagram of saturated fat

```
   H   H   H   H   H   H
   |   |   |   |   |   |
H— C — C — C = C — C — C — COOH
   |   |           |   |
   H   H           H   H
```

Diagram of unsaturated fat

Sources of monounsaturated fat

Sources of polyunsaturated fat

The composition of fats

Lipid is a term used for fats and oils. Fats are solid at room temperature, while oils are liquid at room temperature. Fats are a macronutrient, important for health and wellbeing.

Fats are made up of the chemical elements carbon, hydrogen and oxygen. These elements combine to make fatty acids and glycerol. Fatty acids may be saturated or unsaturated, according to the way in which their carbon and hydrogen atoms are arranged. Three fatty acids and one unit of glycerol make a triglyceride.

In saturated fats, all the carbon atoms are saturated with hydrogen atoms.

In unsaturated fats, some carbon atoms are joined to other carbon atoms by a double bond in the molecule, and so are not completely saturated by hydrogen atoms.

Saturated fats

Saturated fats are solid at room temperature. They are mainly found in foods that originate from animals, although palm and coconut oils also contain high levels of saturated fat.

Foods high in saturated fat contain high levels of cholesterol, a natural fat manufactured in the liver and transported by the blood around the body. Foods containing animal fat contain some cholesterol.

Saturated fats are unhealthy because they can cause the build up of fatty deposits in and around major organs, leading to coronary heart disease (CHD), obesity and high blood pressure.

Trans fatty acids are produced when manufacturers add hydrogen to vegetable oils using a process called hydrogenation. This allows the fat to change from a liquid to a solid state, changing unsaturated fats to saturated fats. This improves the texture, storage life and working characteristics of the fat, as it can be used for spreading and baking.

Unsaturated fats

Unsaturated fats are found in a range of foods originating from plants and oily fish. There are two types of unsaturated fat.

- Monounsaturated fats are soft at room temperature. Research has found that they are healthier for you, by potentially lowering blood cholesterol and reducing the risk of cancer and diabetes. Monounsaturated fats contain only one pair of carbon atoms with one hydrogen atom.
- Polyunsaturated fats are liquid or very soft at room temperature. They contain two or more pairs of carbon atoms, and are therefore capable of holding more hydrogen atoms.

Essential fatty acids (EFA) cannot be made in the body, but are vital for the health and function of the body.

- Omega 3 EFA helps to protect the heart and is found in oily fish, seeds and green leafy vegetables.
- Omega 6 EFA helps to lower blood cholesterol and is found in vegetables, grains, seeds and poultry.

Nutritionists encourage people to eat less saturated fat and trans fat as these have been linked to high blood cholesterol levels, coronary heart disease, obesity and diabetes.

Dietary functions of fat

Fat in the diet:

- provides energy
- forms an insulating layer under the skin
- protects and surrounds vital organs in the body
- is a source of the fat-soluble Vitamins A, D, E and K
- provides texture and flavour to foods
- promotes a feeling of satiety (fullness).

Sources of fat

Fats come from both animal and plant sources. Animal sources include meat, lard, suet, dairy products and oily fish. Plant sources include nuts, pulses, seeds and some fruits (e.g. avocado and olives).

Many manufactured foods contain high levels of fat. It is important that you understand the source and function of fat in your diet, to allow you to make the right choice when choosing, designing or making foods. Many manufacturers are trying to reduce the amount of saturated fat and trans fat in commercial products, and labelling their products accordingly. This allows you to make an informed decision about the fat content of foods.

Function of fats in food preparation

Fat is used in food preparation for:

- spreading on bread
- creaming fat and sugar together to trap air in cakes
- adding colour and flavour to baked products and sauces
- shortening properties for pastries and doughs, used to create a tender, flaky texture
- cooking foods using deep or shallow frying, due to the high boiling point of fats
- oiling baking tins
- creating emulsions, such as salad dressing and mayonnaise.

Support Activity

Investigate the fat content of a range of manufactured foods available in supermarkets. Record your findings in a table like this:

Manufactured food product	Fat content per 100g	Ingredients containing fat

Stretch Activity

1. Discuss the difference between saturated and unsaturated fats.
2. Evaluate the use of hydrogenated fats in the manufacture of foods.

Apply it!

In your Design and Make activities, analyse the different types of fat in your products and comment on their health implications.

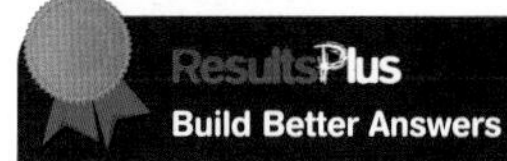

Give three reasons for using fat in a pastry recipe. (3 marks)

■ **Basic answers (0–1 marks)**
At this level, answers gave one or no reasons.

● **Good answers (2 marks)**
At this level, answers gave two reasons.

▲ **Excellent answers (3 marks)**
At this level, answers gave three reasons. For example:

1. To shorten pastry to create a crisp texture.
2. To add colour.
3. To add flavour.

Stretch and support activities provide extra support to ensure understanding and opportunities to stretch your knowledge.

Apply it activities bring your learning into the practical context of your controlled assessment, encouraging you to apply your knowledge to your own products.

ResultsPlus features combine real exam performance data with examiner insight to give **guidance on how to achieve better results**.

A dedicated suite of revision resources for **complete exam success**.

We've broken down the six stages of revision to ensure that you are prepared every step of the way.

Zone in: How to get into the perfect 'zone' for your revision.

Planning zone: Tips and advice on how to effectively plan your revision.

Know zone: All the facts you need to know and exam-style practice at the end of every chapter.

Chapter overview: Outlines the key issue that the chapter examines. Keep this issue in mind as you work through the Know Zone pages.

Key terms: A matching exercise to ensure that you can **understand and apply important food terminology**.

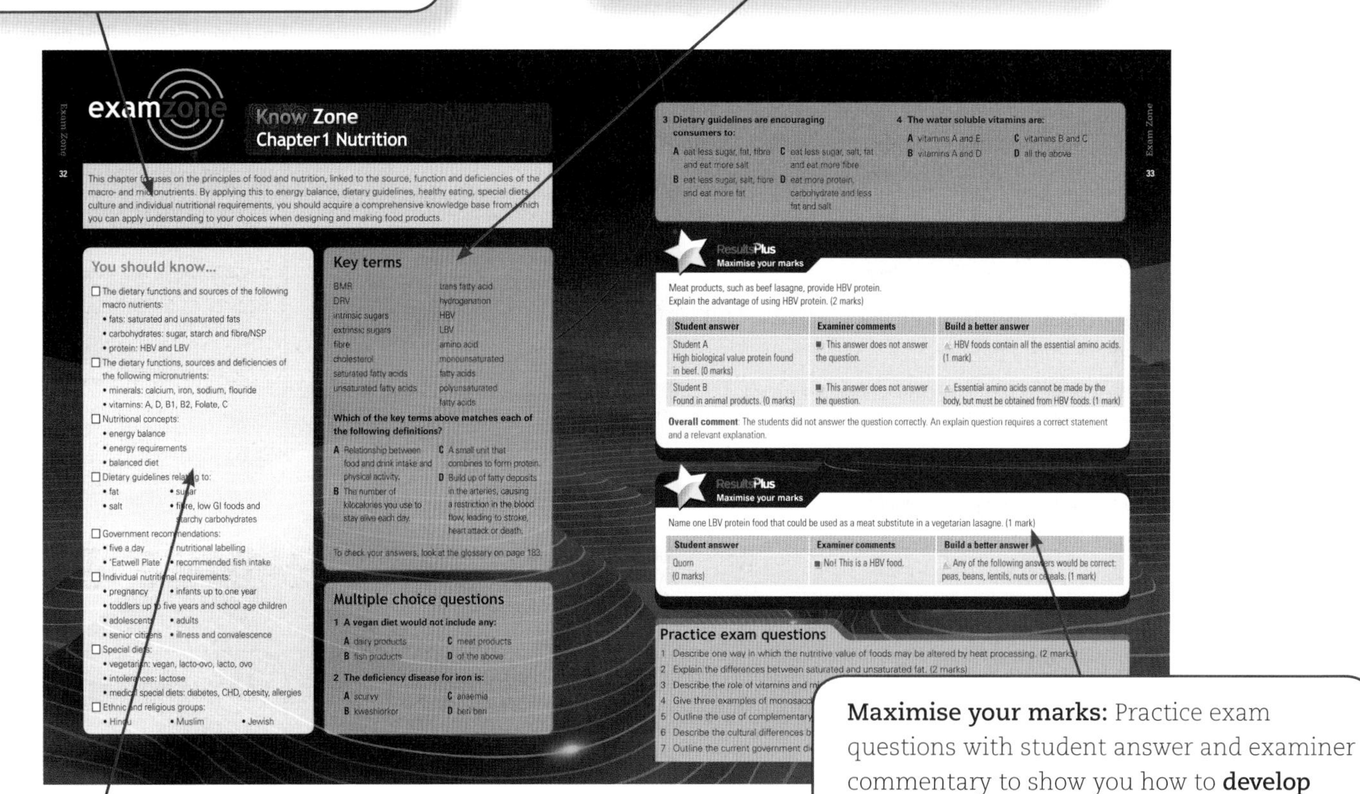

Exam Zone 32

examzone

Know Zone
Chapter 1 Nutrition

This chapter focuses on the principles of food and nutrition, linked to the source, function and deficiencies of the macro- and micronutrients. By applying this to energy balance, dietary guidelines, healthy eating, special diets, culture and individual nutritional requirements, you should acquire a comprehensive knowledge base from which you can apply understanding to your choices when designing and making food products.

You should know...

- ☐ The dietary functions and sources of the following macro nutrients:
  - fats: saturated and unsaturated fats
  - carbohydrates: sugar, starch and fibre/NSP
  - protein: HBV and LBV
- ☐ The dietary functions, sources and deficiencies of the following micronutrients:
  - minerals: calcium, iron, sodium, flouride
  - vitamins: A, D, B1, B2, Folate, C
- ☐ Nutritional concepts:
  - energy balance
  - energy requirements
  - balanced diet
- ☐ Dietary guidelines relating to:
  - fat
  - sugar
  - salt
  - fibre, low GI foods and starchy carbohydrates
- ☐ Government recommendations:
  - five a day
  - nutritional labelling
  - 'Eatwell Plate'
  - recommended fish intake
- ☐ Individual nutritional requirements:
  - pregnancy
  - infants up to one year
  - toddlers up to five years and school age children
  - adolescents
  - adults
  - senior citizens
  - illness and convalescence
- ☐ Special diets:
  - vegetarian: vegan, lacto-ovo, lacto, ovo
  - intolerances: lactose
  - medical special diets: diabetes, CHD, obesity, allergies
- ☐ Ethnic and religious groups:
  - Hindu
  - Muslim
  - Jewish

Key terms

BMR	trans fatty acid
DRV	hydrogenation
intrinsic sugars	HBV
extrinsic sugars	LBV
fibre	amino acid
cholesterol	monounsaturated
saturated fatty acids	fatty acids
unsaturated fatty acids	polyunsaturated fatty acids

Which of the key terms above matches each of the following definitions?

A Relationship between food and drink intake and physical activity.
B The number of kilocalories you use to stay alive each day.
C A small unit that combines to form protein.
D Build up of fatty deposits in the arteries, causing a restriction in the blood flow, leading to stroke, heart attack or death.

To check your answers, look at the glossary on page 183.

Multiple choice questions

1 A vegan diet would not include any:
A dairy products **B** fish products **C** meat products **D** of the above

2 The deficiency disease for iron is:
A scurvy **B** kweshiorkor **C** anaemia **D** beri beri

3 Dietary guidelines are encouraging consumers to:
A eat less sugar, fat, fibre and eat more salt
B eat less sugar, salt, fibre and eat more fat
C eat less sugar, salt, fat and eat more fibre
D eat more protein, carbohydrate and less fat and salt

4 The water soluble vitamins are:
A vitamins A and E **B** vitamins A and D **C** vitamins B and C **D** all the above

ResultsPlus
Maximise your marks

Meat products, such as beef lasagne, provide HBV protein.
Explain the advantage of using HBV protein. (2 marks)

Student answer	Examiner comments	Build a better answer
Student A High biological value protein found in beef. (0 marks)	■ This answer does not answer the question.	▲ HBV foods contain all the essential amino acids. (1 mark)
Student B Found in animal products. (0 marks)	■ This answer does not answer the question.	▲ Essential amino acids cannot be made by the body, but must be obtained from HBV foods. (1 mark)

Overall comment: The students did not answer the question correctly. An explain question requires a correct statement and a relevant explanation.

ResultsPlus
Maximise your marks

Name one LBV protein food that could be used as a meat substitute in a vegetarian lasagne. (1 mark)

Student answer	Examiner comments	Build a better answer
Quorn (0 marks)	■ No! This is a HBV food.	▲ Any of the following answers would be correct: peas, beans, lentils, nuts or cereals. (1 mark)

Practice exam questions

1 Describe one way in which the nutritive value of foods may be altered by heat processing. (2 marks)
2 Explain the differences between saturated and unsaturated fat. (2 marks)
3 Describe the role of vitamins and mi
4 Give three examples of monosacc
5 Outline the use of complementary
6 Describe the cultural differences b
7 Outline the current government di

33 Exam Zone

Maximise your marks: Practice exam questions with student answer and examiner commentary to show you how to **develop stronger answers** (see next page).

You should know: A check-yourself list of the concepts and facts that you should know before you sit the exam. Use this list to **identify your strengths and weaknesses** so you can plan your revision wisely.

Don't panic zone: Last-minute revision tips for just before the exam.

Exam zone: Some exam-style questions for you to try, an explanation of the assessment objectives, plus a chance to see what a real exam paper might look like.

Zone out: What do you do after your exam? This section contains information on how to get your results and answers to frequently asked questions on what to do next.

ResultsPlus

These features are based on the actual marks that students have achieved in past exams. They are combined with expert advice and guidance from examiners to show you **how to achieve better results**.

There are four different types of ResultsPlus feature throughout this book:

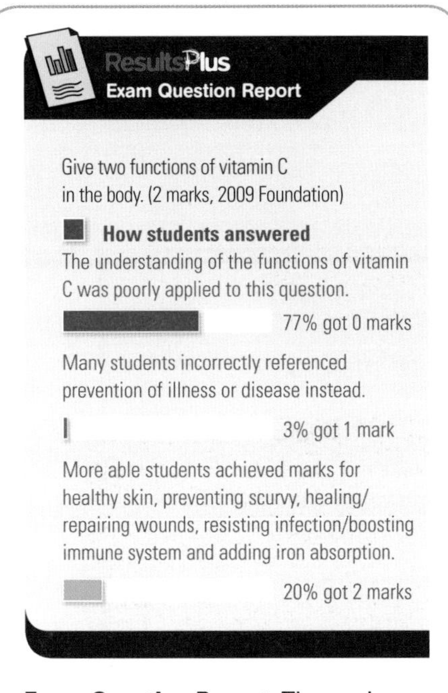

ResultsPlus
Exam Question Report

Give two functions of vitamin C in the body. (2 marks, 2009 Foundation)

■ **How students answered**

The understanding of the functions of vitamin C was poorly applied to this question.

77% got 0 marks

Many students incorrectly referenced prevention of illness or disease instead.

3% got 1 mark

More able students achieved marks for healthy skin, preventing scurvy, healing/repairing wounds, resisting infection/boosting immune system and adding iron absorption.

20% got 2 marks

Exam Question Report These show previous exam questions with details about how well students answered them.

- Red shows the number of students who scored low marks (less than 35% of the total marks)
- Orange shows the number of students who did okay (scoring between 35% and 70% of the total marks)
- Green shows the number of students who did well (scoring over 70% of the total marks).

They explain how students could have achieved the top marks so that you can make sure that you answer these questions correctly in future.

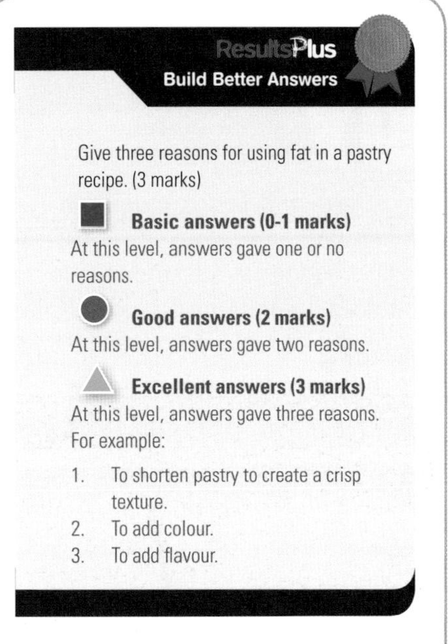

ResultsPlus
Build Better Answers

Give three reasons for using fat in a pastry recipe. (3 marks)

■ **Basic answers (0-1 marks)**
At this level, answers gave one or no reasons.

● **Good answers (2 marks)**
At this level, answers gave two reasons.

▲ **Excellent answers (3 marks)**
At this level, answers gave three reasons. For example:

1. To shorten pastry to create a crisp texture.
2. To add colour.
3. To add flavour.

Build Better Answers These give you an opportunity to answer some exam-style questions. They contain tips for what a basic ■, good ● and excellent ▲ answer will contain.

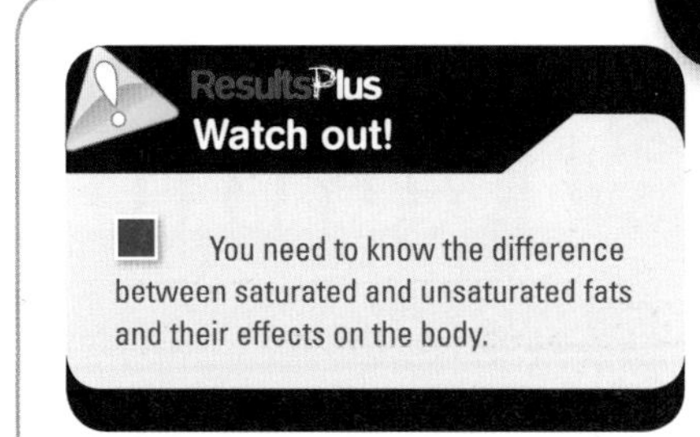

ResultsPlus
Watch out!

■ You need to know the difference between saturated and unsaturated fats and their effects on the body.

Watch out! These warn you about common mistakes and misconceptions that examiners frequently see students make. Make sure that you don't repeat them! The ■, ● and ▲ symbols highlight the severity of the error.

Maximise your marks These are featured in the Know Zone pages at the end of each chapter. They include an exam-style question with a student answer, examiner comments and an improved answer so that you can see how to build a better response.

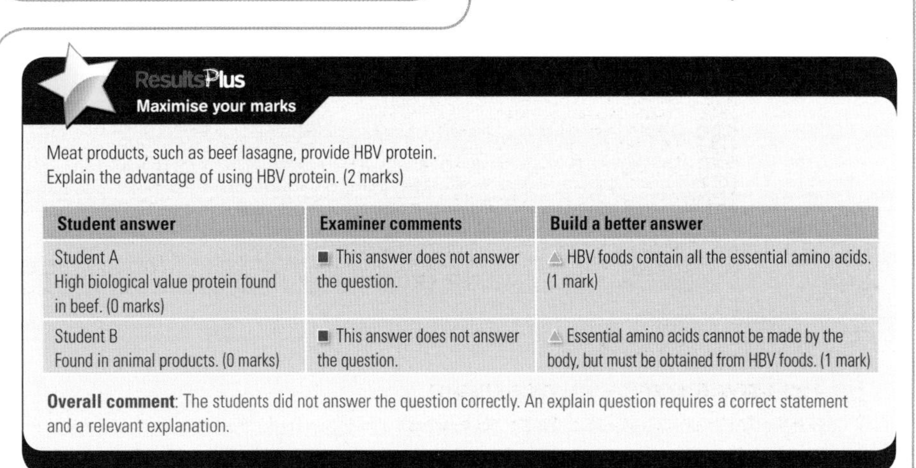

ResultsPlus
Maximise your marks

Meat products, such as beef lasagne, provide HBV protein.
Explain the advantage of using HBV protein. (2 marks)

Student answer	Examiner comments	Build a better answer
Student A High biological value protein found in beef. (0 marks)	■ This answer does not answer the question.	▲ HBV foods contain all the essential amino acids. (1 mark)
Student B Found in animal products. (0 marks)	■ This answer does not answer the question.	▲ Essential amino acids cannot be made by the body, but must be obtained from HBV foods. (1 mark)

Overall comment: The students did not answer the question correctly. An explain question requires a correct statement and a relevant explanation.

Knowledge and understanding of Food Technology

This unit focuses on the development of knowledge, understanding and skills for a wide range of ingredients, components and materials. It does this through a range of practical and theoretical activities using **primary and secondary foods**, allowing you to understand how their working characteristics can be used to create new and existing recipes and food products.

Food preparation, **processing and preservation** topics focus on the equipment, skills, techniques and processes used within home, school and industry contexts. The topics give you the opportunity to apply your design decisions to their selection and use, whilst considering health and safety implications, when designing and making food products.

The importance of **nutrition** and current health issues are explored in detail, together with technological developments within the food industry to give you scope for **product analysis**, innovative development and **product manufacture** work within your food technology course.

Topics:
- Chapter 1: Nutrition
- Chapter 2: Primary and secondary foods
- Chapter 3: Preservation and processing
- Chapter 4: Product manufacture
- Chapter 5: Analysing products

Your assessment

The exam is based on a structured exam paper that is worth 40% of the final GCSE grade. The 90 minute exam is worth a total of 80 marks and contains the following different types of questions:
- multiple choice
- short answer
- design questions
- product analysis
- extended writing.

Tips for success in the exam
- Remember to always read the question carefully before responding.
- Check how many marks are awarded for the question. This will give you a good indication of the level of detail needed in the answer or the number of points that need to be raised in order to gain maximum marks.
- Check your spelling, punctuation, grammar and use of subject specific terminology. Questions with a * will be marked based on the quality of written communication (*QWC).
- Check the 'command' word at the beginning of the question. This will help you to identify what you need to do in order to gain the marks. See the Examzone section (page 182) for more guidance.

Chapter 1: Nutrition

Fats

Objectives

- **Describe** the functions of saturated and unsaturated fats
- **Understand** the dietary sources of different types of fat

ResultsPlus
Watch out!

You need to know the difference between saturated and unsaturated fats and their effects on the body.

The composition of fats

Lipid is a term used for fats and oils. Fats are solid at room temperature, while oils are liquid at room temperature. Fats are a macronutrient, important for health and wellbeing.

Fats are made up of the chemical elements carbon, hydrogen and oxygen. These elements combine to make fatty acids and glycerol. Fatty acids may be saturated or unsaturated, according to the way in which their carbon and hydrogen atoms are arranged. Three fatty acids and one unit of glycerol make a triglyceride.

In saturated fats, all the carbon atoms are saturated with hydrogen atoms.

In unsaturated fats, some carbon atoms are joined to other carbon atoms by a double bond in the molecule, and so are not completely saturated by hydrogen atoms.

Saturated fats

Saturated fats are solid at room temperature. They are mainly found in foods that originate from animals, although palm and coconut oils also contain high levels of saturated fat.

Foods high in saturated fat contain high levels of cholesterol, a natural fat manufactured in the liver and transported by the blood around the body. Foods containing animal fat contain some cholesterol.

Saturated fats are unhealthy because they can cause the build up of fatty deposits in and around major organs, leading to coronary heart disease (CHD), obesity and high blood pressure.

Trans fatty acids are produced when manufacturers add hydrogen to vegetable oils using a process called hydrogenation. This allows the fat to change from a liquid to a solid state, changing unsaturated fats to saturated fats. This improves the texture, storage life and working characteristics of the fat, as it can be used for spreading and baking.

Unsaturated fats

Unsaturated fats are found in a range of foods originating from plants and oily fish. There are two types of unsaturated fat.

- Monounsaturated fats are soft at room temperature. Research has found that they are healthier for you, by potentially lowering blood cholesterol and reducing the risk of cancer and diabetes. Monounsaturated fats contain only one pair of carbon atoms with one hydrogen atom.
- Polyunsaturated fats are liquid or very soft at room temperature. They contain two or more pairs of carbon atoms, and are therefore capable of holding more hydrogen atoms.

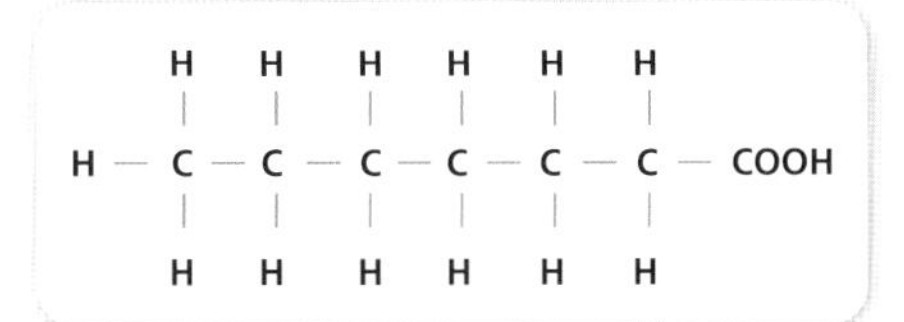

Diagram of saturated fat

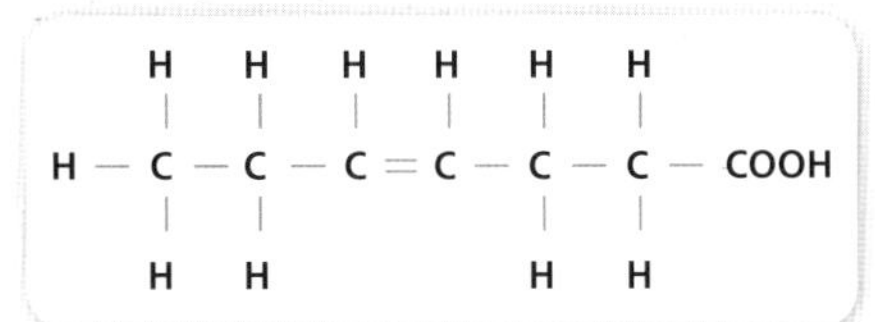

Diagram of unsaturated fat

Sources of monounsaturated fat

Sources of polyunsaturated fat

Essential fatty acids (EFA) cannot be made in the body, but are vital for the health and function of the body.

- Omega 3 EFA helps to protect the heart and is found in oily fish, seeds and green leafy vegetables.
- Omega 6 EFA helps to lower blood cholesterol and is found in vegetables, grains, seeds and poultry.

Nutritionists encourage people to eat less saturated fat and trans fat as these have been linked to high blood cholesterol levels, coronary heart disease, obesity and diabetes.

Dietary functions of fat

Fat in the diet:

- provides energy
- forms an insulating layer under the skin
- protects and surrounds vital organs in the body
- is a source of the fat-soluble Vitamins A, D, E and K
- provides texture and flavour to foods
- promotes a feeling of satiety (fullness).

Sources of fat

Fats come from both animal and plant sources. Animal sources include meat, lard, suet, dairy products and oily fish. Plant sources include nuts, pulses, seeds and some fruits (e.g. avocado and olives).

Many manufactured foods contain high levels of fat. It is important that you understand the source and function of fat in your diet, to allow you to make the right choice when choosing, designing or making foods. Many manufacturers are trying to reduce the amount of saturated fat and trans fat in commercial products, and labelling their products accordingly. This allows you to make an informed decision about the fat content of foods.

Function of fats in food preparation

Fat is used in food preparation for:

- spreading on bread
- creaming fat and sugar together to trap air in cakes
- adding colour and flavour to baked products and sauces
- shortening properties for pastries and doughs, used to create a tender, flaky texture
- cooking foods using deep or shallow frying, due to the high boiling point of fats
- oiling baking tins
- creating emulsions, such as salad dressing and mayonnaise.

Support Activity

Investigate the fat content of a range of manufactured foods available in supermarkets. Record your findings in a table like this:

Manufactured food product	Fat content per 100g	Ingredients containing fat

Stretch Activity

1. Discuss the difference between saturated and unsaturated fats.
2. Evaluate the use of hydrogenated fats in the manufacture of foods.

Apply it!

In your Design and Make activities, analyse the different types of fat in your products and comment on their health implications.

Build Better Answers

Give three reasons for using fat in a pastry recipe. (3 marks)

Basic answers (0–1 marks)
At this level, answers gave one or no reasons.

Good answers (2 marks)
At this level, answers gave two reasons.

Excellent answers (3 marks)
At this level, answers gave three reasons. For example:

1. To shorten pastry to create a crisp texture.
2. To add colour.
3. To add flavour.

Carbohydrates

Objectives

- **Understand** the dietary sources of different types of carbohydrate
- **Describe** the composition and functions of sugar, starch and fibre

Apply it!

In your Design and Make activities, consider the dietary benefits of using starchy carbohydrate ingredients in your food products.

Support Activity

1. Describe the role of fibre in the diet.
2. Outline the differences between intrinsic and extrinsic sugars.

Stretch Activity

Investigate the use of pectin and gums in manufactured foods by identifying these products from the list of ingredients on food labels.

The composition of carbohydrates

Carbohydrates are macronutrients and are made up of the elements carbon, hydrogen and oxygen. The three main types of carbohydrates are: sugar, starch and fibre. The process of photosynthesis produces carbohydrates, which are found in all plant foods.

Table 1.1 shows how carbohydrates can be classified according to their type and structure.

Type of carbohydrate	Structure	Examples	Sources
sugars (sweet)	simple sugars: **mono-saccharides**	• glucose	• fruit, onions, potatoes
		• fructose	• fruit, honey
		• galactose	• milk
	double sugars: **disaccharides**	• maltose (glucose + glucose)	• barley
		• sucrose (glucose + fructose)	• sugar beet or sugar cane
		• lactose (galactose + galactose)	• milk
non-sugars (not sweet)	simple **poly-saccharides**	• starch	• root vegetables, seeds, unripe fruit, rice, potatoes and cereals
		• cellulose / fibre / NSP (non-starch poly-saccharide)	• skins of fruit and vegetables, bran and wholegrain **cereal** products
	complex poly-saccharides	• pectin	• orchard and citrus fruits • berries used in jam, gels and jellies
		• gums	• seaweed, carrageenan and stems of plants and fruit used as thickeners, stabilisers and emulsifiers

Table 1.1: Types of carbohydrate, their structures and sources

Dietary functions of carbohydrates

Carbohydrate in the diet:

- provides energy (sugar and starch)
- aids digestion (fibre)
- sweetens and flavours food (sugar)
- adds bulk to your diet (fibre and starch)
- helps to lower blood cholesterol levels (fibre).

Sugars

Sugars come in two different forms.

- Intrinsic sugars are found naturally in the cells of fruit and vegetables.
- Extrinsic sugars are processed sugars, and include granulated, caster, Demerara, icing sugars, treacle and syrup that are added to cakes, biscuits, sweets, desserts, sauces, soft drinks and soups.

A diet high in extrinsic sugar can lead to tooth decay, obesity and diabetes. Sugar provides 'empty' calories, as it is deficient in any other nutrient.

Starch

Starch is found in cereals (wheat, rice, barley, oats, maize and rye), bread, potatoes, pasta and root vegetables. They are filling and provide you with many other nutrients: for example, cereals contain the Vitamin B complex.

Fibre

Fibre or non-starch polysaccharides (NSP) is the cellulose found in the outer skins and flesh of fruit and vegetables.

Fibre can be split into two different groups:

- Soluble fibre is found in the flesh of fruit and vegetables, oats, beans and lentils. Digestion partially breaks it down to form a gel-like substance that can coat the digestive tract. This helps to speed up digestion, helping to lower blood cholesterol levels and prevent cancer and other digestive problems.
- Insoluble fibre is found in the outer skins of fruit and vegetables, cereals and wholegrain food products. The body cannot digest insoluble fibre. Insoluble fibre acts as a bulking agent, absorbing the end-products of digestion to allow waste products to be removed from the body.

Too little soluble and insoluble fibre in your diet can lead to digestive problems such as constipation, diverticular disease (distortion and inflammation of the digestive tract), appendicitis and haemorrhoids (piles).

Sources of intrinsic sugars

Sources of extrinsic sugars

Sources of starch

Sources of fibre

Describe the difference between the two types of fibre found in foods. (4 marks)

Basic answers (0–1 marks)
At this level, answers gave one or no descriptions of fibre.

Good answers (2 marks)
At this level, answers named and described one type of fibre or named the two types of fibre. For example:

1. Soluble fibre
2. Insoluble fibre

Excellent answers (3–4 marks)
Answers gave two types of fibre and their differences. For example:

1. Soluble fibre is a jelly-like substance.
2. Insoluble fibre cannot be digested by the human body.

Protein

Objectives

- **Describe** the composition and functions of proteins, and deficiency of protein
- **Understand** the dietary sources of different types of protein

Support Activity

1. Describe the difference between HBV and LBV proteins.
2. Compare the cost of LBV and HBV protein foods. Record and evaluate your findings.

Food	HBV/LBV protein	Cost per 100g

The composition of protein

Protein is an essential macronutrient in your diet. Proteins are made up of complex chains of amino acids. There are 20 different amino acids, each with a specific function in the body. For healthy growth and repair of the human body, you need all 20 amino acids.

Some amino acids can be made in the body, but others have to be obtained from the food you eat; these are called essential amino acids. Adults need ten essential amino acids, and children need eight.

High biological value (HBV) protein

Foods containing all the essential amino acids are said to have a high biological value. Foods originating from animal sources (meat, poultry, fish, eggs and dairy products) are all HBV protein foods; soya is the only HBV food originating from a plant. Soya beans can be used as whole beans or soya sprouts, or processed as soya milk, tofu, tempeh, soya sauce, miso or TVP. Quorn™ is another HBV protein food product, but is made from edible fungus; a mycoprotein, bound together with egg. Soya products and Quorn™ have been promoted as a result of consumer demand for vegetarian, healthy, high-protein foods, or low-fat meat substitutes.

HBV fooods

Low biological value (LBV) protein

Foods that are deficient in one or more of the essential amino acids are said to have a low biological value (LBV). Foods originating from plants (cereals, nuts, seeds, lentils, beans, pulses) are LBV protein foods.

LBV foods

Complementary proteins

With careful meal planning, you can mix HBVs with LBVs or combine different LBV foods to create a complementary protein that contains all the essential amino acids your body needs. Good examples are jacket potato and beans or vegetable chow mein. As well as having a nutritional benefit, combining protein foods provides a more varied diet and can save you money, because LBV proteins are cheaper to produce than HBV proteins.

Dietary functions of proteins

Protein is needed in the diet:

- for growth
- to repair body tissues
- to promote the manufacture of enzymes, vital for metabolism
- as a constituent of hormones, needed to regulate bodily functions
- as a secondary source of energy if the body receives insufficient energy from carbohydrate and fat sources.

Deficiency

A deficiency of protein would cause:

- slow growth in children's physical development
- digestive problems due to insufficient enzyme production
- malfunction of the liver
- muscles to become weak, limbs thin and stomach distended.

Kwashiorkor is a protein energy malnutrition disease that occurs in children more frequently in less developed countries, where they are weaned from breast milk to a low-protein diet.

Kwashiorkor

Dietary sources of protein

Table 1.2 shows the dietary sources of protein.

HBV protein	LBV protein
meat: poultry, game, offal	cereals
fish	beans, peas
dairy foods: milk, cheese, cream, yogurt	nuts
eggs	seeds
Quorn™	lentils
soya	

Table 1.2: Sources of HBV and LBV protein

ResultsPlus
Build Better Answers

Give two dietary functions of protein. (2 marks)

■ **Basic answers (0–1 marks)**
At this level, answers gave one or no function.

● **Good answers (2 marks)**
At this level answers gave two functions. For example: Protein is needed for growth and repair.

Stretch Activity

1. Research the different types, uses and production methods of soya and Quorn™ food products available to consumers.
2. Using sketches and labels, design a food product to demonstrate the use of complementary proteins.

Quick notes

- **Proteins** are made up of chains of amino acids.
- **Protein value** is based on biological value (HBV or LBV).
- **HBV protein** contains all the essential amino acids.
- **Essential amino acids** adults need ten, children need eight.
- **LBV protein** contains some of the essential amino acids.
- **Complementary proteins** mix HBVs with LBVs or combine LBV protein foods to supply all the essential amino acids the body needs.
- **Kwashiorkor** is one example of protein deficiency.

Vitamins and minerals

Objectives

- **Describe** the dietary function, sources and deficiency of the fat-soluble and water-soluble vitamins
- **Understand** the dietary composition, sources, function and deficiency of calcium, iron, sodium and fluoride

Apply it!

In your Design and Make activities, consider how you could limit the loss of water-soluble vitamins during preparation, processing and cooking techniques.

Support Activity

Keep a three-day meal diary of what you eat and drink. Evaluate your intake of vitamins, minerals and water.

Stretch Activity

Food products can be fortified by adding nutrients or food components to improve nutritional status. Using a supermarket website, investigate why foods are fortified. Then complete the table below.

Food product	Fortified with which vitamin/mineral?	Reasons and comments

ResultsPlus Watch out!

- Make sure you don't confuse fat- and water-soluble vitamins.
- The deficiency diseases need to be learned thoroughly for the exam!

The composition of vitamins

Vitamins are micronutrients. They must be included in your daily diet. If you eat a wide variety of foods, you should get all the vitamins that the body needs, without taking additional vitamin supplements. In general, you need vitamins to prevent illness and maintain good health, to aid maintenance and repair of body tissue and to control the release of energy needed by the body. A diet lacking in one or more vitamins will result in specific deficiency diseases.

Vitamins can be split into two groups.

- Fat-soluble – Vitamins A and D. Fat-soluble vitamins can dissolve in fat and can be stored in minute quantities in the body.
- Water-soluble – Vitamins B complex and C, folate/folic acid. These vitamins dissolve in water. They cannot be stored in the body. They can be destroyed or lost through preparation, processing and cooking.

Tables 1.3 and 1.4 show the sources, functions and deficiencies of both types of vitamins.

Vitamin	Source	Function	Deficiency
A (retinol and beta carotene) Carotene is an anti-oxidant vitamin and helps to protect against cancer	retinol (animal sources): liver, oily fish, egg yolk, milk, cheese carotene (plant sources): carrots, green leafy vegetables	• maintenance and health of the skin • produces a substance called 'visual purple', which helps night vision and keeps eyes healthy	• night blindness • skin infections • *excess may contribute to liver and bone damage*
D (cholecalciferol)	liver, oily fish, egg yolk, milk and dairy foods, margarine, sunlight	• proper formation of teeth and bones • aids absorption of calcium	• **rickets** • **osteomalacia**

Table 1.3: Sources, functions and deficiencies of fat-soluble vitamins

Sources of vitamins and minerals

Vitamin	Source	Function	Deficiency
B1 (thiamin)	wholegrain cereals, liver, kidney	• maintenance and function of nerves	• **beriberi** • depression
B2 (riboflavin)	meat, milk, green vegetables	• normal growth • aids the release of energy from food	• poor growth • skin disorders • swollen tongue
folate/ folic acid	leafy vegetables, seeds, beans, fruit, liver, fortified cereal products	• essential for all bodily functions • important during rapid periods of growth • production of healthy red blood cells	• **anaemia** • **neural birth defects**
C (ascorbic acid)	citrus fruit, green leafy vegetables	• formation of connective tissue • aids absorption of iron	• **scurvy** • poor health of gums, teeth and skin

Table 1.4: Sources, functions and deficiencies of water-soluble vitamins

The composition of minerals

Minerals are micronutrients, needed by the body for good health. Minerals are used in building the body and controlling how it works.

Table 1.5 shows the sources, functions and deficiencies of minerals.

Mineral	Source	Function	Deficiency
calcium	milk, yoghurt, cheese, green vegetables, sardines	combined with Vitamin D and phosphorous, calcium helps the formation of strong teeth and bones	• stunted growth • rickets
iron	liver, kidney, red meat, bread, potatoes, egg yolk, green vegetables	combined with protein, forms haemoglobin, to give blood its red colour, and helps transport oxygen around the body	• anaemia
sodium	salt, cheese, bacon, fish, processed foods	maintains water balance in the body	• deficiency: cramps • *excess: high blood pressure, stroke and coronary heart disease*
fluoride	fish, water, tea	strengthens teeth against tooth decay	• tooth decay

Table 1.5: Sources, functions and deficiencies of minerals

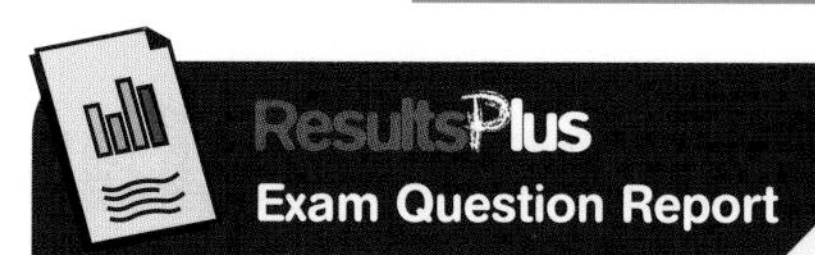

Give two functions of vitamin C in the body. (2 marks, 2009 Foundation)

How students answered

The understanding of the functions of vitamin C was poorly applied to this question.

77% got 0 marks

Many students incorrectly referenced prevention of illness or disease instead.

3% got 1 mark

More able students achieved marks for healthy skin, preventing scurvy, healing/repairing wounds, resisting infection/boosting immune system and adding iron absorption.

20% got 2 marks

ResultsPlus
Build Better Answers

Explain the consequences of having a diet high in sodium. (2 marks)

Basic answers (0–1 marks)

At this level, answers gave one or no reason.

Good answers (2 marks)

At this level, answers gave one reason and an explanation. For example: A diet high in sodium (salt) can cause high blood pressure, which can lead to stroke or heart attack.

Quick notes

- **Fat-soluble vitamins**: A and D
- **Water-soluble vitamins**: B complex and C, folate/folic acid.
- **Nutritional fortification** involves the addition of nutrients to foods, whether the nutrients were originally present in the food or not.
- **Minerals** are used in building the body and controlling how it works.

Energy balance

Objectives

- **Understand** the different uses of energy in the body
- **Describe** the factors affecting the energy requirements for individuals
- **Understand** the concept of a balanced diet
- **Explore** the uses of the dietary reference values

1g protein	4 kcal
1g carbohydrate	3.75 kcal
1g fat	9 kcal
1g alcohol	7 kcal

Table 1.6: Energy in foods

Mechanical energy

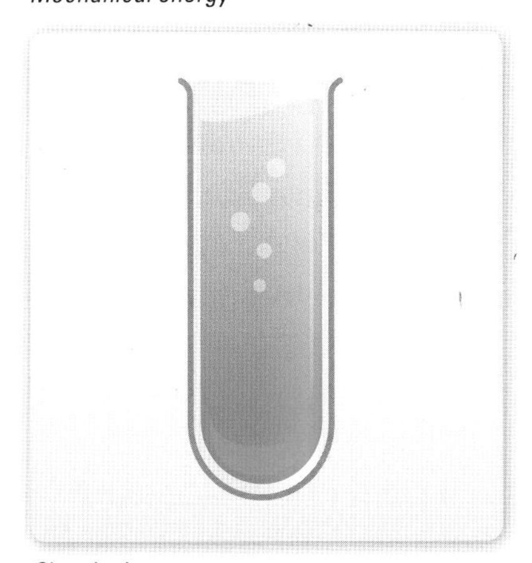

Chemical energy

The uses of energy in the body

The human body is a complex living structure composed of millions of individual units called cells. These cells group together to make tissues and organs, which each perform unique functions. Within the body, chemical reactions and changes take place all the time. These reactions enable the body to perform all the necessary functions and processes, as well as allowing the growth, repair and maintenance of the body's cells. This complex collection of chemical reactions is called metabolism.

Food provides a variety of substances and nutrients that are essential for the growth, repair and maintenance of the body. Energy is needed for all these metabolic reactions. Foods supply energy and essential chemicals that the body cannot make. The three macronutrients (protein, carbohydrate and fat) provide energy from food.

Energy is measured in kilocalories and kilojoules.

kcal	kilocalorie	=	1000 calories
kJ	kilojoule	=	1000 joules
1 calorie		=	4.184 kJ

Your energy needs depend on your body type and the amount of physical activity you do. How you use or store energy can influence your weight, shape and physical activity performance.

Types of energy

Your body needs four main types of energy: mechanical energy, chemical energy, heat energy and electrical energy.

Mechanical energy

Muscles in your body need energy to perform basic functions. There are a variety of different muscles in your body, controlling internal organs and movement. Your body uses mechanical energy to work all these muscles.

Chemical energy

Respiration is the chemical reaction that allows cells to release energy from food. The metabolic rate is the speed at which such chemical reactions take place in your body. Your metabolic rate increases as you exercise, and stays high for a while afterwards. Your basic metabolic rate (BMR) is the amount of energy needed by your body to stay alive.

Heat energy

The heat in your body is generated from the breakdown of chemicals inside your body's cells. Your body takes the chemicals from the food you eat and turns them into energy. Heat is generated when the body cells break these chemicals down.

Heat energy

Electrical energy

Electrical energy in your body is used by the nervous system. Your sense organs (ears, eyes, tongue, nose and skin) contain receptors that are sensitive to stimuli, and turn them into electrical impulses. These impulses can be used for reflex actions: fast, automatic and protective responses.

Electrical energy

Energy requirements

The energy your body takes from food and drink is measured in kilojoules or kilocalories. You need enough energy to meet the demands of your BMR and PAL.

- BMR stands for Basic Metabolic Rate, the number of kilocalories you use just to stay alive each day. BMR is different for different people.
- PAL stands for Physical Activity Level, the number of kilocalories you use to fuel all of your physical activity.

BMR + PAL = your daily energy requirement.

The relationship between food and drink intake and physical activity is called energy balance.

- If your energy intake from food and drink is greater than the energy you use, you will gain weight.
- If your energy intake from food and drink is less than the energy you use, you will lose weight.

If your energy intake from food and drink is the same as the energy you use, your weight will stay the same.

People who are overweight need more energy for BMR. Athletes in endurance events and hard training need more energy for PAL.

Support Activity

Describe what you understand by the term 'balanced diet'.

What is the difference between energy balance and energy inbalance?

Stretch Activity

Outline how the Dietary Reference Values (see page 21) can be used to aid meal planning for different groups of the population.

Describe the role of energy in relation to the BMR and PAL.

Support Activity

Describe the factors that influence our need for energy.

Stretch Activity

Evaluate the contribution that each of the macronutrients makes towards the daily energy requirement of an adult.

- Protein, fat and carbohydrate are the three macronutrients that can contribute energy to our diet. Remember that fat contributes double the amount of calories per 100g of energy compared to protein and carbohydrate.
- Many protein foods contain high levels of fat. Remember to consider this when designing and making your food products. Consider alternative sources of energy which are low in fat but high in starchy carbohydrate, for example cereals, pasta, rice, bread.
- Many starchy carbohydrate foods are often served with rich sauces, fillings or dressings that have a high fat content, for instance, chicken tikka masala, pasta carbonara, green thai curry. Remember to consider the total energy value of a dish rather than individual ingredients. A nutritional analysis programme can help you to do this.

Varying needs for energy

Our need for energy is based on a number of factors.

- **Age** During childhood, periods of rapid growth and development create a greater need for energy, to allow the body to perform these functions. Older people find their metabolism slows down and their physical activity levels reduce, leading to less need for energy.
- **Gender – male or female** Men and women have different needs for energy because of their different body structure, build, weight and activity levels.
- **Occupation** People in different occupations use different amounts of energy. For example, eight hours of active work might use 1800 kcal; eight hours sitting at a desk might use 900 kcal.
- **Exercise and other physical activity** It is important to have exercise in your daily life at all ages. This helps to keep you fit and active, with a healthy body and mind. Every time you move, you use energy. The more strenuous the activity, the more energy you use.
- **Life stage** Our need for energy can depend on our life stage. For example, during pregnancy, an expectant mother must consider herself and her unborn baby's needs, to allow for the healthy growth and development of the baby as well as her own health.

Balanced diet

A healthy, balanced diet contains a variety of foods including plenty of fruit and vegetables, starchy foods such as wholegrain bread, pasta and rice, some protein-rich foods such as meat, fish, eggs and lentils, and some dairy foods. A balanced diet should also be low in fat (especially saturated fat), salt and sugar.

Life stages

Dietary Reference Values

In the UK, Dietary Reference Values (DRVs) are estimated requirements of nutrients and energy for particular groups of the population. These draw on advice given by the Committee on Medical Aspects of Food and Nutrition Policy (COMA) back in the early 1990s, based on scientific evidence and research. COMA has been superceded by the Scientific Advisory Committee on Nutrition (SACN). It is likely that SACN will review the UK nutritional requirements soon, as these are now more than 10 years old.

DRVs comprise a series of estimates of the amount of energy and nutrients needed by different groups of healthy people in the UK population. DRVs include RNIs, EARs and LRNIs.

- Reference Nutrient Intakes (RNIs) show estimated amounts of protein, vitamins and minerals needed for 97% of the population. This will be far too much for some people.
- Estimated Average Requirements (EARs) give an average estimate of the requirement for energy, for a certain group of people.
- Lower Reference Nutrient Intake (LRNI) is the amount of a nutrient that is enough for a small number of people who have low energy needs.

Nutritional databases and software allow you to analyse recipes and foods by comparing your food product to the EAR, as well as identifying opportunities for recipe development and adaption.

ResultsPlus
Build Better Answers

Give four factors that contribute towards a healthy lifestyle. (4 marks)

Basic answers (0–1 marks)
At this level, answers gave one or no factors.

Good answers (2 marks)
At this level, answers gave two factors.

Excellent answers (3 marks)
Answers gave three or four factors.
For example:

1. Eat a variety of foods.
2. Eat a well-balanced diet.
3. Eat five portions of fruit and vegetables a day.
4. Exercise regularly.

Quick notes

- **The body** needs four main types of energy:
  - mechanical energy
  - chemical energy
  - heat energy
  - electrical energy.
- **Metabolism** is the set of chemical reactions that occur in living organisms to maintain life.
- **The energy** your body takes from food and drink is measured in kilojoules or kilocalories.
- **You need** enough energy to meet the demands of your BMR and PAL.
- **Your need** for energy is based on:
  - age
  - gender – male or female
  - occupation
  - exercise and other physical activity
  - life stage.

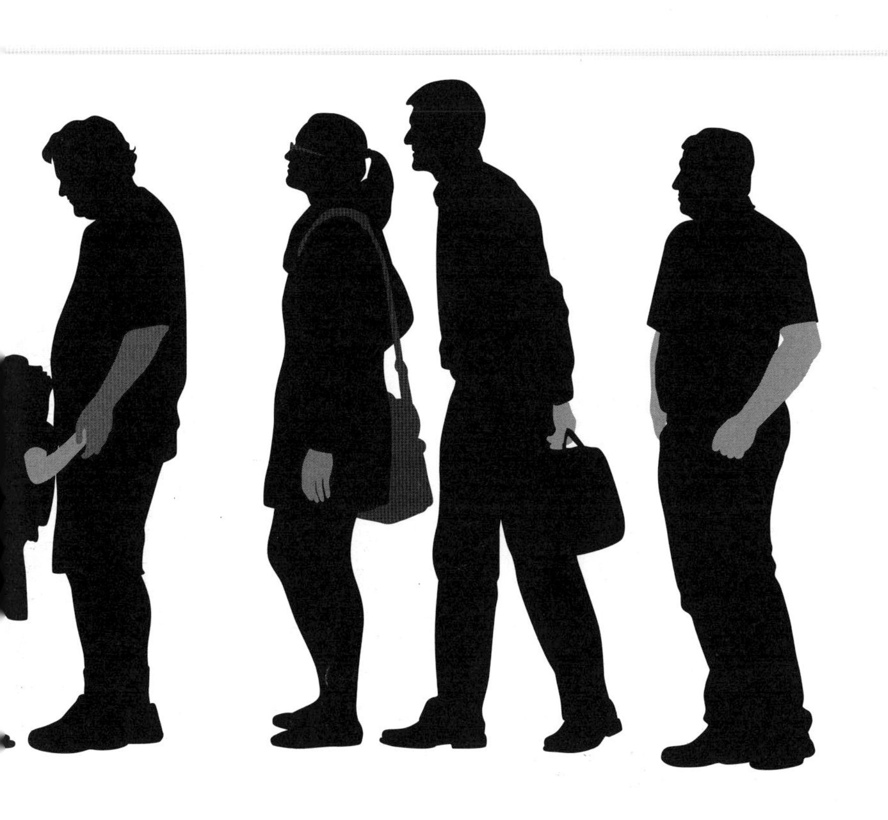

Dietary guidelines and government recommendations

Objectives

- **Describe** the nutritional concepts of healthy eating
- **Understand** how healthy eating concepts can be applied to achieve a healthy, balanced diet

Support Activity

Research and identify the symbols found on food labels and packaging that promote healthy living.

Stretch Activity

The *Eatwell Plate* says you should eat five portions of fruit and vegetables a day. Keep a meal diary to record your intake of fruit and vegetables over a week. Evaluate your diet – are you getting 5 a day?

ResultsPlus
Build Better Answers

Give **four** guidelines that people should follow based on the *Eatwell Plate*. (4 marks)

Basic answers (0–1 marks)
At this level, answers gave one or no guidelines.

Good answers (2 marks)
At this level, answers gave two guidelines.

Excellent answers (3–4 marks)
Answers gave three or four guidelines.
For example:

1. Base your meals on starchy foods.
2. Eat lots of fruit and vegetables.
3. Eat more fish.
4. Cut down on saturated fat and sugar.

The *Eatwell Plate*

The *Eatwell Plate* is a visual guide showing the proportion and types of food needed for a healthy, balanced diet. Produced by the Food Standards Agency, it is based on extensive research that made links between what people eat and their health and wellbeing. It is designed to help people understand and enjoy healthy eating.

The *Eatwell Plate* is based on the government's eight guidelines for a healthy diet. Here is what they recommend.

The Eatwell Plate

- Base your meals on starchy foods.
- Eat lots of fruit and vegetables.
- Eat more fish.
- Cut down on saturated and hydrogenated fat and sugar.
- Try to eat less salt – no more than 6g per day.
- Get active and try to be a healthy weight.
- Drink plenty of water.
- Don't skip breakfast.

The *Eatwell Plate* supports previous dietary advice to reduce fat, sugar, salt and alcohol, and to increase fibre.

The *Eatwell Plate* is based on the five food groups. To achieve a healthy, balanced diet, choose different types and proportions of foods from the first four groups every day, to get a wide range of nutrients, in the correct proportion to each other. Try to eat less of foods in the purple group.

Water

Water is essential for life. The human body is made up of nearly 70 per cent water. You need water every day. A lack of water to drink is more serious than a lack of food.

Water: controls body temperature by perspiration; lubricates joints; maintains healthy skin; aids digestion; prevents constipation; prevents dehydration; helps to remove harmful excess or foreign substances from the blood; transports nutrients, oxygen and carbon dioxide around the body.

Around the world, many people cannot get clean, safe drinking water and this is a major cause of disease, illness, infection and malnutrition.

Fresh water on tap

	Starchy foods	Fruit and vegetables	Milk and dairy foods	Meat, fish, eggs, beans and other non-dairy sources of protein	Foods and drinks high in fat, salt and/or sugar
Recommendations	Should be 33% of the food we eat • eat at least one portion with every meal	Should be 33% of the food we eat • eat five portions a day	eat two to three portions a day	• eat two portions a day • try to eat fish twice a week, with one portion being oily fish (e.g. mackerel)	• not essential to a healthy balanced diet • eat in very small amounts • choose lower-sugar, lower-fat and lower- or no-salt alternatives • no more than 6g per day of salt
Food	bread, rice, pasta, couscous, bulgar wheat, maize, cornmeal, oats, squash, lentils, peas, noodles, potatoes, other wholegrain cereals • low-GI (**glycaemic index**) foods are digested and absorbed slowly, allowing the carbohydrate to be used more efficiently	fresh, frozen, tinned, dried or juiced fruit and vegetables One portion (80g) • 1 apple/pear/ orange or 2 plums • 3 tbsp vegetables • 3 tbsp beans/ pulses • 3 tbsp fruit salad or stewed fruit • 1 tbsp dried fruit • 150ml fruit juice	milk, cheese, yoghurt, fromage frais and crème fraîche	meat, fish, eggs, beans, soya, Quorn™, textured vegetable protein (TVP)	carbonated drinks, squash, alcohol, cakes, biscuits, pastries, processed foods, crisps and confectionary, hydrogenated and saturated fats
Adaptions to diet	• eat more starchy food (pasta or rice) and less sauce • add beans, lentils to casseroles • try different varieties of wholegrain bread • eat thicker slices of bread	try to avoid adding fat or rich sauces to vegetables or adding syrup or sugar to fruit	always choose lower-fat versions, or use less of the product but a more flavoursome alternative (e.g. mature cheddar)	• choose lower-fat meat products or leaner cuts of meat, or remove visible fat and skin • use cooking methods that use no fat: poach, steam, bake, microwave, grill	• limit your intake of sugary drinks and foods in between meals • try not to add any fat when cooking

Table 1.7: Summary of the Eatwell Plate *guidelines*

Individual nutritional requirements

Objectives

- **Describe** the nutritional requirements for different groups of the population
- **Understand** how these nutritional requirements can be applied to achieve a healthy, balanced diet

Support Activity

Make a list of the factors to consider when planning meals for pregnant women.

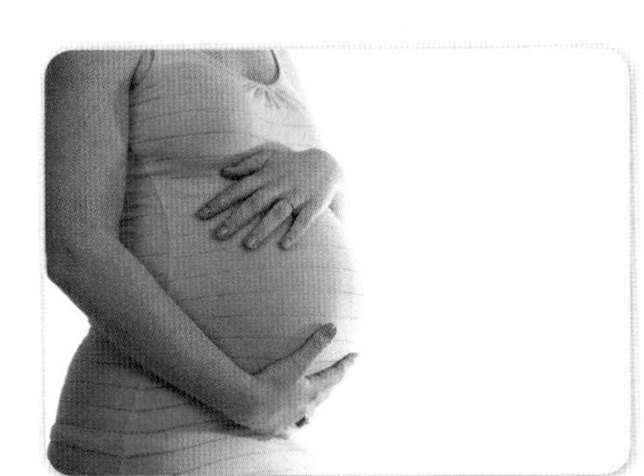

Pregnant woman

Baby

Toddler

Food is an essential part of our lives. Everyone has different needs and requirements for food depending on their: age; gender; health; physical activity levels; climate in which they live; customs and culture (see Ethnic and religious groups on pages 30–1)

Pregnant women have the following nutritional requirements:

- Diet must meet the needs of the mother and the unborn baby.
- Energy, protein, iron, calcium, folate, and Vitamins C and D are essential for the development of muscle, bone and blood.
- A folate supplement is recommended for women who are planning a pregnancy or who are pregnant. This can reduce the risk of development defects in the brain of developing embryos.

Pregnant women should:

- avoid taking in high levels of Vitamin A, which can cause birth defects
- avoid soft cheeses, paté, uncooked eggs, unpasteurised milk and milk products
- avoid shellfish
- ensure all meat and poultry is thoroughly cooked
- a mother choosing to breastfeed must ensure a healthy, balanced diet to support her and her baby's energy and nutritional needs.

Infants up to one year have the following nutritional requirements:

- Babies need essential nutrients for growth and development. Milk (breast or formula) is the main food source for the first six months of a baby's life.
- As babies grow, they need more energy, so babies are weaned onto solid food.
- Babies are born with body stores of iron that last for only a few months after birth.

Toddlers up to five years

The main nutrional needs of a toddler are affected by:

- parents - for choosing and providing food
- eating habits and patterns, which can be established from an early age
- the fact that they are growing and developing rapidly
- the need for a healthy balanced diet containing protein, starchy carbohydrates, vitamins and minerals.

Toddlers need:

- breakfast, lunch and tea, with healthy snacks as appropriate
- easy-to-hold food
- suitable sized portions
- interesting shapes, textures, colours and flavours
- a variety of foods.

School-age children

Use the *Eatwell Plate* dietary guidelines. The main nutritional requirements of school-age children are affected by:

- increasing activity levels, leading to a greater need for energy
- media and peer pressure, which can be influential.

School age children need:

- a variety of foods
- breakfast, lunch and tea, with healthy snacks as appropriate.

Adolescents

Continue to use the *Eatwell Plate* dietary guidelines and ensure they eat a variety of foods. The main nutritional requirements of adolescents are affected by:

- environmental, social, economic, moral and health issues
- puberty, which brings rapid development, growth and change in the human body. (Girls have a greater need for iron to replace that lost during menstruation. Boys need more energy from starchy carbohydrates to feed their larger appetites.)

Adolescents need:

- breakfast, lunch and tea, with healthy snacks as appropriate
- quick, easy-to-prepare food that is suited for a busy and energetic lifestyle
- affordable food.

Adults

Continue to use the *Eatwell Plate* dietary guidelines and eat a variety of foods. An adult's main nutritional needs are affected by: lifestyle and occupation; the energy balance of intake and expenditure.

Many adults enjoy luxury/fusion/hybrid/foreign/sociable cuisine.

Senior citizens

Continue to use the *Eatwell Plate* dietary guidelines and eat a variety of foods. A senior citizen's main nutritional needs are affected by:

- increased life expectancy; as people live longer, food needs and eating patterns change according to health, activity and companionship
- income – it may be limited
- mobility – may have difficulty with shopping (distance, transport, weather, limited access to internet shopping)
- may lose appetite.

Senior citizens need: smaller quantities as energy levels decrease; easy-to-prepare meals.

Illness and convalescence

The nutritional needs of people who are ill vary depending on the type of illness and length of convalescence. Protein, vitamins and minerals are essential for good health and wellbeing. When they are sick, people may lose their appetite. Meals should be: easy-to-prepare; in small portions.

Stretch Activity

Plan a day's menu suitable for a young child convalescing in hospital, compared to an active teenager, who participates in lots of sports.

Apply it!

In your Design and Make activities, your target group is a collection of people who will use your product. Consider their needs carefully when designing and making food products.

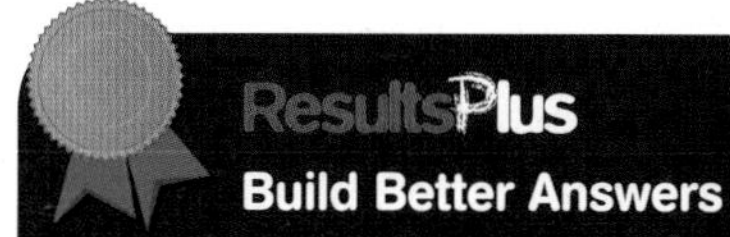

Describe two nutritional requirements for a young pre-school child. (4 marks)

Basic answers (0–1 marks)

At this level, answers gave one or no nutritional requirements.

Good answers (2 marks)

At this level, answers gave one nutritional requirement and a reason, or two nutritional requirements.

Excellent answers (3–4 marks)

Answers gave two nutritional requirements and at least one reason. For example:

1. Regular meals each day to avoid snacking on foods high in fat and sugar.
2. Protein, starchy carbohydrates, vitamins and minerals form a healthy balanced diet to aid growth and development.

Elderly couple

Special diets

Objectives

- **Understand** the differences between a range of special diets
- **Describe** the nutritional requirements, good food sources of nutrients and modification of ingredients and recipes to suit user needs

Many people have special dietary needs. This might be because of their culture, religion or moral beliefs. Some people's health and well being are affected by the foods they eat, causing intolerances to specific foods and other medical issues.

There are many different special diets, but in this topic we will focus on:

- vegetarian and vegan: lacto, ovo and lacto-ovo
- intolerances: lactose intolerance
- medical conditions: diabetes mellitus, coronary heart disease (CHD), obesity, nut allergy, coeliac disease.

The most common form of special diet is vegetarianism. For more on this, see Chapter 4 Food issues on pages 124–125.

ResultsPlus
Watch out!

- The word ovo at the beginning of a word refers to eggs.
- The word lacto at the beginning of a word refers to milk. Therefore, lacto-ovo vegetarians will eat eggs and milk, but not meat or fish.

Vegetarianism

The most common special diets are the various forms of vegetarianism. A vegetarian is someone living on a diet of grains, pulses, nuts, seeds, vegetables and fruit, with or without the use of dairy products and eggs.

Vegetarians may object to the use of animal products because of moral, cultural, ethical or social issues.

Types of vegetarian

Vegan

A vegan is a strict vegetarian who does not eat any meat, dairy products, eggs or honey.

Vegetarian Society

Meal planning for vegans:

- Vegan children need nutrient-rich foods, high in protein, calcium, vitamins and minerals.
- Overuse of high-fibre foods can lead to poor mineral absorption. Dairy products can be replaced with soya products.
- Commercial egg-replacer products are also available from health food shops.

Vegans need to make sure they have enough:

- LBV protein: (plant sources) nuts, beans, lentils and pulses.
- Essential fatty acids (EFA): soyabean or rapeseed oils.
- Vitamin B2: whole grains, mushrooms, almonds and leafy vegetables.
- Vitamin B12: (main source is from meat, dairy and eggs) many foods are fortified with Vitamin B12, e.g. veggie burgers, breakfast cereals, vegetable margarines and soya milk.
- Vitamin D: fortified foods, including soya milk, vegetable margarines.

Lacto-ovo

A lacto-ovo vegetarian is someone who eats both dairy products and eggs (the most common type of vegetarian diet).

Meal planning for lacto-ovo vegetarians:

- A healthy balanced diet easily achievable with planning.
- Remove all meat, game, poultry, fish, rennet and gelatine from the diet.
- Purchase free-range eggs.
- Make sure there is enough LBV and HBV protein in the diet and essential fatty acids (EFA).

Lacto

A lacto vegetarian is someone who eats dairy products but not eggs.

Meal planning for lacto vegetarians:

- A healthy balanced diet easily achievable with planning.
- Remove all meat, game, poultry, fish, eggs, rennet and gelatine from the diet.
- Make sure there is enough LBV and HBV protein in the diet and essential fatty acids (EFA).

Ovo

An ovo vegetarian is someone who eats eggs but not dairy product.

Meal planning for ovo vegetarians:

- Remove all meat, game, poultry, fish, dairy products, rennet and gelatine from the diet.
- Purchase free-range eggs.
- Soya products are a good food source for this group.

Intolerances

Many people have intolerances to various types of food. One of the most common is lactose intolerance. This is the body's inability to break down and use lactose, a sugar found in milk and other dairy products, because the required enzyme lactase is absent in the intestinal system or its availability is lowered.

Meal planning for lactose intolerance:

- Watch out for hidden lactose in foods such as sausages, bread, breakfast cereals, cakes and biscuits.
- Calcium and Vitamin D work together for the development of healthy bones. Good sources of each are needed.
- Use lactose-free foods: rice milk, soya milk; goat's milk is acceptable for some people.

Support Activity

The following recipe was used to produce a prototype fishcake product.

500g mashed potato
20g butter
250g cooked or tinned fish
seasonings
herbs or spices to flavour
1 egg
50g breadcrumbs

Describe two modifications that would make the fishcake product suitable for:

- a lacto vegetarian
- someone with coeliac disease (see page 29)
- someone following a low-fat diet.

Support Activity

Describe the four different types of vegetarian diet.

There has been an increase in identifying allergies and intolerances because medical research has improved, enabling people to be diagnosed with these medical issues.

In the West, we eat a highly refined diet (where food has been extensively processed and altered). This has had an impact upon the health and well-being of people.

Medical

There are many medical reasons why some people need special diets. The following are some of the most common.

Diabetes mellitus

This is an illness where production of the hormone insulin in the body is ineffective at controlling the blood sugar level.

Meal planning for diabetes mellitus:

- Careful control of sugar intake.
- Regular meals to support the body in controlling blood sugar levels.
- High-fibre diet to satisfy appetite.
- Sweeten foods with natural sugars from fruit, vegetables and juices.
- Use artificial sweeteners sparingly.

British Heart Foundation

Coronary heart disease (CHD)

This covers various diseases of the heart.

As well as a healthy diet, regular exercise, being aware of dangers such as smoking, drinking, high blood pressure and stress also help children to be heart healthy.

Meal planning for coronary heart disease:

- starchy carbohydrate foods to satisfy appetite and aid digestion
- diet low in saturated fat
- low-salt diet
- high-fibre diet
- low-fat products: vegetable spreads, low-fat cheese
- 5 a day (fruits and vegetables).

Obesity

When excess body fat has accumulated to the extent that it may have an adverse effect on health, leading to reduced life expectancy and/or increased health problems. Body mass index (BMI) compares weight and height. It defines a person as overweight (pre-obese) when their BMI is between 25 kg/m^2 and 30 kg/m^2, and obese when it is greater than 30 kg/m^2. Obese people should follow a healthy, balanced diet containing a variety of foods in smaller portions.

Meal planning for obesity:

- Eat less fat. Fat provides significantly more energy than carbohydrate or protein. Saturated fat can also contribute to CHD.
- Eat more fibre to satisfy appetite and add a variety of flavours, colours and textures to meals.
- Eat less salt to reduce blood pressure.
- Eat less sugar as this provides empty calories.
- Increase exercise and decrease energy intake.
- Share and support a weight loss diet by asking friends and family to help achieve weight loss.

Nut allergy

This is when eating nuts can cause someone to go into anaphylactic shock, where the skin itches and develops a rash, together with more serious symptoms such as a swelling of the tongue and trachea (windpipe). This can be very frightening and can even be fatal.

Meal planning for nut allergy:

- Be aware that processed foods produced in a factory can also contain nuts. Always check the label.
- Avoid all nut oils, walnuts, hazelnuts, almonds, pecans, Brazil nuts, macadamia nuts and cashew nuts.

Fruit & Fibre

Whole wheat flakes with mixed dried fruit and roasted chopped mixed nuts fortified with vitamins and iron.

Ingredients

Whole wheat, Raisins (15%), Sugar, Banana slices (6%) (banana, coconut oil, sugar, honey, flavouring), **Coconut chips (3%), Malted barley extract, Dried apple (1.5%)** (preservative (sulphur dioxide)), **Roasted chopped nuts (1.5%)** (hazelnuts, almonds), **Salt, Niacin, Iron, Pantothenic acid (B5), Thiamin (B1), Vitamin B6, Riboflavin (B2), Folic acid, Vitamin B12.**

! Allergy advice: Contains gluten, nuts and sulphite

! Produced in a factory which uses milk ingredients

Allergy advice label

Coeliac disease

This is an autoimmune disease, where the body's immune system attacks its own tissues. This immune reaction is triggered by gluten, a collective name for a type of protein found in the cereals.

Meal planning for coeliac disease:

- Avoid gluten, found in the cereals wheat, rye and barley. A few people are also sensitive to oats.
- Use 'Free from' foods sold in supermarkets, which use gluten-free flours and other products.

Quick notes

- **Vegan**: strict vegetarian, eating no meat, dairy, eggs or honey.
- **Lacto vegetarian**: eats dairy products, but not eggs.
- **Ovo-lacto vegetarian**: eats eggs and dairy products.
- **Ovo vegetarian**: eats eggs, but not dairy products.
- **Coeliac disease**: intolerance to gluten.
- **Diabetes**: ineffective control of blood sugar levels by insulin.
- **Obesity**: energy imbalance causing someone to be seriously overweight.
- **Nut allergy**: allergy to nuts that can cause anaphylactic shock.
- **Lactose intolerance**: intolerance to milk sugar.
- **Coronary heart disease (CHD)**: build-up of fatty deposits and cholesterol in arteries.

Stretch Activities

1. Research the alternative ingredients available for each of the special diets, using the internet, recipes and supermarkets.
2. Investigate the information available to consumers when making food choices. Use packaging, labelling and website research to analyse the use, role and success of this information.

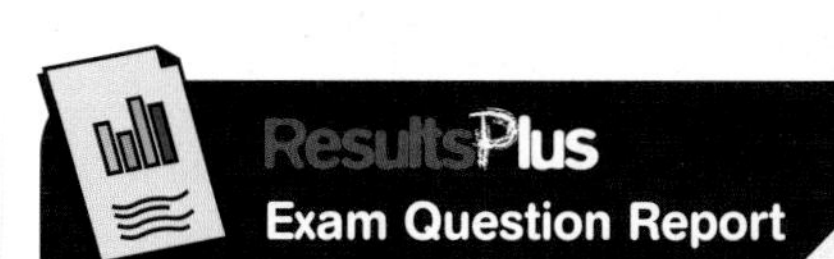

Give two reasons why people choose not to eat meat. (2 marks, 2009 Higher)

How students answered

There was poor understanding of the reasons why people choose not to eat meat.

28% got 0 marks

Many students repeated the answer in the question stem, or repeatedly referred to different rearing conditions (e.g. crowding and quality of life), limiting their potential marks.

11% got 1 mark

Two different, original reasons were required in order to achieve full marks, such as the cruelty of rearing methods and a dislike of the texture and flavour of meat.

61% got 2 marks

Ethnic and religious groups

Objectives

- **Understand** that different cultures and customs can influence food choices
- **Describe** the main dietary food rules and restrictions for the Christian, Hindu, Sikh, Muslim and Jewish faiths

Customs and cultures

Culture refers to the shared customs, traditions and beliefs of a large group of people, such as a nation, race, or religious group. These customs are part of what defines a group's identity.

Food customs are one aspect of culture. Every culture has its own traditional way of preparing, serving and eating foods. Some religions have dietary restrictions, and all have foods that are associated with religious festivals, where food is shared among family and friends for pleasure and celebration.

The UK is a multicultural society

Food and religious groups

Some religions have very specific dietary requirements and/or customs. Here are three examples:

Hinduism

Orthodox Hindus are vegetarians who believe it is wrong to kill animals. They do not eat meat, fish or eggs. Milk and dairy products are eaten, together with other widely used foods such as yoghurt (dahi), cottage cheese (panir and chenna) and butter (ghee). Combinations of pulses and cereals are important sources of protein. Typical bread products include chapatis, puri and paratha.

Examples of Hindu food

Apply it!

Multicultural food products might be a topic that you wish to use for your controlled assessment: Unit 1 (coursework). Remember to consider the wider implications of food choices in relation to the festivals, dietary restrictions, customs and cultures that are reflected in our multicultural society. You might choose to use those explored in detail in the main text in addition to those listed below:

Christianity

Christianity is better known for its festive foods than for dietary restrictions. Festive celebrations at Easter, Rogation, Harvest and Christmas have developed over centuries, with traditions and customs playing a major factor in food choices. By contrast, the seriousness of Shrove Tuesday and Lent, traditionally a time of fasting, are reflected in food choices.

Sikhism

The dietary pattern of Sikhs is similar to that of non-orthodox Hindus. Sikhs have food at the temple on special days. Favourite foods are chapatis and vegetable curry.

Non-orthodox Hindus eat poultry, eggs and white fish, but the cow is regarded as sacred and the pig as unclean, so neither pork nor beef products are eaten, including gelatine. Traditional cooking methods include tandoori and tikka dishes, involving marinades made of yoghurt, lemon juices and spices. Special sweets and savouries are prepared during the Hindu festivals, such as Diwali (festival of lights).

Islam (Muslim)

Beef, lamb and poultry are eaten, but the pig is thought to be unclean, so Muslims do not eat pork or any pork products. Other meats must be slaughtered in a particular way to remove all traces of blood, after which it can be called 'halal' meat.

There are many different cuisines associated with Muslim culture, reflecting the diversity of ingredients, cooking processes and techniques from different parts of the world. Islamic cuisine can have many different Far Eastern influences; Arabian, Chinese, Bengali, Persian and Syrian cooking styles are associated with their customs, traditions, fasting and festivals.

Halal prepared food for Muslims

Judaism

The bible is the source of all Jewish food laws. Animal flesh that can be eaten includes beef, lamb, goat, chicken, turkey, duck and goose. Pork and birds of prey are not permitted. All meat must be ritually slaughtered, soaked and treated with kosher salt, and can then be called 'kosher'. Meat and dairy produce must not be prepared or eaten together at the same meal.

Support Activity

Discuss how different customs and cultures affect the food choices that we make.

Stretch Activity

Investigate the various religious festivals and food customs that we celebrate in the UK as a multicultural society.

ResultsPlus
Build Better Answers

Give two foods associated with religious festivals. (2 marks)

Basic answers (0–1 marks)
At this level, answers gave one food product.

Good answers (2 marks)
At this level, answers gave two food products. For example:

1. Hot cross buns
2. Christmas pudding

Know Zone
Chapter 1 Nutrition

This chapter focuses on the principles of food and nutrition, linked to the source, function and deficiencies of the macro- and micronutrients. By applying this to energy balance, dietary guidelines, healthy eating, special diets, culture and individual nutritional requirements, you should acquire a comprehensive knowledge base from which you can apply understanding to your choices when designing and making food products.

You should know...

- ☐ The dietary functions and sources of the following macronutrients:
  - fats: saturated and unsaturated fats
  - carbohydrates: sugar, starch and fibre/NSP
  - protein: HBV and LBV
- ☐ The dietary functions, sources and deficiencies of the following micronutrients:
  - minerals: calcium, iron, sodium, flouride
  - vitamins: A, D, B1, B2, Folate, C
- ☐ Nutritional concepts:
  - energy balance
  - energy requirements
  - balanced diet
- ☐ Dietary guidelines relating to:
  - fat
  - sugar
  - salt
  - fibre, low GI foods and starchy carbohydrates
- ☐ Government recommendations:
  - five a day
  - nutritional labelling
  - *Eatwell Plate*
  - recommended fish intake
- ☐ Individual nutritional requirements:
  - pregnancy
  - infants up to one year
  - toddlers up to five years and school age children
  - adolescents
  - adults
  - senior citizens
  - illness and convalescence
- ☐ Special diets:
  - vegetarian: vegan, lacto-ovo, lacto, ovo
  - intolerances: lactose
  - medical special diets: diabetes, CHD, obesity, allergies
- ☐ Ethnic and religious groups:
  - Hindu
  - Muslim
  - Jewish

Key terms

BMR
DRV
intrinsic sugars
extrinsic sugars
fibre
cholesterol
saturated fatty acids
unsaturated fatty acids
trans fatty acid
hydrogenation
HBV
LBV
amino acid
monounsaturated fatty acids
polyunsaturated fatty acids

Which of the key terms above matches each of the following definitions?

A Relationship between food and drink intake and physical activity.

B The number of kilocalories you use to stay alive each day.

C A small unit that combines to form protein.

D Build up of fatty deposits in the arteries, causing a restriction in the blood flow, leading to stroke, heart attack or death.

To check your answers, look at the glossary on page 183.

Multiple choice questions

1 A vegan diet would not include any:

A dairy products
B fish products
C meat products
D of the above

2 The deficiency disease for iron is:

A scurvy
B kwashiorkor
C anaemia
D beri beri

3 Dietary guidelines are encouraging consumers to:

A eat less sugar, fat, fibre and eat more salt

B eat less sugar, salt, fibre and eat more fat

C eat less sugar, salt, fat and eat more fibre

D eat more protein, carbohydrate and less fat and salt

4 The water soluble vitamins are:

A vitamins A and E

B vitamins A and D

C vitamins B and C

D all the above

ResultsPlus
Maximise your marks

Meat products, such as beef lasagne, provide HBV protein.
Explain the advantage of using HBV protein. (2 marks)

Student answer	Examiner comments	Build a better answer
Student A High biological value protein found in beef. (0 marks)	■ This answer does not answer the question.	△ HBV foods contain all the essential amino acids. (1 mark)
Student B Found in animal products. (0 marks)	■ This answer does not answer the question.	△ Essential amino acids cannot be made by the body, but must be obtained from HBV foods. (1 mark)

Overall comment: The students did not answer the question correctly. An explain question requires a correct statement and a relevant explanation.

ResultsPlus
Maximise your marks

Name one LBV protein food that could be used as a meat substitute in a vegetarian lasagne. (1 mark)

Student answer	Examiner comments	Build a better answer
Quorn (0 marks)	■ No! This is a HBV food.	△ Any of the following answers would be correct: peas, beans, lentils, nuts or cereals. (1 mark)

Practice exam questions

1 Describe one way in which the nutritive value of foods may be altered by heat processing. (2 marks)
2 Explain the differences between saturated and unsaturated fat. (2 marks)
3 Describe the role of vitamins and minerals in the diet. (4 marks)
4 Give three examples of monosaccharides, disaccharides and polysaccharides. (6 marks)
5 Outline the use of complementary proteins when meal planning. (6 marks)
6 Describe the cultural differences between Muslim, Islam and Hindu diets. (6 marks)
7 Outline the current government dietary guidelines in the UK. (6 marks)

Chapter 2: Primary and secondary foods

Cereals

Objectives

- **Understand** the nutritional content, uses, and types of cereals

In their simplest form, cereals are primary foods, which can be processed into other useful ingredients and products. These are called secondary foods. Cereals are crops cultivated for the edible components of their seeds (grains). Cereals are grown in greater quantities and provide more food energy worldwide than any other crop. These staple crops are cheap to produce in comparison with protein foods.

Mixture of grains

Nutritional content

In their natural form as a whole grain, cereals are rich sources of carbohydrates, fats and oils, LBV protein, Vitamin B complex and minerals. All cereals are similar in structure.

Storing cereals

Cereals should be stored in a cool dry place, in an airtight container, for short periods of time. Wholegrain cereals have a shorter shelf life due to their fat content.

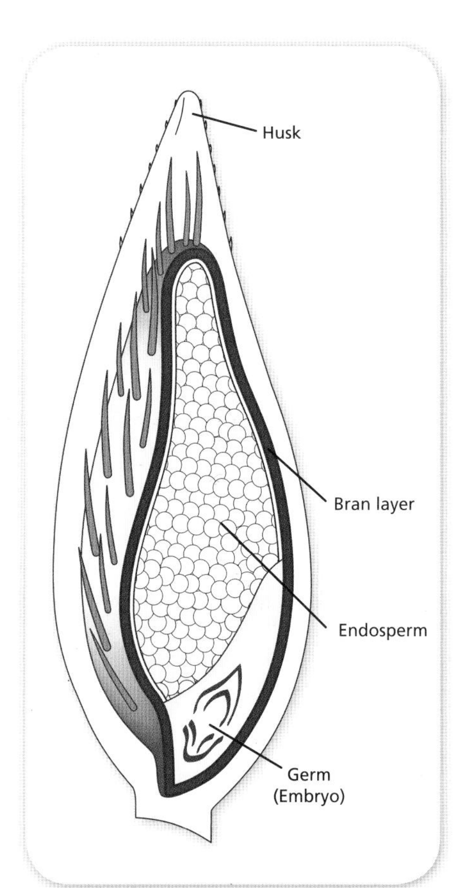

Cross-section of a cereal grain

Types of cereal

Wheat

Wheat is milled to make flour, by separating the endosperm from the rest of the grain. These small, fine particles are used in the production of semolina, couscous, pasta and breakfast cereals. During milling, the nutritional content of the grain can be altered due to the extraction of different particles of the grain. The extraction rate is the percentage of the whole grain used.

Types of wheat flour

- **Wholemeal flour** (100%) contains 100% of the germ, bran and endosperm, and has a brown colour and coarse, grainy texture.
- **Brown flour** (85-90%) contains 85% of the germ, bran and endosperm, and has a light brown colour and grainy texture.
- **White flour** (70%) is white and smooth, and contains endosperm, but the bran and germ have been removed during milling. In the UK, white flour must be fortified by law with iron, calcium, thiamin and niacin, to replace the nutrients lost during processing. This flour is white and has a smooth texture.

Many different variations of flours are available, including:

- **strong plain flour** – white or wholemeal flour with high gluten content suitable for bread making
- **self-raising flour** – white or wholemeal flour with the addition of a raising agent
- **soft flour** – flour with a low gluten content used for making cakes and pastries

- **gluten-free flour** – in which the protein gluten is removed, so it can be used by people who have intolerance to gluten (coeliac disease)
- **wheatmeal** – white flour with 10% finely ground germ added.

Bulgar wheat is made by soaking and cooking the whole wheat grain, drying it, removing part of the bran and cracking the remaining grain into small pieces. It is used in salads, soups, couscous and breads.

Rice

Brown rice is the whole of the grain, with only the husk removed. It is a highly nutritious food product, rich in fibre, starchy carbohydrate, Vitamin B complex and LBV protein. Brown rice takes longer to cook than white rice and has a nutty flavour and chewy texture. White rice has had the bran and germ removed during milling and polishing. As a result, it is less nutritious than brown rice, with fewer B vitamins, minerals and protein.

Brown rice

Rice is the staple food of many millions of people in Asia and Africa. It is popular in the UK as it is economical, easy to prepare and cook, and has a long shelf life. There are three main types of rice: long, medium and short grain. The grains of long grain rice (basmati and patna) separate when cooked and remain fluffy, so are good for savoury dishes. Medium and short grain rice (Carolina) grains become softer and stickier when cooked, and are better for sweet dishes.

Maize/corn

Traditionally grown in the Americas and Europe, maize is used as popping corn, is milled into corn flour or is used to manufacture breakfast cereals (cornflakes). It can also be eaten as a vegetable (corn on the cob). Cornflour is made from ground maize – it contains no gluten. This is a useful thickening agent for liquids and sauces. These are secondary foods. Maize is a staple food still in Mexico and Latin America.

Corn

Oats

Scotland and northern Europe are the main growers of oats. Manufacturers roll and crush oats between heated rollers to soften and partially cook them. They are found in porridge, muesli-type breakfast cereals and biscuits. These are secondary foods.

Explain how cereals can be processed to create other food components. (4 marks)

Basic answers (0–1 marks)

At this level, answers gave one or no processing method used to change the primary food into the secondary food.

Good answers (2 marks)

At this level, answers gave either a method and an explanation or two methods. For example: Wheat may be milled into flour and this can be mixed with eggs and water to make pasta.

Excellent answers (3–4 marks)

Answers gave two methods and at least one explanation. For example: Maize can be ground and milled into cornflour. Cornflour is used in sauces and soups as a thickening agent. Wheat may be milled into flour and this can be mixed with eggs and water to make pasta.

Support Activity

List the different types of flour available to consumers.

Stretch Activity

Research the main uses of each type of flour in food preparation.

Milk and dairy foods

Objectives

- **Understand** the nutritional content, uses, and types of milk and dairy foods

Milk

ResultsPlus
Exam Question Report

Give **two** nutrients, other than calcium, found in milk. (2 marks, 2008 Foundation)

How students answered

This question was poorly answered. Frequently, candidates used the stem of the question in their answer, and were unable to achieve a mark for 'calcium'.

51% got 0 marks

About half of students achieved a mark for protein.

9% got 1 mark

Fat, carbohydrate and vitamin A were also acceptable answers.

40% got 2 marks

Milk is a primary food product. Its secondary food products are: cream; cheese; yoghurt; butter (see Fats and oils on page 48).

Milk is a highly nutritious, useful and valuable food for all age groups. All mammals produce milk to feed their young. Milk used in this country comes mainly from cows, but also from goats and sheep.

Nutritional content

Milk is rich in protein, carbohydrate (lactose), Vitamins A, D and B (riboflavin, thiamin and niacin), calcium and phosphorous, water and fat (saturated and unsaturated fats). Processing techniques can affect the nutritional quality of milk, by reducing the water-soluble vitamins or removing fat to produce reduced-fat milks (skimmed and semi-skimmed).

Table 2.1 shows the main types of milk and their nutritional values.

Source	Type	Nutritional information
cow	whole milk	3.8% fat – nothing added or removed
	semi-skimmed	1.7% fat reduced fat content of whole milk
	skimmed	0.1% fat lower levels of fat-soluble vitamins
	Channel Islands	approximately 5% fat creamy flavour due to high fat content higher content of fat-soluble vitamins
sheep	milk	higher in fat than cow's milk excellent cheese-making properties
goat	milk	acceptable for certain intolerances to cow's milk
soya	milk	dairy free. Soya beans are ground with water to make soya milk. Lactose free. HBV protein, lower in fat than whole milk

Table 2.1: Types of milk and their nutritional values

Milk can also be made from rice and oats. These are dairy-free milks.

Treatment and storage

Milk is a perishable, nutritious food you can store for four to five days if refrigerated. Keep it in a clean, covered carton. Check date marks and use it on a rotational basis. Processing and preservation techniques increase the shelf life of milk and dairy products. Follow product instructions carefully to preserve the best qualities of the milk product.

Milk is subjected to different preservation techniques to increase its shelf life and sensory properties.

- Pasteurisation.
- Sterilisation.

- UHT (ultra heat treatment).
- Homogenisation: breaks up fat particles and distributes them evenly throughout the milk.
- Dehydration.
- Evaporation: evaporated, homogenised and sealed into cans and sterilised at 120°C for 10 minutes.
- Condensation: evaporated, homogenised and with added sugar instead of sterilisation.

For more on pasteurisation, sterilisation, UHT and dehydration see Chapter 3, pages 72–3.

Types of dairy product: secondary foods

Cream

Cream is the butterfat layer skimmed from milk before homogenisation. To whip cream into a stable foam, the fat content must be 30–38%.

- Types: the main types of cream are single (18% fat), double (48%), whipping (35%) and clotted (55%). These may be processed and preserved (like milk) to extend shelf life and use.
- Uses: desserts, cakes, sauces, drinks.
- Nutritional content: fat, protein, calcium and Vitamin A.
- Storage: any cream, once opened, should be covered and refrigerated.

Cheese

Cheese-making is a traditional method of preserving milk, used worldwide. By adding a starter culture, lactic acid is produced in milk, allowing protein to set (coagulate) with rennet. Different production methods can produce the variety of textures, flavours, colours and types of cheese.

- Types: hard (e.g. Cheddar), semi-hard (e.g. Wensleydale), blue-veined (e.g. Stilton), soft (e.g. cottage), ripened soft (e.g. Brie).
- Uses: sauces, savoury and sweet dishes, gratin toppings, sandwiches, bread, salads, pastry, scones.
- Nutritional content: protein, fat, Vitamin A, calcium and water.
- Storage: wrap and store in a cool place to prevent cheese from drying out and to prevent cross-contamination of odours.

Yoghurt

Yoghurt is a cultured milk product made using skimmed or whole milk or cream. The lactose in the milk is changed into lactic acid with a bacterial starter culture to develop the characteristic acidity, flavour and texture.

- Types: low-fat, whole milk, creamy, Greek-style, bio – all variations produced from the two types of yoghurt, set or stirred; adding fruit, jam, chocolate or honey can alter the flavour, texture and nutritional content of the yoghurt.
- Uses: snacks, desserts, sweet and savoury dishes, sauces and dressings, dips, drinks, soups, ice creams.
- Nutritional content: protein, fat, calcium, Vitamin B complex.
- Storage: store in a refrigerator for up to 14 days.

Support Activity

1. Describe the different sensory characteristics of milk and dairy products.
2. List four preservation treatments for milk.

Stretch Activity

Milk is a highly perishable food. Research how it should be stored correctly.

Remember that milk is a primary food. Cream, cheese, yoghurt and butter are secondary foods made from the processing of milk.

Cheese

Yoghurt

Eggs

Objectives

- **Understand** the nutritional content, uses and storage of eggs

Most eggs eaten in the UK are hen's eggs, but goose, quail and duck eggs can also be eaten.

Traditionally, eggs were produced by free-range farming where poultry roam freely and feed naturally in their surroundings. As demand for food increased, producers developed factory farming. Thousands of hens are kept in distressing living conditions and farmed intensively using cages, restricted eating patterns, artificial lighting and heat to stimulate egg production. Currently, consumer groups are campaigning for better animal welfare.

Support Activity

1. Discuss the function of the following parts of an egg: chalazae, membrane, shell and air sac.
2. Describe how eggs could be stored in the home.

Stretch Activity

Discuss why it is possible to have a soft-boiled egg with a runny yolk.

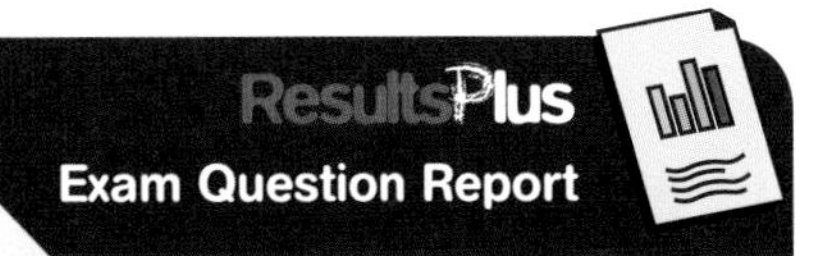

Give **two** nutritional reasons for using eggs in a lemon filling. (2 marks, 2009 Higher)

How students answered

The nutritional reasons for using eggs in a lemon filling were generally poor.

28% got 0 marks

Vague answers commented on vitamins and minerals.

51% got 1 mark

Good answers needed to focus on Vitamins A, B or D, potassium, protein or fat.

21% got 2 marks

Nutritional content

Eggs are a highly nutritious and versatile food product.

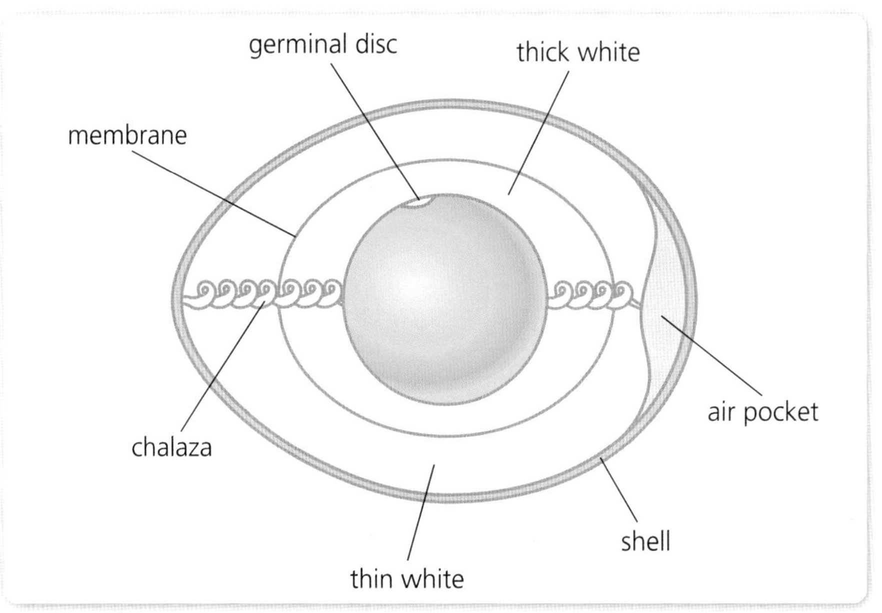

Cross-section of an egg

The eggshell is porous and allows the developing chick to breathe and store oxygen using the air sac. The pores let bacteria and odours in, but the membrane that lines the shell helps to filter this contamination. The colour of the shell varies with the breed of the bird. The egg white has two layers: thick and thin white. The egg yolk colour is related to the diet of the hen. It contains lecithin, which is an emulsifier used in the preparation of cakes, salad dressings and mayonnaise.

Uses

Eggs are used extensively in food preparation due to their versatility and functional properties. Egg white proteins start to coagulate at 60°C until the whole egg white is opaque and solid. The proteins of egg yolk start to coagulate at 70°C and continue until the egg yolk is dry and hard.

Eggs can be used:

- as foams, created by trapping air as protein is stretched and denatured in egg white and egg yolk (with/without egg white)
- as a raising agent in cakes by holding and trapping air
- for aerating mousses and soufflés
- to thicken sauces, custards and soups due to the coagulation of proteins
- to allow oil and water to be mixed to an emulsion without separating (mayonnaise) due to emulsifying properties
- to bind ingredients together to create different flavours and textures through the use of coagulation of proteins (e.g. in fish cakes or meatballs)
- to coat fried food, on their own or combined with breadcrumbs, to create a protective layer around food
- for glazing pastries, bread and scones, to enhance the colour of baked products
- to enrich sauces, soups and puddings by adding additional protein and fat
- in hard-boiled form to garnish salads and sandwiches.

Storage

Store eggs in a cool place, away from strong-smelling foods and extreme temperatures. Don't wash them as this will destroy the protective layer on the shell. Eggs will remain in good condition for 14–21 days. A stale egg will float in a bowl of water, as the air sac increases in size as the egg gets older. Eggs stamped with the Lion mark come from hens that are salmonella-free.

Forms of processed egg

Frozen whole egg, removed from the shell, is produced in large quantities for use in the food industry.

Dried egg is an alternative to frozen egg and is usually made by spray-drying or freeze-drying egg to a powder. It can then be reconstituted with water.

Liquid egg is sold specifically to the catering and food manufacturing industry. This product is pasteurised, refrigerated and sold in cartons or bags in box packages for food service operators. These methods of processing greatly increase the shelf life and improve the transportation of egg products within the food industry.

ResultsPlus
Build Better Answers

Evaluate the benefits of using frozen and dried egg products in the food industry. (4 marks)

Basic answers (0–1 marks)
At this level, answers gave one or no uses of using frozen and dried egg products in the food industry.

Good answers (2 marks)
At this level, answers gave a use and an advantage or two uses. For example: Dried egg has been dehydrated into a powder. This is easy to store.

Excellent answers (3–4 marks)
Answers gave two uses and at least one explanation. For example: Dried egg has been dehydrated into a powder. This is easy to store. Frozen egg has the shell removed and the egg is then frozen. This can increase the storage life of an egg from 14 days (fresh) to one month (frozen).

Apply it!

Eggs are a highly nutritious and versatile food product. In your Design and Make activites, consider the preparation, processing and storage implications for foods containing egg in your food products.

Meat

Objectives

- **Know** the nutritional content, uses and types of meat

ResultsPlus
Watch out!

Meat and fish are high- risk foods. They must be stored, cooked and handled correctly to ensure that they are safe to eat.

ResultsPlus
Watch out!

Varieties of meat and fish can also be seasonal foods and this can affect their taste, texture and flavour. Look in your local butcher or fishmonger to see what varieties of food are sold during the year.

ResultsPlus
Watch out!

Sustainability issues related to meat and fish might include sourcing the meat or fish locally, farming techniques, use of any by-products (waste products from the food industry used elsewhere in other industries) or the traceability of the food product from farm to fork.

Meat and poultry are primary foods, which can be processed into many other secondary products: for example, burgers, sausages, meatballs, pâté and cured meat products.

Different types of meat are eaten around the world and have been an important part of the human diet for centuries. Meat is more expensive to produce than cereal, due to the time, care and effort it takes to rear animals for meat. Large quantities of food (cereals, animal feed and pasture) as well as land and shelter have to be provided and this all contributes to the cost of meat.

Types of meat eaten in the UK include:

- beef
- veal (young calf)
- lamb
- mutton
- pork
- bacon
- poultry (chicken, turkey, duck, goose)
- game (venison, rabbit, pheasant).

Nutritional content of meat

Meat is composed of different proteins. An animal's muscle fibres are held in bundles by connective tissue. Each individual muscle fibre is surrounded by a sheath and, within this, the fibre is divided into myofibrils, which are surrounded by fluid. The myofribrils are made up of two proteins: myosin (which are thicker filaments) and actin (thinner filaments). These proteins are responsible for the contraction of muscle and for rigor mortis. Collagen is a soluble protein found around muscle bundles, forming a layer of connective tissue. Myoglobin carries oxygen to the muscles, giving meat its characteristic colour.

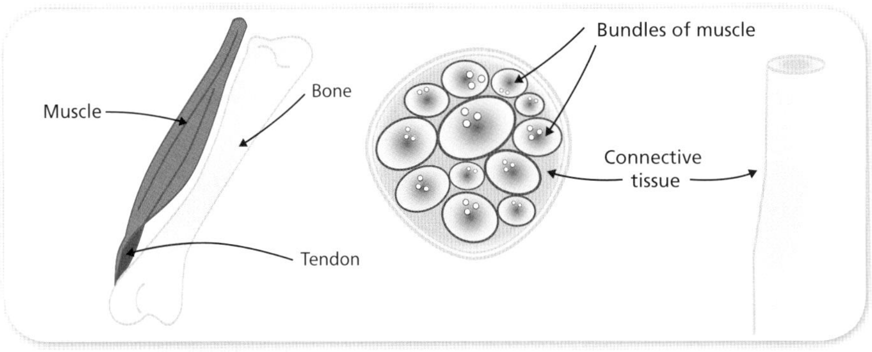

A cross-section of muscle

Fat is stored in the adipose tissue of meat under the skin, around vital organs (kidneys – suet) and between the bundles of muscle fibres as marbled fat. The quality of lean meat is often judged on the marbling, which affects the flavour, colour, texture and price of the cut of meat.

Meat is rich in Vitamins A, B and D. Iron is found in red meat and offal.

Marbled fat

Uses of meat

People use meat extensively in a wide range of recipes all over the world. Each type of meat has different cuts and uses, according to their suitability for different cooking methods. A butcher prepares the meat into joints or cuts according to the position and quantity of lean meat, bones and fat in various parts of the body. Lean, tender cuts are more expensive. This may be due to the rearing methods or the nutritional content of the meat.

Muscle fibres increase in size as the animal gets older; the older the animal, the tougher the meat from it. Those parts of the animal's body that do the most physical activity have the largest muscle fibres and make tougher meat. Generally, lean and tender cuts of meat are suitable for dry methods of cooking (grilling, roasting and frying), tougher cuts of meat are more suitable for moist methods of cooking, where the cooking liquid and increased cooking time can convert collagen to gelatine and tenderise the meat. The adipose tissue becomes soft and tender when cooked. The fat melts into the meat, allowing the texture to develop further. On the skin of roasted, grilled or fried meat, the fat becomes crisp and brown, enhancing flavour and texture.

Poultry has less connective tissue and so the meat is more tender.

Apply it!

In your Design and Make activities, meat and fish must be stored correctly to avoid cross-contamination and the risk of food poisoning. Consider the storage, preparation and processing implications when using these food products, to avoid cross-contamination.

Buying, preparing and storing meat

You can buy meat for preparation at home or ready prepared. It should have a fresh smell, good colour and moist, soft texture.

You should wrap meat and store it in a refrigerator. You can also freeze it on the day of purchase for up to a month.

Meat is a highly perishable, nutritious food. Make sure that you practise good hygiene when storing, preparing and cooking meat. Store raw and cooked meat on different shelves in refrigerators and prepare it using separate boards and knives to prevent cross-contamination. Defrost frozen meat thoroughly before cooking. Cook meat carefully and thoroughly to ensure quality and safety.

The Red Tractor is an independent mark of quality that guarantees the food that you buy comes from farms and food companies that meet high standards of food safety, hygiene, animal welfare and environmental protection.

Support Activity

Why is it important to be able to trace the origin of meat/animals back to the farm where it was reared?

The Red Tractor logo

Fish and other sources of protein

Objectives

- **Know** the nutritional content uses, and types of meat and fish
- **Describe** the alternative protein sources available to consumers

The MSC logo

Stretch Activity

Discuss the main factors to consider when choosing how to cook and prepare fish.

Stretch Activity

Discuss the nutritional contribution meat and fish make to our diet.

Fish stall

Fish

Fish is a primary food, which can be processed into many other food products, such as fish cakes, pâtés and fish fingers. You can buy a great many varieties of fish. You can buy fish frozen, smoked, salted or canned. However, with an increase in fishing over many decades, there is growing concern about fish stocks, farming methods and sustainability. The Marine Stewardship Council's fishery certification program and seafood ecolabel recognise and reward sustainable fishing. As a global organisation, MSC works with fisheries, seafood companies, scientists, conservation groups and the public to promote the best enviro-friendly seafood.

You can classify fish in four ways:

- origin: freshwater (e.g. trout) or seawater (e.g. plaice)
- shape: flat (e.g. plaice) or round (e.g. herring)
- fat content: oily fish have more than 5% fat in their flesh (e.g. mackerel, sardine, tuna); white fish have less than 5% fat in their flesh, but they have oil in their liver (e.g. cod, haddock, sole)
- physical structure: shellfish are either molluscs (small soft-bodied sea animals, which live inside a hard shell, such as cockles and mussels), or crustaceans (soft-bodied, jointed sea animals covered in a hard external skeleton, such as lobster, shrimp and crab).

Nutritional content of fish

Fish contains protein, but far less connective tissue than meat, so it is much easier to tenderise and quicker to cook. If you overcook it, fish becomes tough and dry. The fat in fish is mainly oils that are high in essential fatty acids, which can lower blood cholesterol and protect the heart. Oily fish is also high in the fat-soluble Vitamins A and D. Most fish contain small amounts of Vitamin B complex. Fish bones contain calcium. In some canned fish, bones softened during processing may be eaten. Fluoride is found in all fish, and sodium is found in seawater fish.

Uses of fish

You can use fish in many recipes, using many different preparation and cooking methods. The size of fish, desired flavour, texture and recipe will determine how you cook it: for example, you can marinate fish, coat with batter or breadcrumbs, season with flour or cook it in a liquid or with dry heat to grill, fry, bake, roast or microwave.

Buying, preparing and storing fish

With fresh fish, check that the skin is shiny and the eyes are clear. The flesh should be firm but springy to the touch. The gills should be bright red. Fresh fish should have a mild, pleasant smell. Fish deteriorates quickly after being caught due to the enzymes in it, so it is important to eat fresh fish as soon as possible after purchase. Store fish in the coolest part of the refrigerator, wrapped to prevent strong odours contaminating other foods.

Alternative protein sources

Alternative protein foods offer a variety of plant-based protein foods that can complement a range of different dietary requirements.

Alternative protein sources - tofu burger

Soya

Soya is the only food originating from a plant that is HBV. As a primary food product, soya beans can be used as whole soya beans or soya sprouts, or processed into secondary foods, such as soya milk, tofu, tempeh, soya sauce or miso.

Textured vegetable protein (TVP)

Textured vegetable protein is made from dehydrated soya beans that have had all their starch removed. Mixed with water into a paste, TVP can be shaped, then dried or frozen into a range of different products that can resemble meat. TVP is very bland: you need to use strong flavourings to enhance its taste and texture.

Quorn™

Quorn™ is another HBV protein food product, made from edible fungus (myco-protein) bound together with egg and processed into different shapes. You can use it to replace or extend meat dishes.

Manufacturers have developed these foods as a result of consumer demand for vegetarian, healthy, high-protein, low-fat meat substitutes.

Pulses and nuts

Pulses and nuts are also valuable sources of LBV protein. Pulses are sourced from the seeds of the legume plant family, which includes beans, peas and lentils. There are many varieties grown all over the world. Their preparation and use depends on the variety chosen for a recipe. They can be used in soups, stews and salads, and as vegetable accompaniments for flavour and texture.

Nuts are generally only eaten in small amounts because they are expensive. The most common nuts used in this country are peanuts, walnuts, almonds, chestnuts and cashews. They are also used in baking and confectionary to give flavour and texture to recipes. Some people experience severe allergic reactions to nuts. As a result, food labelling aims to inform consumers of the likely presence of nuts wherever a factory handles nuts during the preparation or manufacture of foods.

Stretch Activity

Explain why animal protein foods are often more expensive than plant-based protein foods.

ResultsPlus
Exam Question Report

Name **one** LBV protein that could be used as a meat substitute in a vegetarian lasagne. (1 mark, 2008 Higher)

How students answered

Students struggled with this question; many were unable to name a single food containing LBV protein. Inaccurate references were given to soya or Quorn products. Both of these are HBV proteins.

92% got 0 marks

Desirable answers would include: lentils, pulses, beans and legumes.

8% got 1 mark

Quick notes

- **Meat** is expensive to produce compared to cereals.
- **Meat and fish** are composed of many different proteins. These affect the structure and composition of the food.
- **Meat and fish** are highly perishable, nutritious foods.
- **Plant-based proteins** have been developed as a result of consumer demand for vegetarian, healthy, high-protein, low-fat meat substitutes. Pulses and nuts are also valuable sources of protein.

Fruit and vegetables

Objectives

- **Understand** the nutritional content, uses, types and storage of fruit and vegetables

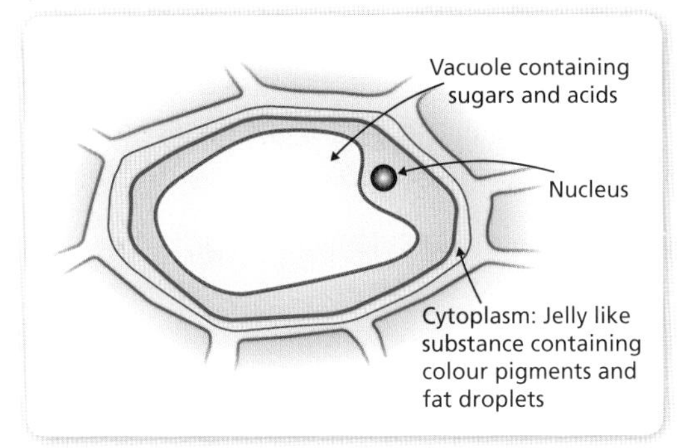

A plant cell

ResultsPlus
Watch out!

Make sure you understand the structure of a plant cell. It consists mainly of water, found in the vacuole containing the cell sap. Once the supply of water to the cell is reduced or cut off, water is lost and the cell starts to collapse. This is seen as wilting or leathery skin.

The water content of fruit and vegetables varies enormously. Those with a high water content, such as strawberries, cannot be successfully frozen as water expands as it turns to ice, causing the structure of the plant cell to collapse on thawing.

Fruit and vegetables are primary foods. They may be processed into secondary foods such as jams, marmalades, chutneys, pickles or couli sauces. They are vital for good health and wellbeing. They offer vibrant colour, intense flavour and a delicious range of textures to your diet.

Nutritional content

The nutritional content of different fruit and vegetables is determined by their type, freshness, seasonality and preparation, and by any processing and preservation techniques used. Fruit and vegetables are composed mainly of water and contribute valuable vitamins, minerals and carbohydrate to your diet.

Preparation and processing techniques can alter the nutritional content of fruit and vegetables due to the loss of water-soluble vitamins, which are sensitive to heat treatment and exposure to air.

Nutrients in food and vegetables include:

- protein – LBV protein in pulses and beans and HBV protein in soya beans
- carbohydrate – root vegetables and tubers are the best sources of starchy carbohydrates
- fibre – soluble fibre: flesh of fruit and vegetables; insoluble fibre: skins of vegetables (potatoes)
- Vitamin A – apricots, peppers, carrots, spinach
- Vitamin B – pulses and most green leafy vegetables
- Vitamin C – citrus fruits, blackcurrants and soft berry fruit, sprouts, cabbage, spinach, watercress
- iron – apricots and leafy green vegetables
- calcium – leafy green vegetables.

Types of fruit and vegetables

You can classify fruit and vegetables into two groups:

- climacteric, which ripen rapidly, so are often picked at full size but before they are fully ripe, then allowed to mature after harvesting (banana, mango, pear, avocado)
- non-climacteric, which ripen slowly and tend to maintain whatever quality they had at harvest (citrus fruit, apples, kiwi, pineapple, grapes and most vegetables).

You can also classify fruit and vegetables according to their growing system, structure and origin. Tables 2.2 and 2.3 are grouped by type.

Fruit type	Example
stone	plum, peach, greengage
hard	apple, pears
soft	strawberries, raspberries, grape
citrus	lime, lemon, orange
tropical	banana, pineapple, kiwi
dried	sultana, currant

Table 2.2: Classifying fruit by type

Vegetable type	Example
root	carrot, beetroot, parsnip, radish, swede
tuber	Jerusalem artichoke, potatoes, yams
bulb	garlic, onions, shallots, leeks
leaf	spinach, chard, watercress, lettuce
brassica	cabbage, sprouts, cauliflower, broccoli
pods and seeds	beans, peas, sweetcorn, mange tout, okra
fruiting	courgettes, tomatoes, pumpkin, squash, peppers, cucumber, aubergine
stems and shoots	asparagus, bean sprouts, celery, kale
mushrooms and fungi	ceps, chanterelles, oyster, field mushrooms

Table 2.3: Classifying vegetables by type

Support Activity

Discuss the nutritional benefits of eating a diet including lots of fruit and vegetables.

Stretch Activity

Investigate seasonal fruit and vegetables. Identify five fruit and /or vegetables that are in season for each of the twelve months of the year.

Fruit and vegetables

Organic fruit and vegetables

Growing, buying and storage

Select fruits and vegetables for their freshness and sensory properties. There are extensive ranges of fruit and vegetables available all year, some grown in this country and others imported from abroad. Farmers, growers and producers use a range of farming practices to meet consumer expectations for variety, quality, nutritional content and sensory properties. Farming practices might include the use of intensive farming to extend growing seasons and increase crop yields, increased pest and weed control, genetic modification or more traditional farming methods such as organic farming or cultivating home-grown fruit and vegetables.

These days, more consumers expect good quality, fresh, local, seasonal produce. Growing your own fruit and vegetables also has many benefits, including:

- fresh, local food
- seasonal produce
- no air miles from transportation
- no chemicals/pesticides/herbicides, so no side effects of these chemicals or uncertainty over long-term effects
- keeps you healthy – gardening is good physical exercise
- excellent taste/higher nutritive value because picked and eaten on the same day
- less expensive.

When choosing fruit and vegetables, make sure they are:

- clean
- undamaged, unblemished and disease-free
- of good shape, colour and appearance.

After purchase:

- handle gently to avoid bruising
- wash and remove dirt
- remove from packaging.

Storage:

- store in a cool, dry place
- use stock rotation
- store frozen vegetables and fruit in a freezer
- store tubers in a cool, dark place to avoid sprouting
- keep salad in drawer of refrigerator.

ResultsPlus
Build Better Answers

Give four reasons why it is good to grow your own fruit and vegetables. (4 marks)

Basic answers (0–1 marks)
At this level, answers gave one or no reasons why it is good to grow your own fruit and vegetables.

Good answers (2 marks)
At this level, answers gave two reasons.

Excellent answers (3–4 marks)
Answers gave at least three reasons why it is good to grow your own fruit and vegetables. For example:

1. Keeps you healthy because gardening is good physical exercise!
2. Excellent taste/higher nutritive value because picked and eaten on the same day.
3. Less expensive to grow your own fruit and vegetables.
4. Fresh, local produce.

Tables 2.4 and 2.5 show the various uses of fruits and vegetables.

Use	Fruit
raw	apples, pears, kiwi, grapes, plums, peaches
stewed	apples, blackberries, rhubarb, gooseberries, plums
dried	currants, sultanas, cherries, apricots, papaya, banana
vacuum-packed	apricots, dates
jam and marmalade	orchard fruits and berries, citrus fruits
sauces and coulis	berries and other soft fruits
desserts	cheesecakes, trifle, gateau, ice cream, mousses, flans and tarts
baked products	scones, bread, biscuits, cakes and pastries
savoury dishes	sauce accompaniments: apple, redcurrant jellies, gammon with pineapple, lemon and limes with fish dishes

Table 2.4: Uses of fruit

Orchard fruits

Citrus fruits

Use	Vegetables
raw	carrots, lettuce, cucumber, radish
steamed	bean sprouts, courgettes, peas, chard, spinach, leeks, asparagus
baked	potatoes
roasted	potatoes, carrots, parsnips, onions, peppers, pumpkin, squash, garlic
fried / sautéed	potatoes, courgettes, aubergine, mushrooms, onion
boiled	potatoes, carrots, cauliflower, corn on the cob, beetroot
microwaved	broccoli, leeks, cauliflowers
in savoury dishes	accompaniments, sandwiches, snacks, soups, pastries

Table 2.5: Uses of vegetables

Steamed vegetables

Roasted vegetables

Fats and oils

Objectives

- **Understand** the nutritional content, uses, types and storage of fats and oils

Fat and oil products are available in many varieties. Fats come from animal, fish or plant origin. Animal fats may come from the flesh of an animal (e.g. suet, lard) or be manufactured from an animal source (e.g. butter). Fish are rich sources of oils, which are found in their liver and flesh. Plant oils can be extracted from seeds, nuts, beans, flowers, cereals, fruit and vegetables.

A fat is solid at room temperature and has a high melting point. Oil is liquid at room temperature with a lower melting point. Each fat is made up of a unique combination of fatty acids, resulting in many different functional properties and working characteristics.

Fat type	Description	Nutritional content	Uses
butter	made from pasteurised, churned cream; buttermilk drained off and the resulting fat chilled, washed and hardened; salt added to improve flavour and shelf life; colour varies with breed of cow and quality of feed	82% saturated fat, 15% water, 0.4% protein, 2.3% minerals and fat-soluble Vitamins A and D	icing, sauces, pastry, glazing, biscuits, bread and cakes
lard	a hard, white, bland fat made of rendered and clarified pork fat	100% saturated fat	pastry for shortening properties, deep and shallow frying
suet	solid, hard fat made from animal fat; sold either in cartons or shredded	70–99% saturated fat	pastry, puddings and dumplings
margarine	made from animal fats or hydrogenated oils by adding hydrogen to harden oils into soft cooking fats or margarines; plant oils are unsaturated fatty acids and can hold more hydrogen, which converts them from oils to solids (this increases saturation of the fat, and resulting fatty acids are known as trans fatty acids, which increase risk of coronary heart disease by raising cholesterol levels)	varies depending on the origin of the fat or oil; Vitamin A and D added to margarine by law, and it must contain no more than 16% water; where water is used, an emulsifier is needed to blend the water to the fat or oil to prevent separation	block and soft margarines used as a substitute for butter
low-fat spreads	made from butter or margarine, with water, blended with fat, and an emulsifier added to produce a low energy value (compared to normal fats) product	varies depending on the origin of the fat and oil and water content	spreading; variable success with baking and cooking due to high water content
plant oils	made from nuts or the seeds of cereals (e.g. corn), fruit (e.g. olives) or flowers (e.g. sunflower); oil contained in the cells of seeds and nuts; each oil has distinct colour, taste and smell; refined after extraction to remove impurities; often hydrogenated and blended with other fats to make margarine or cooking fats	varies depending on the origin of the oil: (figures approximate) olive oil = 73% unsaturated fat and 15% saturated fat sunflower oil = 90% unsaturated fat corn oil = 60% unsaturated fats and 13% saturated fats	ice cream, salad dressings, marinades and sauces; blended oils used to produce cooking fats and oils

Table 2.6: Types of fat and oil

Storage

Keep butter, margarine, low-fat spreads, suet and lard covered or wrapped in a cool dry place or a refrigerator. Keep oils in a cool, dry, dark place in an airtight bottle.

After prolonged storage, fat deteriorates and goes off. This is called rancidity.

There are two types of rancidity.

- Hydrolytic rancidity occurs when, in the presence of water, butter, cream and margarine are attacked by enzymes that alter their chemical structure, resulting in intense odours. This can be useful in cheese-making but is undesirable in butter and margarine.
- Oxidative rancidity occurs when, in the presence of oxygen, unsaturated fats are attacked by highly reactive particles called free radicals, resulting in undesirable odours, and a change in colour and texture of the oil or fat.

ResultsPlus
Build Better Answers

Evaluate the use of fats in food preparation and cooking in a test kitchen. (4 marks)

Basic answers (0–1 marks)

At this level, answers gave one or no uses of fats in food preparation and cooking in a test kitchen.

Good answers (2 marks)

At this level, answers gave one use and an advantage/disadvantage or two uses. For example: Butter is a secondary food product made from churned cream. It has a distinctive colour and flavour that is useful in baked products.

Excellent answers (3–4 marks)

Answers gave two uses and at least one evaluative comment. For example: Butter is a secondary food product made from churned cream. It has a distinctive colour and flavour that is useful in baked products. Low-fat spread is made from butter or margarine. Water is added, it is blended with fat, and an emulsifier is added to produce a product with a low energy value compared to normal fats. This would be useful for weight-control diets.

Support Activity

1. Identify the three main sources of fats and oils, giving two examples for each source.
2. Using the ingredients list and nutritional information on food labels, research the fat content in food products. Record your information in a table like the one below.

Food product	Ingredients containing fat	Grams of fat per 100g

Apply it!

When you are using recipes in your Design and Make activities, consider how fats are used to create specific characteristics in food: for example, using white fat and a hard yellow fat (margarine or butter) in shortcrust pastry.

Stretch Activity

Investigate the range of fats and oils available to consumers for food preparation and production.

Fats and oils

Sugar

Objectives

- **Understand** the nutritional content, uses, types and storage of sugar

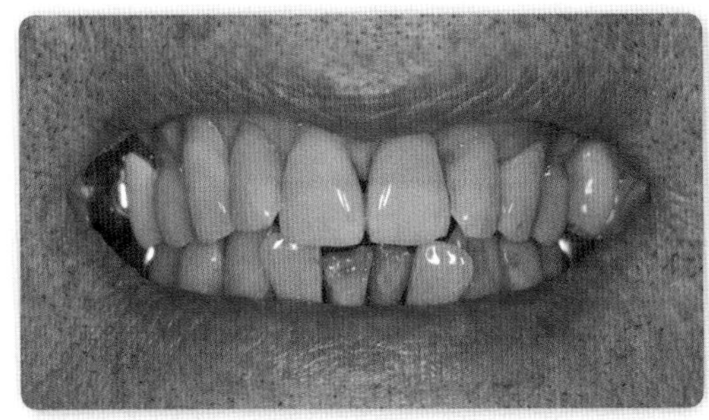

Tooth decay: the dangers of eating too much sugar

ResultsPlus
Build Better Answers

Give two reasons for using sugar in a cake recipe. (2 marks)

Basic answers (0–1 marks)
At this level, answers gave one or no reasons.

Good answers (2 marks)
At this level, answers gave two reasons. For example:

1. To sweeten the cake product.
2. To colour the baked product using the Maillard reaction.

Sugar is a carbohydrate and can be found in food as a simple sugar (monosaccharide) or double sugar (disaccharide). Sugar is an important ingredient in the confectionery, baking and drinks industries, adding flavour, colour and texture to food products, as well as increasing their shelf life by acting as a preservative, as high concentrations of sugar can prevent bacterial growth. For this reason, many processed foods have sugar and sweeteners added to their recipes. Apart from having a high energy value, it has no other nutritional value. An excess of sugar is bad for you because it can lead to obesity and tooth decay.

Uses of sugar in food preparation

Caramelisation is an important process in the production of a number of food products. When sugar crystals or syrup are heated, they decompose to produce a range of brown products called caramel.

During cooking and processing, in dry heat, where sugars are mixed with protein in baked products, browning occurs and a pleasant baked aroma is produced. This is called the Maillard reaction.

Both caramelisation and the Maillard reaction are useful in the baking, confectionary and drinks industries.

Storage

Store sugar in a cool, dry place to prevent clumping of crystals.

Sugar is used in a wide variety of products

Types of sugar

Table 2.7 shows the types of sugar available.

Sugar type	Description
sugar cane	• grown in tropical countries • cane crushed and sprayed with water to extract molasses; impurities removed and water evaporated off to leave raw brown sugar
sugar beet	• grown in the UK • sugar stored in the root of sugar beet; beets shredded and soaked in hot water, then impurities removed and water evaporated off, leaving raw brown sugar
granulated sugar	• raw brown sugar processed to reduce size of crystals; impurities and colour removed • uses: cakes, biscuits, drinks, confectionery and desserts
caster sugar	• as above, but with smaller sugar crystals • uses: cakes, pastries, biscuits, drinks, confectionery and desserts
icing sugar	• crystals milled into fine powder; anti-caking agent often added to prevent lumps forming during storage • uses: icings, sauces, coulis and decoration
brown sugar	• crystallised syrup refined into brown sugar; produces moister, richer sugar crystals, which vary in size, colour and flavour, e.g. Demerara, soft brown, dark brown • uses: cakes, biscuits, sauces, confectionery and desserts.
syrup	• sugar syrup • uses: puddings, flapjacks, biscuits, cakes
treacle	• sugar cane molasses and sugar syrup • uses: adds dark flavour and colour to puddings, cakes, biscuits, toffee
natural sweeteners - honey	• produced by bees from nectar obtained from various flowers; sold in liquid (runny) and solid (set) forms • uses: sandwiches, drinks, desserts, cakes, sauces
artificial sweeteners	• low-calorie, intense sweetener e.g. Aspartame, acesulfame-K-based sweeteners

Table 2.7: Types of sugar and their uses

Sugar cane

Sugar beet

Support Activity

Discuss the two main differences between sugar cane and sugar beet.

Stretch Activity

Investigate the functions and different types of sugar and sweetener products used in the food industry. The first example is completed for you.

Food product	Name of sugar/ sweetener	Function
strawberry jam	sucrose	sweetener and preservative
fruit yogurt		
tin of peaches		
packet of crisps		
tomato sauce		

Confectionary

Secondary foods

Objectives

- **Understand** how combining or processing primary foods can create secondary foods
- **Understand** how secondary foods have increased nutrition and improved sensory qualities

Apply it!

In your Design and Make activities, most ingredients must be combined in the correct proportions to each other, if the food product is going to be successful in terms of nutrition and improved sensory qualities.

Secondary foods

Combining raw ingredients

Food technology involves the combining or processing of raw materials into edible food products. The raw ingredients used can be divided into the various categories.

- Primary foods are used raw, or changed from raw materials using only primary processing to make them suitable for either immediate consumption or further processing: for example, milling wheat, pasteurising milk, washing fruit and vegetables.

Primary and their secondary foods

- Secondary foods are combined or processed to make them into food products: for example, flour, water and salt are made into bread, or flour and eggs are made into pasta; meat is combined with egg and breadcrumbs to make burgers; milk and rennet are made into cheese.
- Food components are individual ingredients within a more processed product: for example, tomato sauce, cheese sauce, pasta and meat are the food components used to make a lasagne (a composite food).
- Composite foods are made of different component parts. Some of the parts may have undergone primary processing (meat in the lasagne) and some may have undergone secondary processing (pasta, tomato and cheese sauces in the lasagne).
- Standard components are pre-manufactured components used in the manufacture of commercial and domestic food products. They are useful for ensuring the consistency and quality of food products, but are often expensive and have been highly processed. Examples include ready-made pastry, sauces and pasta, pre-blended herbs and spices or ingredients that have undergone some partial preparation, such as grated cheese or pre-washed vegetables.

Consumers can choose to purchase the basic ingredients to make a lasagne at home, buy some basic ingredients and other standard components (pasta, stock cubes, seasoning) to create their own lasagne at home, or buy a ready-made product from a shop.

Properties of food products

The more processing an ingredient, component or composite food has undergone, the more expensive it is likely to be. Combining or processing primary foods can create other foods with additional properties, such as:

- increased nutrition
- improved sensory qualities.

Table 2.10 shows ways to improve the various properties of secondary food products.

Secondary food product	Increased nutrition
pastry	• add eggs to enrich with protein • add wholemeal flour to increase fibre content
sauces	• add cream, cheese or eggs to enrich with protein
cakes, biscuits, bread, scones	• add fruit or vegetables to increase vitamin and fibre content • replace half the sugar content with dried or fresh fruit to improve natural fruit sugar content and vitamin content • use wholemeal flour to improve fibre content
yoghurt	• add fruit, honey or jam to increase vitamin content
low-fat spreads	• made from butter or margarine with added water and blended with fat and an emulsifier to produce a low energy value (compared to normal fats) product
pasta	• add spinach and carrots to improve Vitamin A and mineral (iron) content
drinks (milk shakes/smoothies)	• add fruit to increase vitamin, mineral or fibre content

Table 2.10: Increased nutrition in secondary food products

Tables 2.11–2.13 below show ways to improve the appearance, texture and taste of secondary foods.

Apply it!

Recipe innovation and development is used in Unit 1 – coursework. Consider how and why you will develop your range of food products to meet the needs of your user group.

Take care when you are altering recipes to ensure that proportions and combinations of ingredients enhance your Design and Make activities.

Support Activity

The following recipe was used to produce a prototype bread product.

500g strong plain flour
50g butter
1 sachet dried easy blend yeast
1tsp salt
1tsp sugar
Water to mix to a dough

Describe two modifications that would make the bread product suitable for a consumer wanting a multicultural bread product.

Secondary food product	Improved appearance
pastry	• egg or milk glaze
cakes, biscuits and puddings	• icing: butter, royal, fondant, glacé, cream • fruit to enhance colour: dried, fresh, purée, fruit glaze
pasta	• gratin topping (cheese and breadcrumbs) • add spinach and carrot to change colour of pasta
meat and fish products	• glazes, marinades, sauces
treacle	• brown colour from sugar cane molasses and syrup

Table 2.11: Improving appearance in secondary food products

Fruit topping

Cheese topping

Secondary food product	Improved texture
pastry, bread, scones and biscuits	• use wholemeal flour to add nutty, coarse texture • add seeds or dried fruit • use correct proportions of ingredients
cake	• use fruit to create different textures, e.g. banana cake • use correct raising agent to aerate mixture • runny texture of syrup/treacle can be added
pasta	• use gratin topping (cheese and breadcrumbs) to create crispy, crunchy texture • add spinach and carrot to change flavour of pasta
meat products	• use different cooking methods to create textures (moist, dry or combination methods)
cheese	• use different cheese-making methods to produce cheese with characteristic textures: hard, soft, cream, blue-veined
yoghurt	• add different types of fruit • process fruit in different ways to create alternative textures (purée, chopped fruit or fruit juice)
margarine	• made from animal fats or hydrogenated oils by adding hydrogen to harden oils into soft cooking fats or margarines

Table 2.12: Improving texture in secondary food products

Apply it!

In your Design and Make activities, consider the combining or processing of primary foods to create additional properties (increase nutrition or improve sensory qualities).

Stretch Activity

Describe five methods of improving the nutritional content of bread products.

Secondary food product	Improved flavour
pastry	• add herbs • use butter
bread, scones, savoury biscuits	• add spices, herbs, cheese, garlic
cakes and biscuits	• add juice or zest of oranges, lemons • add natural essences: vanilla, peppermint, almond • add spices: ginger, mixed spice, cinnamon • add chocolate, dried or fresh fruit
pasta	• use gratin topping (cheese and breadcrumbs) • add spinach and carrot to change flavour of pasta
joints of meat	• glazes, marinades, sauces, stocks
sauces	• add cream, alcohol, herbs or spices to sauces • use seasonings
cheese	• use different cheese-making methods to alter flavour of cheese: mild, mature, blue-veined
butter	• add salt to improve flavour (and shelf life)
treacle	• used instead of other sugar products to create intense flavour

Table 2.13: Improving taste in secondary food products

Treacle on pancakes

Support Activity

Create a collage of pictures (mood board) using the internet and magazines to demonstrate the range of secondary food products available to the consumer.

ResultsPlus

Build Better Answers

List three categories of food products used in food production. (3 marks)

■ Basic answers (0–1 marks)
At this level, answers gave none or one category of food product.

● Good answers (2 marks)
At this level, answers gave two categories of food product.

▲ Excellent answers (3 marks)
Answers gave three categories of food product. For example:

1. Primary food
2. Secondary food
3. Composite food

Functional properties and working characteristics of ingredients

Objectives

- **Understand** the properties and working characteristics of raw materials and ingredients
- **Describe** how the functional properties of ingredients affect finished products

Apply it!

Understanding the functional properties of ingredients is extremely useful when designing and making food products.

Cakes

Functional properties

The properties and working characteristics of raw materials, ingredients and food components are determined by their nutritional structure and composition.

Functions of ingredients

Table 2.8 shows the functions of ingredients.

Ingredient	Functional properties	Use in food
eggs	colour and flavour	cakes
	foam holds air when whisked	meringue, swiss roll
	emulsion allows oil and water to be mixed together without separation	mayonnaise
	binds ingredients together	fish cakes, beef burgers
	a protective **coating** around food	batters
	enriching	sauces, choux pastry
	glazing	egg wash on pastry
flour	gives structure to product through coagulation of wheat protein (gluten), because of high gluten content of strong plain flour	bread
	bulking agent	crumble topping, pastry casing
	raising agent (self-raising flour)	cakes
	thickening and gelation	sauces
fat and oils	adds colour, flavour and texture	shortbread, pastry
	aerates mixtures by holding in air	cakes, biscuits, pastry
	emulsions	salad dressings, cake mixtures, sauces
	extends shelf life	pastry, bread, cakes
	binding agent	salad dressing, tinned foods

➜*continued*

Ingredient	Functional properties	Use in food
sugar	caramelisation-dry heat applied to sugar	crème brûlée
	browning baked products with sugar and protein content	cakes, biscuits, bread, scones
	bulking agent, holds air with fat mixture	cakes
	extends shelf life due to preservation	jam
	aids fermentation	bread, alcohol
liquid	raising agent when converted to steam	cakes, batters, bread
	binding agent	pastry
	glazing (milk)	scones
	enriching (milk)	bread
salt	flavour	pastry
	extends shelf life	fish
	develops gluten in flour and controls action of yeast	bread
yeast	fermentation (produces carbon dioxide, which acts as a raising agent) **aeration**	bread
baking powder	aeration	make cakes rise
gelatine	coagulation or gelatinisation (setting)	jelly, cheesecakes, soufflés, mousses
fruit and vegetables	thickening	soups, purées
chocolate and icing	coating and decoration	biscuits, cakes, desserts

Table 2.8: Functions of ingredients

Biscuits

Jams

Gelotine cubes

Thickening and gelatinisation (gelation)

When you moisten and heat starch, it thickens. This process is called gelatinisation. Starch is insoluble in cold water, but heat causes liquid to penetrate the starch granule, making it swell and burst. This creates a gel.

The degree of gelatinisation is affected by three factors:

- the proportion and type of starch
- the temperature of the liquid: gelation occurs at 75°C so if dry starch is added to hot water, lumps will form because the surface of the starch grain will gelatinise immediately
- effects of other ingredients: for example, acids decrease thickening power, and sugars soften gels, making them runny.

Dextrinisation

When starch is subjected to dry heat (such as with bread in a toaster), the starch is converted to sugar and then to caramel. This is known as dextrinisation and gives the food product a characteristic golden brown colour.

Caramelisation

Caramelisation is an important process in the production of a number of food products. When you heat sugar crystals or syrup, they decompose to produce a range of brown products called caramel.

Browning

During cooking and processing, in dry heat, where sugars are mixed with protein in baked products, browning occurs and a pleasant baked aroma is produced. This is called the Maillard reaction.

Setting (coagulation)

When you heat proteins, their chemical structure is denatured (changed). This is irreversible. As heating continues, proteins coagulate (set) and become less soluble.

Coagulation is affected by:

- heat (proteins found in food ingredients coagulate at different temperatures)
- mechanical action creating heat (e.g. whisking, creaming, beating)
- acid (by adding a starter culture, lactic acid is produced in milk, allowing protein to set with rennet; this process is used in cheese and yogurt making)
- alcohol (some marinades use alcohol to allow proteins in meat to denature, to alter the texture and flavour of meat).

Aeration

You can add raising agents to cake and bread mixtures to give lightness to a food product. For a mixture to rise, it must have the capacity to stretch and hold its shape once risen. Gases expand when heated, causing a mixture to rise. The gases used are air, CO_2 and H_2O vapour.

- Use raising agents carefully to ensure success when cooking.
- Always follow recipes carefully, and use the raising agent in the correct proportion.
- Sieve dry ingredients.
- Add and mix thoroughly to ensure even distribution.
- Store in a cool, dry place.
- Use an airtight container to prevent deterioration.

Foaming

Egg white is capable of holding up to seven times its own volume of air due to the ability of the protein ovalbumin to stretch. If you over-beat it, it will overstretch and break, returning to a liquid.

Whole egg and sugar whisked together will trap a large volume of air.

Stretch Activity

Discuss the function of a raising agent.

Stretch Activity

Discuss the functionality of ingredients and their uses in food preparation and production.

Setting

Aeration

Fermentation

If you give yeast the correct conditions for growth, it will produce carbon dioxide gas and alcohol during a series of chemical reactions called fermentation. The conditions needed for yeast to grow are:

- food source (sugar or flour)
- warm temperature (25°C-37°C); if too hot, yeast will be destroyed; if too cold, yeast will remain inactive
- moisture
- time (critical stages during bread-making: kneading, proving and knocking back).

Shortening

Fat is used in cake, biscuit and pastry mixtures. The fat forms layers between the strands of gluten to create a tender, flaky texture. You can use different types of fat and oil in varying combinations to create shortness, and to add a variety of flavour and colour to food products.

Fortification

Foods are fortified to improve and enhance their nutritional content. To add protein, sauces, soups, baked products and puddings can be enriched with egg and butter.

Some foods are fortified with additional nutrients, as shown in Table 2.9. Those marked with *must be fortified by law, to improve the nutritional content of those foods.

Binding

Ingredients can be bound together to create different flavours and textures through the coagulation of proteins (fish cakes, meatballs).

Glazing

Egg, milk and syrup (water and sugar) can be used to enhance the appearance of pastries, bread and cakes. Fruit juices, honey and marinades of oil and spices can be used to glaze meat and fish, and to add flavour and texture to roasted, barbecued, baked and grilled meats.

Coating

Coating fried food with egg (batter) or a combination of egg and breadcrumbs creates a protective layer around food, due to the coagulation of the egg proteins.

Emulsification

Emulsifying properties allow you to mix oil and water so they do not separate (for example, in mayonnaise, sauces, drinks and soups). A stabiliser works by absorbing large quantities of water and binding to create a stable mixture that does not separate.

Without an emulsifying agent, food becomes unstable and separates into watery and fatty layers.

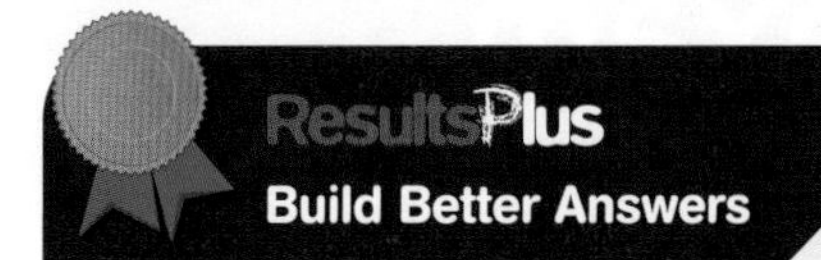

Describe two functions of eggs in recipes. (4 marks)

■ Basic answers (0–1 marks)

At this level, answers gave one or no function.

● Good answers (2 marks)

At this level, answers gave two functions or one function and a description. For example:

1. Eggs contain protein and coagulate when heated.
2. Eggs can aerate a mixture.

▲ Excellent answers (3–4 marks)

Answers gave two uses and at least one description. For example: Eggs contain protein and coagulate when heated. Eggs can aerate a mixture by stretching and trapping air.

Fortified food	Nutrients
White flour*	Calcium
Breakfast cereals	Iron and Vitamin B complex
Margarine*	Vitamins A and D

Table 2.9: Fortified food nutrients

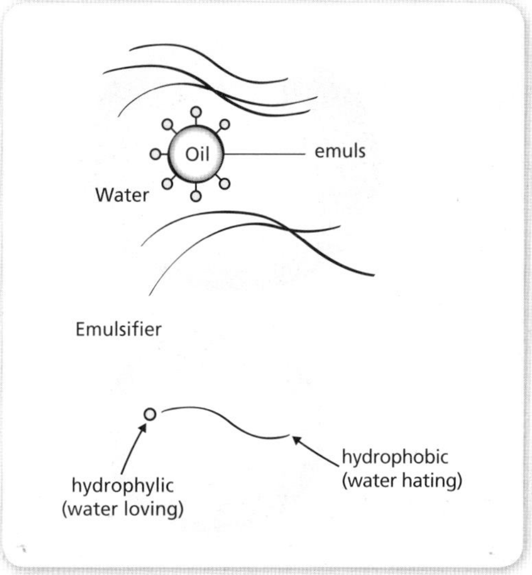

Emulsification

Know Zone
Chapter 2 Primary and secondary foods

By understanding primary and secondary foods, you can utilise the properties and working characteristics of raw materials and ingredients to explore how their functional properties affect finished products in your practical development work of food products.

You should know...

☐ The nutritional content, uses, types and functional properties of:
- cereals
- meat and fish
- fruit and vegetables
- fats and oils
- milk and dairy
- alternative protein sources
- eggs
- sugar

☐ Functional properties and working characteristics:
- thickening and gelatinisation
- aeration
- shortening
- browning
- glazing
- dextrinisation
- setting: coagulation and gelatinisation
- foaming
- fortification
- coating
- emulsification
- caramelisation

☐ Secondary foods created for increased nutrition and improved sensory qualities.

Key terms

staple crops	rancidity
extraction rate	Maillard reaction
pasteurisation	emulsification
sterilisation	gelatinisation
UHT	dextrinisation
homogenisation	standard components

Which of the key terms above matches each of the following definitions?

A The amount of the whole grain that is used to make flour.

B An important process in the production of a number of food products. When sugar (crystal or syrup) is heated, it decomposes to produce a range of brown products called caramel.

C During cooking and processing, in dry heat where sugars are mixed with protein in baked products, browning occurs and a pleasant baked aroma is produced.

D Allows oil and water to be mixed to an emulsion without separating. (mayonnaise)

To check your answers, look at the glossary on page 183.

Multiple choice questions

1 Foods classified as dairy foods would be:

A milk, fish and eggs
B milk, meat and eggs
C milk, cereals and fruit
D milk, cheese, cream and yoghurt

2 Sources of fats originating from animals are:

A lard, suet and butter
B butter and corn oil
C sunflower oil and low fat spreads
D suet, lard and olive oil

3 The gases used to make food mixtures rise are:

A nitrogen and oxygen
B air and nitrogen
C water vapour and nitrogen
D water vapour, air and carbon dioxide

4 A stabiliser works by:

A absorbing large quantities of water to bind the mixture together
B allowing fats and oils to mix
C setting protein
D thickening starch

ResultsPlus
Maximise your marks

Chicken is cooked in a white sauce which is made from fat, flour and milk.
One reason for using milk in the white sauce is that it keeps the filling moist.
Give two other reasons why milk is a suitable ingredient to make white sauce.

Student answer	Examiner comments	Build a better answer
Student A Provides vitamins. (0 marks)	■ This is too vague. Specific vitamins must be mentioned.	△ Vitamins A and D (1 mark)
Student B Makes the mixture soft. (1 mark)	■ Milk contributes to the organoleptic properties of the sauce, by aiding flavour, colour and viscosity.	△ To allow the thickening of starch during gelatinisation. (1 mark)

Overall comment: The student answers are too vague, lacking knowledge and understanding of specific foods.

Practice exam questions

1 Outline the difference between fats and oils. (2 marks)

2 List six uses of eggs in food production. (6 marks)

3 When food products are designed, the ingredients are chosen because of their function. Discuss the ways in which food designers can use the functions of ingredients in new product development. (6 marks)

Chapter 3: Preservation and processing

Preservation and food safety

Objectives

- **Understand** food issues relating to spoilage, poisoning and food, kitchen and personal hygiene

For raw food materials to be used in food production, manufacturers need to process or preserve the foods, to make them suitable for either further processing or immediate consumption.

Food processing and preservation involve the primary and secondary treatment of food to transform the food material into other food components and composite foods. This is the process of treating food to prevent natural and microbial decay, by modifying the conditions that favour enzyme activity and the growth of microorganisms.

Food spoilage

Food contamination and food spoilage may occur due to natural decay, enzyme action or microorganisms. Foods that spoil rapidly are called perishable foods, and usually have a high water content and good nutritional content. Foods with a high protein and/or moisture content are called high-risk foods. Examples include raw and cooked meat, poultry and fish, cheese, milk and dairy products, eggs and cooked rice.

High-risk foods

Natural decay

All food is susceptible to natural decay. Natural decay in food is the result of moisture loss and the action of enzymes. The rate of natural decay depends on:

- time
- storage conditions
- temperature
- type of food
- nutritional content of foods.

Quick notes

- **Mould**: A form of fungi.
- **Toxin**: Poison produced by a pathogen, such as moulds and bacteria.
- **Bacteria**: Small microscopic organisms found all about us. They may be useful or harmful.
- **Yeast**: Microscopic, single celled fungi which reproduce and give off CO_2 in the process called fermentation.

These fruit are susceptible to decay

The effects of natural decay can be identified by a change in colour, flavour, texture and smell: for example, bread goes stale, dry and mouldy. Meat and fish lose their characteristic colour and texture, but gain a putrid smell. After harvesting, fruit and vegetables continue to respire and ripen. Natural decay can then cause them to shrink, become soft and limp, with leathery and wrinkled skins. They often go and mouldy, with a change in colour. Milk becomes sour, while cheese becomes hard and rancid.

Mug of tea

Action of enzymes

The actions of enzymes can be positive and negative.

- **Positive actions** – uses in food preparation: for example, in cider and tea production, which develop their characteristic colour and flavours due to enzyme activity.
- **Negative actions** – spoilage: enzymes naturally present in foods cause food to decay. When you peel apples, pears or bananas, for example, they start to develop a brown colouration. Browning occurs due to the activity of an enzyme (polyphenol oxidase) when the plant tissue is damaged, cut, bruised or diseased. You can prevent this browning by destroying enzymes with heat, immersing fruit or vegetables in cold water to exclude oxygen from food, increasing salt concentrations (aubergines are traditionally salted to halt enzyme activity) or placing food in lemon juice. This works due to its acidity. During storage, fruit and vegetables start to dry out and decay through enzyme activity.

Conditions for growth of enzymes: oxygen, prolonged storage, warm temperatures.

Contamination by microorganisms

Microorganisms are microscopic living organisms. They are found in air, soil, water and during natural decay. Some foods contain microorganisms (salmonella can be found in poultry); other microorganisms can be transferred to food through cross-contamination. This means that the food has been infected with harmful microorganisms and is therefore not safe to eat.

Microorganisms can also have useful functions in the production of food products: for example, when making cheese, yoghurt, Quorn™, bread and beer.

There are three types of microorganism responsible for contamination of food: yeasts, moulds and bacteria.

Apply it!

There are six factors affecting the growth of microorganisms:

- food
- warmth
- time
- moisture
- neutral pH
- oxygen.

Make sure that you control these factors to prevent their growth as much as possible in your Design and Make activities.

Yeasts, moulds and bacteria

Yeasts

Yeasts

Yeasts are microscopic, single-celled fungi which reproduce and give off CO_2 during fermentation.

Uses: During the process of fermentation, yeast is used to make bread and alcohol. Sugars break down into alcohol and carbon dioxide.

Spoilage: Yeasts are found in the air, in soil and on the surface of fruit. They can spoil jams and fruit yoghurts by fermenting sugars in moist, warm conditions with food for growth and reproduction.

Conditions: Yeast does not need oxygen (anaerobic) to grow.

Moulds

Moulds

Moulds are a form of fungi

Uses: During the production of blue-veined cheeses, harmless moulds are used to produce specific flavours and textures.

Spoilage: Moulds are visible microorganisms that grow on the surface of foods.They can be black, white or blue in colour.

Conditions: Warm (20°C–30°C), moist conditions are the ideal conditions for moulds to grow, but they will also grow on food that is dry, acidic, alkaline, or has a low concentration of salt or sugar.

Bacteria

Bacteria

Bacteria are small, microscopic organisms that may be harmful or useful.

Uses: Cheese and yogurt manufacture use cultures of lactic acid bacteria to produce the characteristic flavours and textures of these products.

Spoilage: Bacteria may be classified as causing:

- *Infection*: pathogenic bacteria can cause food poisoning, which is a serious infection causing illness or even death; infected foods often look and smell as they should, but the presence of these bacteria can make them very dangerous to eat (see next section).
- *Toxins*: bacteria may also produce toxins as waste products or spores, which cause irritation to the intestine and food poisoning symptoms, even when only a small number of bacteria are present. Toxins are not destroyed by normal cooking temperatures, as some spores remain dormant. Germination of bacterial spores is usually accompanied by the production of highly poisonous substances.

Conditions: For optimum growth, bacteria require food, warmth, moisture and oxygen. Reproduction is very rapid, as they divide into two every two minutes. Bacteria can grow in neutral pH conditions, but pathogenic bacteria cannot reproduce in acid or alkaline conditions.

Cross-contamination can occur in many different ways.

- food to food
- food handler to food
- pests to food
- pet to food
- equipment to food.

Food poisoning

Table 3.1 shows the bacteria that are the main causes of food poisoning.

	Salmonella	Listeria monocytogenes	Clostridium perfringens	Bacillus cereus	Staphylococcus aureus
Type	infectious	infectious	toxic	toxic	toxic
Onset time	6–48 hours	1–14 days	8–22 hours	1–7 hours	1–7 hours
Duration of illness	1–7 days	2–3 days	variable	3 days	1–6 days
Causes	fish, poultry, eggs, dairy foods	soft cheese, ice cream, pâtés, raw vegetables, raw meat, raw and cooked poultry	meat and meat products, gravy	cooked rice and other cereals and starchy foods	poor hygiene leading to cross-contamination
Symptoms	vomiting, fever, diarrhoea, death	vomiting, fever, diarrhoea, meningitis in newborn babies	vomiting, fever, diarrhoea	vomiting, fever, diarrhoea	vomiting, fever, diarrhoea
Prevention	• good personal hygiene • preparing, storing raw and cooked foods separately • refrigerate all high-risk foods • good stock rotation	• good stock rotation • cooking food adequately • washing vegetables thoroughly	• preparing, storing raw and cooked foods separately • good personal hygiene • refrigerate all high-risk foods	foods must be thoroughly cooked, rapidly cooled and stored at the correct temperature	• good personal hygiene • refrigeration of high-risk foods

Table 3.1: Bacteria related to food poisoning, symptoms and prevention

The main reasons for the increase in food poisoning are:

- Poor food hygiene: incorrect handling, cooking and storage of foods; failure to follow storage, reheating or cooking instructions correctly.
- Poor personal hygiene.
- Cross-contamination between food and food handlers, pests, pets and rodents.
- More food prepared and consumed outside of the home.
- Lack of training for food handlers.
- Confusion about food labelling (storage and reheating instructions) and the date mark system.

Food hygiene

Objectives

- **Describe** the main features of the Food Safety Act 1990 and The Food Hygiene (England) Regulations 2006

Food probe

ResultsPlus
Build Better Answers

Give four principles of food preservation. (4 marks)

■ **Basic answers (0–1 marks)**
At this level, answers gave one or no principles.

● **Good answers (2 marks)**
At this level, answers gave two or three principles.

▲ **Excellent answers (3–4 marks)**
Answers gave four reasons. For example:

1. Make food safe to eat.
2. Extend the storage life of food.
3. Increase the variety and range of foods.
4. Make use of foods when they are cheap and in plentiful supply, to use at a later date.

Food hygiene

If you practise good food hygiene, you can prevent the contamination and infection of food.

To ensure correct handling

- Check date mark of food.
- Use good stock rotation of foods.
- Prepare and store raw and cooked meat and poultry separately.
- Defrost food (meat, poultry and fish) thoroughly before using for food preparation and cooking.

To ensure correct cooking

- Ensure that all meat, fish and poultry has been cooked correctly, by checking the internal temperature of food. If internal meat juices are clear and meat is the correct colour, then the internal temperature should have reached the safe temperature of 75°C. You can check this with a food probe.
- When using cooked foods at a later stage, always cool the cooked foods rapidly. Store them at the correct temperature.
- Reheat any previously cooked food until piping hot (75°C).

To ensure correct storage

- Cover high-risk foods and refrigerate.
- Keep dry foods (cereals, flour, and sugar) in airtight containers, in cool, dry conditions.
- Never put warm foods into the fridge.
- Avoid opening the fridge and freezer door more than necessary to prevent hot air raising the internal temperature.
- Use the star rating system for storage of foods in the freezer.
- If tamper-proof packaging has been damaged, do not use the product.

Danger zone

The danger zone is the temperature range at which bacterial growth is most rapid. The danger zone is 5°C to 63°C. The optimum temperature is 37°C (body temperature). Below 0°C bacteria are dormant; most bacteria cannot survive temperatures of above 70°C.

Kitchen hygiene

To ensure good kitchen hygiene:

- Keep pets, pests and rodents out of the kitchen.
- Keep all surfaces and equipment clean by using hot water and a detergent to remove dirt, grime and to dissolve grease. Disinfectants reduce levels of bacteria. Sanitisers remove dirt, grime and bacteria.

- Keep kitchen waste and cleaning materials away from food preparation areas.

Personal hygiene

To ensure good personal hygiene:

- Tie long hair back or wear a hairnet or hat.
- Wash hands before and after preparing food.
- Wear an apron.
- Cover cuts and wounds.
- If suffering with food poisoning symptoms (vomiting and diarrhoea), do not prepare, cook or serve food.

The Food Safety Act 1990

This provides the framework for all food legislation in Britain. The main responsibilities for all food businesses under the Act are:

- to ensure you do not include anything in food, remove anything from food or treat food in any way which means it would be damaging to the health of people eating it
- to ensure that the food you serve or sell is of the nature, substance or quality which consumers would expect
- to ensure that the food is labelled, advertised and presented in a way that is not false or misleading.

The Food Hygiene (England) Regulations 2006

This legislation is designed to protect public health and is enforced by Environmental Health Officers and the Trading Standards Institute. All food business operators (except farmers and growers) are required to implement and maintain HACCP (Hazard Analysis and Critical Control Points) principles.

The basic requirements of the Food Hygiene Regulations are:

- controls throughout the food chain, from primary production to sale or supply to the final consumer (from 'farm to fork')
- controls focus on what is necessary for public health protection
- food business operators take primary responsibility to produce food safely
- hygiene of foodstuffs within the food industry
- specific hygiene rules and requirements for food of animal origin intended for human consumption
- general hygiene requirements for all food business operators.

See page 97 for on HACCP.

Pests and rodents

Stretch Activity

Discuss the properties of microorganisms in the manufacture and production of food.

- Make sure you remember the danger zone – the temperature range within which multiplication of pathogenic bacteria is possible (5°C–63°C).

Quick notes

- **Date mark**: Food labels must carry a 'use by' or 'best before' date to show the storage life of a food product.
- **Food hygiene**: A process of working cleanly and hygienically to make sure the food is safe to eat after preparation, cooking and storage.
- **Food poisoning**: Illness caused by bacteria, chemicals or poisons in food. They may be useful or harmful.

Preservation methods

Objectives

- **Understand** the principles food preservation
- **Understand** the methods of preservation
- **Understand** industrial and home preservation methods

ResultsPlus
Watch out!

Before preserving food, manufacturers prepare the food to ensure that it is in perfect condition. This might include washing and cleaning, blanching, size reduction or homogenisation.

Support Activity

Using the principles of preservation, give examples of foods that illustrate why food is preserved. The first one has been done for you.

Principles of preservation	Examples of foods
extend the storage life of foods	canned fruit and vegetables dried milk powder frozen vegetables

What is food preservation?

Food preservation is the process of treating food to prevent natural decay and spoilage by microorganisms and enzyme action. By removing the favourable conditions for decay and microorganism growth (food, warmth, moisture and oxygen), food can be preserved and its shelf life can be extended.

Principles of food preservation

The main principles of food preservation are to:

- Make food **safe** to eat by creating conditions unfavourable to microorganism growth.

- Extend the **storage life** of food.

- Increase the **variety** and range of foods by preserving them so that they may be eaten out of season, with altered sensory properties or as a different composite food.

- Make use of foods when they are **cheap** and in plentiful supply, to store for later use.

- Retain the **nutritional and sensory characteristics** of food beyond their normal storage life as fresh ingredients.

Table 3.2 shows the methods of food preservation and the principles upon which they are based.

Method	Principles of preservation	Example
hot	• heat treatment to kill microorganisms and enzymes • high temperature required to kill microorganisms	pasteurisation sterilisation UHT (ultra heat treatment) **canning**
cold	• removal of heat to create low temperature preservation treatments to slow down or stop microbial growth	**chilling** freezing
dry	• removal of water through dehydration (drying) of foods to stop microbial growth • reduce the amount of available water in a food using high concentrations of sugar, salt and dehydration	**sun drying** **spray drying** **AFD (accelerated freeze drying)**
chemical (salt, sugar and acid)	• chemical preservatives (additives) destroy microorganisms or prevent them reproducing • high concentrations of salt, sugar or acid prevent microbial growth	additives preservatives salt, sugar, acid preservation treatments
packaging	• protects food from spoilage and contamination • alters the internal conditions of the packaged food to restrict microbial growth • protects food from climatic conditions	**MAP (modified atmosphere packaging)** CAP (controlled atmosphere packaging) vacuum packaging
Irradiation	• low doses of ionising radiation kill bacteria in food • reduces microbial spoilage • reduces insect damage • reduces the need for chemical additives • improves sensory properties and keeping qualities of unrefrigerated foods	radiation sterilisation radiation pasteurisation

Table 3.2: Preservation methods

Apply it!

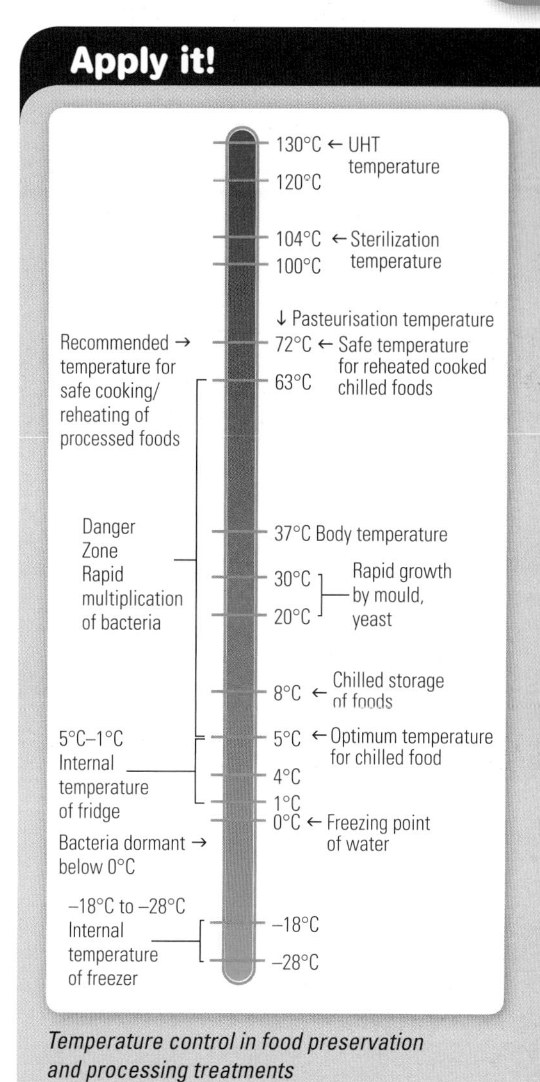

Temperature control in food preservation and processing treatments

Quick notes

- **Chemical Preservative**: Additives (E200 numbers, sugar, acid and salt) prevent food being spoiled by microorganisms.

Home preservation methods

Objectives

- **Describe** the advantages, disadvantages and safety issues of food preservation techniques

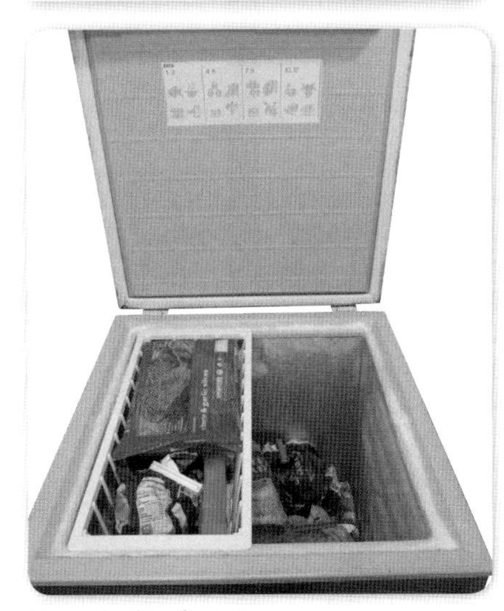

Domestic chest freezer

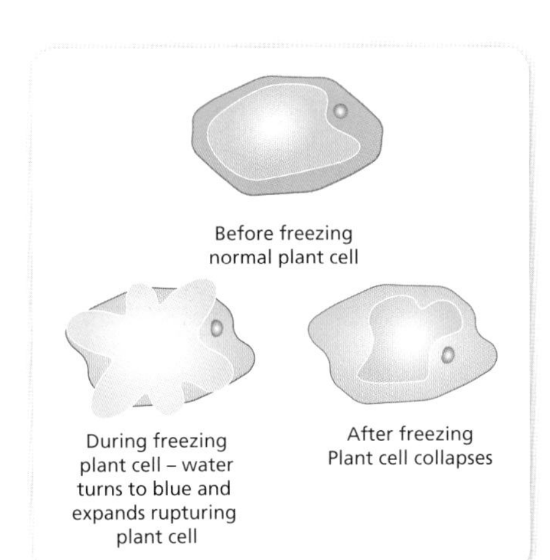

Cell/collapsed cell

Quick notes

The main food preservation techniques used at home are: **freezing**, **drying** and **chemicals** (salt, sugar and acids).

Home preservation techniques have been used for hundreds of years. Pickles, chutneys, marmalades, jellies, jams, bottling and drying helped keep foods in plentiful supply, as well as improving the range and versatility of fruits, vegetables and herbs. Meat and fish were smoked to improve flavour and storage life. More recently, the freezer has aided storage of ready-made foods, as well as fresh produce from the garden.

Freezing

In the process of freezing, microbial growth and enzyme action is slowed down or stopped at very low temperatures. Bacteria remain dormant at low temperatures. As food warms up, bacteria start to grow again.

Foods become frozen as the water content of the food turns to ice and becomes solid.

Advantages

- Storage life is extended from one month to one year, depending on the food.
- Freezing is excellent for storing food when it is plentiful, cheap or seasonal, or after prior preparation, for use at a later date.

Disadvantages

- Freezer burn to badly packaged foods causes grey marks to appear on foods.
- The structure of food can be damaged during thawing and refreezing, affecting:
  - nutritional loss through thawing (of water soluble vitamins)
  - colour loss
  - flavour loss.
- Textures can change, particularly in foods with a high water content, causing the structure of these foods to collapse and become mushy when thawed.

Safety issues

- During the defrosting and thawing of food, the temperature increases and bacterial reproduction resumes. Food must be stored in a fridge to prevent bacterial growth.
- A freezer box within a fridge cannot be used to freeze fresh foods, as the time and temperature to freeze the food are not fast or low enough to stop the reproduction of bacteria.
- Use the fast-freeze function on freezer to freeze fresh foods.
- Food must be in perfect condition before freezing, not bruised, damaged or not fresh.
- Never put warm food into a freezer as this increases the temperature and can cause cross-contamination by microbial growth.

- Never refreeze food after it has thawed, due to contamination by bacteria.
- Blanching (steam or hot water immersion) vegetables before freezing halts enzyme activity.
- Defrost the freezer regularly to aid temperature control.
- Use stock rotation in freezer.
- Label all food with date and contents before freezing.

Drying

Drying is the removal of water through dehydration of foods, using an oven or microwave oven.

Advantages

- Drying food is easy in an oven or microwave oven.
- Storage life is extended (herbs, fruit or vegetables).
- It intensifies taste and flavours.

Disadvantages

- Drying is a slow process.
- Structural damage to fruit and vegetables can cause shrinkage, colour change and leathery texture.

Safety issues

- Wash fruit, vegetables and herbs thoroughly before using.
- Store in an airtight container after drying.

Chemicals

High concentrations of salt, sugar, acid or combinations of these chemicals prevent microbial growth and reproduction and are often used to prolong the life of foods.

Advantages

- Adding chemicals (sugar, salt, acid) is easy.
- Storage life of food is extended.
- Changes flavour, texture, appearance and colour of foods, giving variety to the product range.
- This makes good use of seasonal foods when cheap and plentiful, for use at a later date.

Disadvantages

- High levels of salt and sugar are unhealthy.

Safety issues

- Wash fruit, vegetables and herbs thoroughly before use.
- Sterilise containers before use.
- Store in an airtight container to prevent microbial growth.
- Food must be in perfect condition before chemical preservation.

Give three disadvantages of using chemical additives. (3 marks, 2007 Higher)

How students answered

Three-quarters of students were unable to give any disadvantages.

76% got 0 marks

22% got 1–2 marks

2% got 3 marks

Relevant answers could include concern about artificial additives and the need for clean labels, that chemicals can have unknown side effects, and that they can be unhealthy (addition of chemicals: salt or sugar to prevent microbial growth).

Home preserves

Chemicals		
Sugar	**Salt**	**Acid**
jam marmalade jelly chutney	cheese bacon fish	pickles chutney

Table 3.3: Various sources of sugar, salt and acid

Industrial preservation methods

Objectives

- **Understand** industrial preservation methods

Sterilised drinks

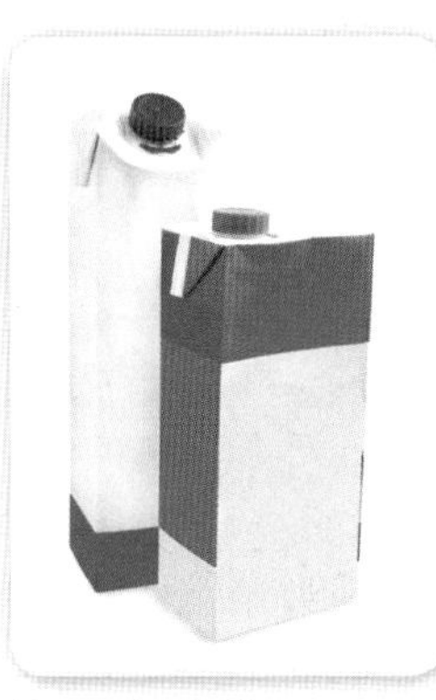
Pasteurised milk

ResultsPlus
Exam Question Report

Processing milk can give it a longer shelf life. Give **two** different ways in which milk can be processed to give it a longer shelf life.
(2 marks, 2008 Foundation)

How students answered

Almost three-quarters of students were unable to suggest a method.

77% got 0 marks

9% got 1 mark

19% got 2 marks

Many students referenced skimmed or semi-skimmed milk in their answers. These methods of processing do not affect shelf life, but rather change the nutritional fat content of the milk.

Possible answers include: pasteurisation, evaporation, condensing, sterilisation, homogenisation, UHT treatment/UHT canning, drying/drying/dried,freezing/frozen, irradiation.

Industrial preservation techniques have evolved over many years, as new technologies emerged to meet the needs of the food industry and consumers. Techniques have been refined as research has driven innovations in equipment and processes.

Hot preservation methods

Pasteurisation

During pasteurisation, pathogenic microorganisms are destroyed (72°C for 15 seconds). Industrial uses include milk and liquid egg.

Advantages: Storage is extended for 2–5 days.

Disadvantages: Limited storage life of food.

Safety issues: Store in refrigerator.

Sterilisation

To sterilise food, manufacturers heat it for a long period of time at very high temperatures (104-130°C for 40 minutes, depending on the food). Industrial uses include milk and fruit juices.

Advantages:

- Sterilisation destroys nearly all microorganisms.
- Storage period is extended (months).

Disadvantages: The taste and texture of sterilised foods can be affected.

Safety issues: Sterilised foods must be used within two days of opening the package and kept refrigerated.

UHT

UHT (ultra heat treatment) uses very high temperatures (130°C for 1–5 seconds). Industrial uses include milk, soups and sauces.

Advantages:

- Extends storage period of unopened milk for up to 6 months.
- Little colour change.
- Little nutritional loss.

Disadvantages: Slight taste change.

Safety issues: Sold in airtight containers.

Canning

During canning, food is packed in cans and sterilised, or food is sterilised and packed in aseptic (sterilised) cans. Temperature and time vary according to the food type. After sterilisation, cans are sprayed with water to cool them and prevent over-cooking.

Advantages:

- Storage life of food is extended (years).
- A wide range of foods may be canned.

- Cans are able to withstand extreme climate conditions.
- It is easy to store canned foods.
- The packaging is recyclable.

Disadvantages:
- The texture of foods may change.
- Nutrients may be lost.
- Acidic foods must be canned in plastic-lined cans to prevent corrosion.

Safety issues:
- Blanching (water, steam or microwave) vegetables before canning halts enzyme activity and aids shrinkage of food product before preservation.
- Cans are sealed with a double seam to prevent leakage and contamination.
- Damage to cans will cause corrosion and rusting.
- There is usually a tamperproof seal.
- There is usually a ring pull to aid opening.
- A blown can indicates growth of bacteria within a can.

Cold preservation methods

Chilling

To chill food, you need a low temperature (1°C–8°C) to slow down enzyme action and reduce microbial growth. Optimum temperature is below 4°C to prevent infection by *listeria* bacteria.

Cook-chill

During cook-chill, foods are prepared, cooked and rapidly chilled to between 0°C and 3°C in 90 minutes or less. This gives a shelf life of five days. Dishes must be reheated to at least 72°C. They must not be further reheated.

Advantages:
- Chilling is good for the short-term storage of fresh, perishable food.
- Chilled foods may be purchased, cooked and eaten without delay.
- Nutritional content or sensory properties are scarcely affected.
- A wide range of products is available.
- Food can be produced in a variety of portion sizes.
- Quality is consistent.
- Food waste is minimal.
- No skill is required to prepare, cook or serve food.
- Cook-chill food can be cooked and served in packaging material.

Disadvantages:
- Expensive due to safety risk assements. These costs are passed onto the consumer.
- Packaging materials can be excessive.
- Ready meals often have high levels of salt, sugar and fat.

This can has a double seam, lacquer coating and a ring pull.

Support Activity

Milk is a very versatile food product, which can be preserved in different ways. List five different milk products and explain each method of preservation used for those products.

Explain one reason why milk has a short shelf life. (2 marks)

■ **Basic answers (0–1 marks)**
At this level, answers gave one or no reasons.

● **Good answers (2 marks)**
At this level answers gave one statement and one explanation. For example:
Milk is a high-risk food because it provides an ideal source of food to enable bacteria to multiply over a short period of time.

Chilled temperature transport system

Safety issues:

- Critical temperature and time control are essential to maintain safety of food.
- Chilled foods are always sold from chilled cabinets (legal temperature 8°C maximum; ideal temperature: 5°C).
- Chilled foods must be refrigerated at home at 5°C or below.
- Good stock rotation is essential to maintain food safety.
- Transportation of chilled products is in controlled temperature distribution systems in vehicles.

Freezing

Freezing preserves food using low temperatures and turns water into ice.

- Blanching (water, steam or microwave blanching) vegetables before freezing halts enzyme activity.
- Blast freezing: cold air is blown onto food.
- Immersion freezing uses liquids.
- Plate freezing is freezing food in contact with a refrigerated plate.
- Cryogenic freezing uses liquid gases (CO_2 or nitrogen) at very low temperatures.

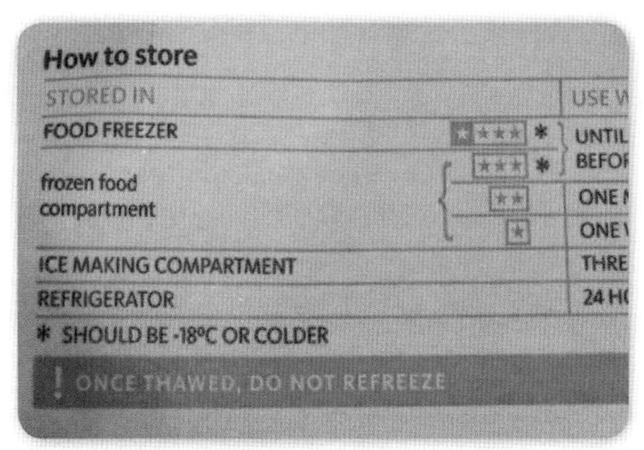

Food label with star marking system

Advantages:

- Rapid freezing retains nutritional value and sensory properties of food.
- A wide range of foods may be frozen.

Disadvantages: Critical temperature and time controls are needed to ensure quality of food. These costs are passed onto consumers.

Safety issues:

- Temperature and time controls are needed during preservation treatment.
- The freezer star rating, found on the packaging of all frozen food, indicates the temperature range and storage life of the food product, needed to maintain the quality of foods.

Star rating	Storage time	Temperature
*	1 week	–6°C
**	1 month	–12°C
***	1 year	–18°C

Table 3.4: Freezer star rating

Drying (dehydration)

This is the removal of water using sun or spray drying, or AFD (accelerated freeze drying).

Sun

Drying in direct sunlight allows moisture to slowly evaporate (raisins, tomatoes, apricots).

Spray

A fine spray of the product (for example, milk, eggs, dessert mixes or coffee) is sprayed into a chamber with hot air. This allows the moisture to evaporate and the fine particles of food to fall and be collected in powder form at the bottom of the chamber (for example, instant mashed potato, baby foods).

AFD

Food is quickly frozen and then placed in a vacuum under reduced pressure. This vaporises the ice, turning it to steam, and drying the food (meat, fruit, vegetables).

Advantages:
- Stops microbial growth and reproduction.
- Food is lightweight and easy to transport.
- Food is easy to hydrate.
- Storage life is extended (months or years).

Disadvantages: Shrinkage and loss of nutrients may occur.

Safety issues:
- Drying through just the removal of water does not kill microorganisms unless very hot temperatures are used.
- Foods must be stored in a dry, airtight container.

Chemical

This is the use of preservatives (additives, E200 numbers), sugar, acid and salt, which prevent food being spoiled by microorganisms.

Advantages:
- Storage life is extended (by months or years).
- Creates different sensory characteristics to food (jams, jellies and marmalades).

Disadvantages:
- High levels of sugar and salt are unhealthy.
- Some people worry about the use of artificial additives in foods.

Safety issues: Once packaging is opened, foods must be stored following manufacturers' instructions.

Specialist packaging

- MAP (modified atmosphere packaging)/CAP (controlled atmosphere packaging): these methods alter the atmosphere within packaged food by decreasing oxygen and increasing carbon dioxide or nitrogen levels.
- Vacuum packaging: removes air from packaged food, by creating a tight seal around the food to prevent bacteria growing.

Advantages:
- Storage life is extended.
- No nutrients are lost.
- The sensory characteristics of food are retained.

Disadvantages:
- Foods are expensive.
- The process relies on the success of the packaging material.
- Uses excessive packaging material.

Safety issues:
- Once opened, food has a normal shelf life.
- Follow manufacturer's instructions for use and storage.

Stretch Activity

1. Describe how high temperature preservation treatments prevent spoilage of foods by bacteria.
2. Discuss the effects of preservation treatments on foods.

Quick notes

The main methods of industrial food preservation are:
- **hot**: pasteurisation, sterilisation, UHT, canning
- **cold**: chilling, freezing, cook-chill/freezing
- **dry**: sun, spray and AFD
- **chemical**: preservatives
- **specialist packaging**: MAP/CAP and vacuum packaging.

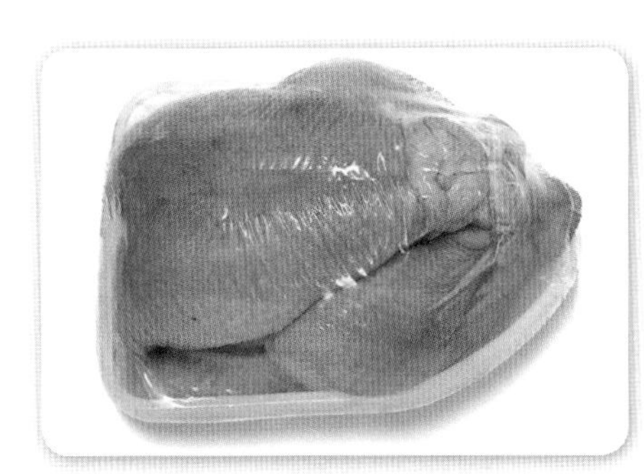

MAP and CAP packaged foods

Vacuum-packaged foods

Processing

Objectives

- **Understand** the principles of primary and secondary food processing

Apply it!

Consider how the ingredients that you use in your Design and Make activities have been processed before use in recipes.

Support Activity

Discuss three primary processing methods.

Quick notes

Primary processing

- removal of unwanted layers
- removal of internal organs
- removal of dirt
- separation of layers
- preservation treatments packaging
- removal of impurities

Definitions of food processing

Primary and secondary food processing techniques may be separate, but are often interlinked, depending on the nature of the raw food, processing treatment and the desired end product.

Primary food processing is the basic treatment of raw food materials to make them suitable for further processing or immediate consumption.

Table 3.5 shows the main treatments in primary processing.

Primary processing	Example of treatment	Food product
removal of unwanted layers	• peeling • shelling and extraction	• fruit and vegetables • nuts, shellfish
removal of internal organs	• gutting of fish • butchering of meat	• fish • meat offal
removal of dirt	• washing and cleaning • polishing	• fruit and vegetables • nuts and cereals • white rice
separation of layers	• milling • milling and polishing • rolling and crushing • skimming of butter fat • rendering and clarification • filleting of fish • jointing of meat	• wheat and maize into flour • rice • oats • milk into cream • pork fat into lard or suet • different fish products (fillets, steaks) • different cuts of meat (steaks, joints, cutlets, breast)
sorting and grading	• by size, weight, colour, quality	• fruit, vegetables, grains, nuts, eggs
preservation treatments	• pasteurisation • sterilisation • dehydration • freezing • curing and salting	• milk, liquid egg • milk • dried egg powder, milk powder • frozen egg, meat, fish • meat and fish
packaging	• MAP/CAP, vacuum	• meat, fish, cheese
removal of impurities	• refining	• oil, sugar

Table 3.5: Primary food processing

Secondary food processing transforms food materials into food components or composite foods.

Table 3.6 shows the main treatments in secondary processing.

Secondary processing	Examples of treatment
size reduction: cut, shape and form	pulping, slicing, dicing, chopping, grating, mincing, shredding and grinding
blanching	a short heat treatment using water or steam; carried out on vegetables before canning, freezing or drying to inactivate enzymes and to shrink the product
methods of cooking	• moist: boiling, poaching, steaming, stewing, braising • dry: baking, roasting, grilling, barbecuing • others: frying, microwave
combining and processing	• formation of dough (bread, pasta, pastry, scones, biscuits) • formation of batters and pastes (cakes, sauces and batters) • formation of dry mixes (dried soups, sauces, blends of herbs and spices) • emulsification of fats to create sauces, ice cream and butter • homogenisation of milk to create a uniform product with no cream/milk layers • cheese production • yoghurt production • meat products: burgers, sausages • processing of mycoprotein and egg white into Quorn™ • processing of soya into tofu and soya milk • hydrogenation of fats and oils
Preservation treatments	• UHT • canning • chemical preservation: acids/sugar/preservatives

Table 3.6: Secondary food processing

Stretch Activity

Research two reasons for blanching food.

ResultsPlus
Build Better Answers

Combining and processing treatments are secondary processing methods. Describe two other secondary methods of processing. (4 marks)

Basic answers (0–1 marks)
At this level, answers gave one or no methods.

Good answers (2 marks)
At this level, answers gave two methods, or one method and one reason.

Excellent answers (3–4 marks)
Answers gave two methods and descriptions. For example:

1. Size reduction of fruit or vegetables using slicing.
2. Blanching to inactivate enzymes and shrink food products.

Quick notes

- size reduction: cut, shape and form
- blanching
- methods of cooking
- combining and processing
- preservation treatments

Home food preparation techniques

Objectives

- **Understand** food preparation techniques used in the home
- **Identify** the advantages, disadvantages and safety issues of these food preparation techniques

Apply it!

Selecting the correct tool is critical to the success of the technique.

In your Design and Make activities, consider:

- shape and size, for example the right size of pan
- form
- use and grip of the tool, for example the right knife for the job
- cleaning and maintenance
- number of parts to dismantle and set up before use
- recipe
- personal preference.

What is food preparation?

Food preparation is the method of preparing ingredients into food for consumption. Food preparation methods can involve the use of small and large pieces of equipment, that can be hand-held and electrical.

The main techniques for food preparation are listed below, with examples of the small equipment needed.

Measuring and weighing

Equipment includes spoons, weighing scales, measuring jugs. Take care to always follow a recipe exactly, noting which unit of measurement you are using throughout the recipe.

Size reduction

Equipment includes knives, graters, scissors, garlic crusher, chopping board. Graters may be different shapes: round, box, rotary and mouli graters. Use a chopping board when using knives. Ensure that all cutting equipment is sharp, with a sturdy grip to prevent accidents.

Ceramic or nylon chopping boards are colour-coded for use with different ingredients to prevent cross-contamination: red – raw meat, blue – raw fish, yellow – cooked meat, white – vegetables, green – salad/fruit. These are more hygienic than wooden chopping boards as they can be put in the dishwasher and cleaned at high temperatures to destroy bacteria and remove dirt.

Cleaning

Equipment includes brushes, cloths and scourers. Make sure you disinfect cleaning brushes regularly and store away from food.

Peeling and coring

Equipment includes vegetable peeler, corer. The grip and size of a peeler or corer will affect the success of these tools.

Measuring and weighing, carving and peeling utensils

Separating

Equipment includes colander, sieve, juicer, slotted spoon, zester. Ensure that small particles of food are removed to avoid build-up of debris in equipment. Colanders are for wet ingredients, sieves for dry ingredients.

Separating equipment: dry ingredients

Forming, shaping and flattening

Equipment includes cutters, piping bags and nozzles, rolling pin, moulds. Make sure you use an effective detergent when washing piping bags and nozzles to prevent cross-contamination. Dismantle equipment to ensure that all parts can be cleaned and dried effectively.

Lifting and mixing equipment

Lifting and spreading

Equipment includes palette knife, fish slice, spatula, scissors. The flexible nature of these tools allows them to be used for a number of different techniques: icing cakes, spreading jam onto a cake, lifting food from a baking tray or cake tin or scraping out a bowl.

Mixing and combining

Equipment includes bowls and basins, whisks and wooden spoons. Bowls and basins may be stainless steel, glass, plastic or ceramic, in a range of shapes and sizes. Whisks are used for adding air to a mixture, and can be operated by hand or electricity; hand whisks can be balloon, coil, spiral, french, aerator ball or rotary in shape and style. Wooden spoons are lightweight, poor conductors of heat and the long handle aids creaming and the combining of ingredients together.

Greasing and glazing equipment

Greasing and glazing

Equipment includes pastry brushes. Ensure that pastry brushes are cleaned regularly to avoid build up of residue. Pastry brushes can allow a liquid to be applied with care and consistency to a food product.

Blanching

Equipment includes saucepans/steamers. A short heat treatment using water or steam carried out on vegetables before canning, freezing or drying to inactivate enzymes and to shrink the product.

Cooking and cooling

Equipment includes cake tins, baking trays, bun and muffin tins, cooling racks, saucepans, woks. The selection of this equipment must be used with care and attention. Non-stick bakeware or the use of oil and baking parchment or cake cases in cake tins will allow easy removal of the food product from the piece of equipment. Cooling racks maybe used for other purposes including decorating cakes, proving bread rolls.

Other

Dredgers can be used for dusting, sprinkling or dredging flour and sugar.

Cooking equipment

Electrical equipment

The correct storage and use of electrical equipment is vital to the health and safety of the person operating the equipment. Below are essential rules to follow when using electrical equipment.

- Switch off the appliance when not in use.
- Ensure that the plug is correctly wired.
- Do not touch with wet hands/do not use near water.
- Ensure that the plug is fully plugged in.
- Do not interfere with a metal object/do not put metal into a microwave.
- Keep away from young children.
- Read the instruction manual before use.
- Do not put hands into equipment when working.
- Ensure that equipment is correctly assembled.
- Clean and maintain equipment after use.
- Check that the flex is not damaged.

The range of electrical equipment is vast, and many new developments allow electrical equipment to perform a wide range of functions.

Some electrical equipment and the techniques related to them are listed below:

Mixers and whisks

Techniques include combining and mixing: kneading, creaming, rubbing in, whisking, liquidising. Free-standing appliances can be heavy, but very sturdy; they may have a number of attachments that can be used for a range of functions. Hand-held mixers are versatile, and easy and quick to use.

Blenders

Techniques include liquidising, puree and pulping. Blenders can be used for dry ingredients (bread, biscuits) or wet ingredients (fruit, vegetables, egg, soups, sauces). Liquid is sometimes used in food, or as an additional ingredient, as a blending agent to soften and blend food together.

Food processors and attachments

Techniques include chopping, pulping, dicing, slicing, grating, mincing and shredding. A lid over the processor bowl allows the mixture to be finely or coarsely processed depending on the desired effect. The range of attachments is vast and this is a versatile piece of equipment. However, it is not successful when used for pastry, cake or bread-making as the lid prevents the mixture becoming aerated. The funnel allows foods to be put into the processor safely and quickly.

Apply it!

All electrical equipment in schools must be checked annually for safety. Look for the label on electrical equipment that identifies this information when using them in your Design and Make activities.

Support Activity

Different tools and equipment are needed to prepare food in the home and in a factory. Give an example of a task that can be carried out using each of the following tools or pieces of equipment: a food processor; a fruit squeezer; a pastry brush; a baking tin; a microwave oven.

Stretch Activity

1. One way a food processor can be used is for rubbing fat into flour. Give three other ways a food processor can be used to prepare foods.
2. Electrical safety rules must be followed when using a food processor.

   Give two other safety rules to follow when using a food processor.

Food processor

Breadmaker

Techniques include mixing and combining, kneading, proving and baking. CAM (Computer-aided Manufacture) allows this appliance to have mixing, time, temperature and weight controls, making it versatile and easy to use with excellent results.

Breadmaker

Microwave oven

Techniques include heating/warming, cooking, reheating, melting, defrosting. CAM time and temperature controls also make this versatile and easy to use. The magnetron inside the appliance converts electrical energy into microwave energy, which is dispersed around the oven, using either a turntable or paddle, to cook, heat, melt or defrost food using convection or conduction heat transference. Cold spots in food can be formed however if the microwave oven is not used correctly; check that food is cooked/defrosted/reheated correctly before serving using a food probe.

Metal containers cannot be used as they will cause microwave rays to reflect against the walls of the appliance, causing damage to the oven. Glass, plastic or ceramic containers may be used: they only become hot from the temperature of the food rather than from the microwave energy, as they cannot absorb this energy.

Microwave oven

Kettle

Techniques include boiling water. A range of styles, shapes, colours and materials are available. The most efficient are those with a visible external measuring system and where only the required amount of water for boiling is used. Cordless electrical styles will automatically turn off once the water has reached 100°C, whereas hob kettles will need removing from the heat source. Filters prevent contamination of water, so kettles need to be cleaned and descaled regularly to prevent the build-up of lime deposits in hard water areas.

Kettle

Blender/electric mixer

ResultsPlus
Build Better Answers

Hand-held blenders can help elderly people to prepare foods such as soup.

Give three ways in which hand-held blenders are suitable for the elderly. (3 marks)

■ **Basic answers (0–1 marks)**
At this level, answers gave one or no way.

● **Good answers (2 marks)**
At this level answers gave two ways.

▲ **Excellent answers (3 marks)**
Answers gave three ways. For example:

1. Easy to use.
2. Lightweight.
3. Small, therefore little storage space needed.

Home food processing techniques

Objectives

- **Understand** food processing techniques used in the home
- **Describe** the advantages, disadvantages and safety issues of food processing techniques

Food processing techniques help you change raw ingredients into food or foods into components or composite foods. In the home, this could include mixing and combining foods, as well as shaping, forming and cooking foods.

Cooking

Cooking food means preparing it by applying heat. You can transfer heat to food using a combination of radiation, conduction and convection.

Heat transference

Convection is when heat travels round liquids and air using convection currents.

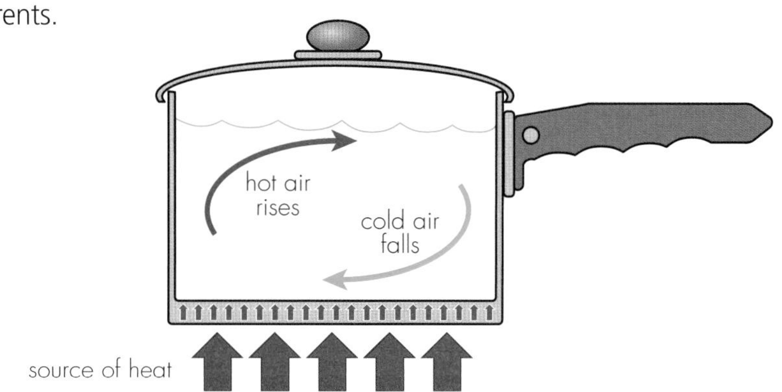

Conduction is when heat is conducted from molecule to molecule in solids or liquids.

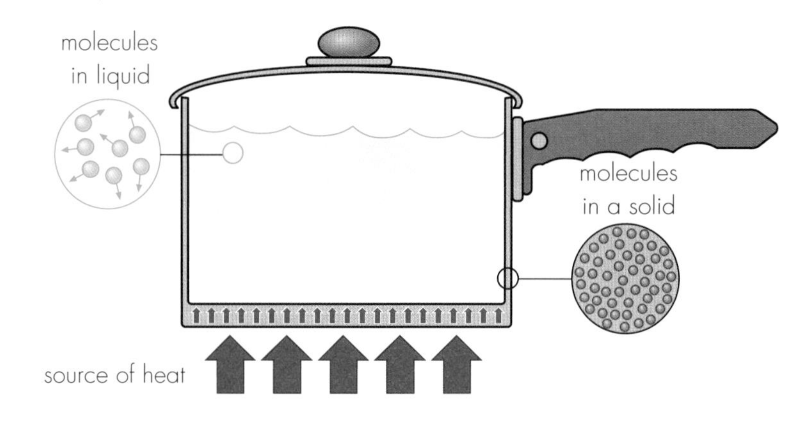

Radiation is when heat travels in waves or rays.

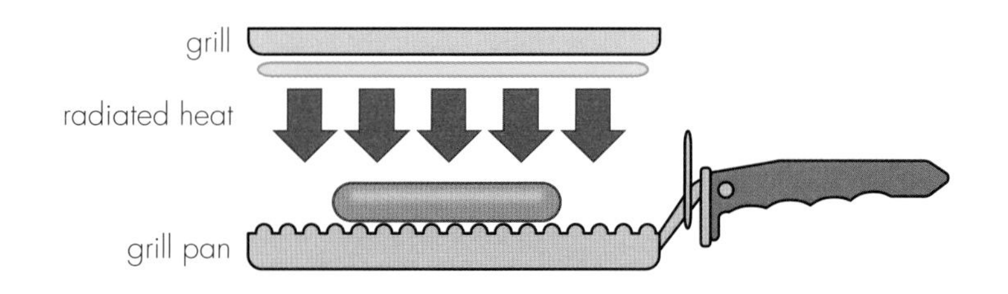

Quick notes

There are three methods of heat transference:

- Convection
- Conduction
- Radiation

There are two main methods of cooking:

- Moist
- Dry

During the cooking process, aspects of the food can change, including:

- its chemical and physical working characteristics
- its sensory properties
- its appearance, flavour, colour, texture and aroma.

The effect of cooking varies depending on the type of food, its structure, its nutritional content, how it interacts with other ingredients and the type of cooking method chosen.

Cooking techniques and ingredients vary widely across the world, reflecting customs and cultures, environmental, social and economic conditions.

Methods of cooking

Cooking uses a combination of at least two methods of heat transference. They are classified according to whether water is involved (moist) or not (dry).

Moist

Moist methods cook food in a liquid, such as water, milk, stock, or fruit juice. Table 3.7 shows the main moist methods of cooking.

Method	Uses	Special points
boiling	vegetables, eggs, starchy foods, jam, sauces and syrups	• quick, simple and no burning of food; 100°C rapidly boiling water • water-soluble vitamin loss (vitamins B and C) • flavour loss due to leaching
poaching	fish, eggs and fruit	• gentle simmering at 85–99°C to retain shape and texture of the food • quick, simple and no burning of food
steaming	fish, vegetables, suet and sponge puddings	• food cooked in steam rising from boiling water retains its nutritional content, texture and flavour • quick, simple and no burning of food • tiered system of steaming several different foods means it saves energy
braising	meat and vegetables	• slow cooking can soften and tenderise tougher cuts of meat to develop good flavour from the reduced liquid stock
stewing	meat, curry, chilli, ratatouille, fruit and vegetables	• slow cooking can soften and tenderise foods to create good flavour and texture

Table 3.7: Features of moist cooking

Apply it!

The choice of cooking method in your Design and Make activities will depend on:

- food
- time available
- tools, equipment and cooking facilities
- your skills
- dietary needs of an individual
- sensory properties for the final product
- your preferences.

Give two moist methods of cooking and an example of a food for each method. (4 marks)

Basic answers (0–1 marks)
At this level, answers gave one or no method.

Good answers (2 marks)
At this level answers gave two methods or one method and a food example.

Excellent answers (3–4 marks)
Answers gave two methods and at least one food. For example:

1. Boiling – rice
2. Poaching – fish

Baking

Roasting

Grilling

Barbeque

Dry

These methods use high temperatures in dry heat to cook food.

Table 3.8 shows the main dry methods of cooking.

Method	Uses	Special points
baking	pastries, bread, cakes, vegetables, fish, fruit and meat	• time and temperature vary depending on the food being cooked • meringues require a low temperature over a long period of time to create a dry, crisp texture • scones are baked at high temperatures for a short time to make them rise and create the desired crumb structure
roasting	meat, fish and vegetables	• fat added to prevent the food drying out and to develop the characteristic flavour
grilling	gratin dishes, small cuts of meat and poultry, steaks, sausages, bacon, fish	• a quick method of cooking using direct, radiated heat • the surface of foods can dry out quickly with prolonged grilling so thin (3–4cm), small foods may be grilled and turned to ensure even cooking • no fat is added and you can also trim excess fat from meat
barbecuing	meat and poultry, burgers, sausages, vegetables and fish	• an increasingly popular method of outdoor cooking, owing to the range of barbecues available (gas, charcoal, wood, brick or metal ovens) and the use of marinades, spices, basting sauces, tools and equipment to aid the cooking process • check that food is thoroughly cooked to ensure the safety of high-risk foods

Table 3.8: Features of dry cooking

Affects of heating on food

Meat and fish: Protein coagulates between 40°C and 60°C, muscle shrinks and fat melts, the colour can change and some Vitamin B may be lost in moist methods.

Eggs: White coagulates at 60°C, becoming transparent; yolk at 70°C. Rapid cooking causes synersis (the egg separates and proteins toughen).

Milk: Forms a skin on its surface during heating.

Cheese: Fat melts, protein coagulates.

Starchy foods: Dextrinisation (starch is converted to sugar and then caramel, giving a characteristic golden-brown colour) and gelatinisation (when starch is moistened and heated, it thickens).

Sugar: Caramelisation (when sugar - crystal or syrup - is heated, it decomposes to produce a range of brown products called caramel) and Maillard reaction (in dry heat, where sugars are mixed with protein in baked products, browning occurs and a pleasant baked aroma is produced).

Fruit and vegetables: Soften, change colour; water-soluble Vitamins B and C are easily destroyed by heat.

Other cooking methods

Apart from moist and dry methods, there are two other main methods of cooking: frying and microwaving.

Frying

You can use frying to cook meat, fish, potatoes, vegetables, eggs.

Dry frying

When you dry fry something, you don't use any fat.

Shallow frying

During shallow frying, you use small amounts of fat to fry lean, tender meat, fish, burgers or bacon.

Deep frying

Some foods may be immersed in oil to create a soft internal texture and crispy coating. Other foods (e.g. fish, sausages) may be coated with batter or breadcrumbs to prevent them from drying out and falling apart. Deep frying adds additional fat to products.

Stir-frying

Stir-frying originated in the Far East, cooking food in a wok. Heat-sensitive nutrients are destroyed. Stir-frying:

- uses minimal fat and relies on a high temperature for a short time to cook food
- is a relatively healthy method of cooking as very little fat or oil is added
- needs fats with a high boiling point (200°C) to be used to prevent burning and an unpleasant taste and aroma to food; low-fat spreads are unsuitable due to the different boiling points of water and fat within the product
- needs great care because of the high temperatures and hot fat.

Microwaving

Foods may be cooked, heated, melted or defrosted quickly in a microwave. You must use the timer carefully to prevent overcooking.

Microwaves use radiation to conduct heat through foods:

- As molecules vibrate, heat is passed through the food during cooking and standing time to complete the cooking process.
- During this time, the centre of the food becomes hotter.

Manufacturers give standing times on food labels, and these should be followed to ensure the safety of the food.

Foods that benefit from microwaving include:

- rapid cooking: fruit and vegetables
- even cooking: custard
- no browning: chicken or fish
- foods without a crisp surface: soups and pasta dishes
- the bright colours of vegetables are retained due to short cooking time.

Stretch Activity

Discuss two effects of heat on meat.

Deep frying

Stir-frying

Microwaving

Other home processing methods

Shaping and forming

There are many methods of giving food products shape and form. Shaping and forming allow a quality finish to be achieved with food products, through consistency in size, thickness, shape, weight, texture and appearance, which aids processing and cooking.

There are a number of different machines and tools used to give consistent shape and form.

Support Activity

Describe how shaping and forming techniques are used in food production within the test kitchen at school, or at home.

Pasta machines

There are a range of different pasta machines available, both electrical and manual. Some mix and combine the ingredients to make the pasta dough and then shape and form the dough. Others only shape and form pasta dough. This variety clamps onto a surface, the pasta dough is then fed through the device to be rolled, shaped and formed into a range of different shapes and sizes, using extrusion plates. These pasta makers are easy and quick to use, with good results. Homemade pasta is much lighter in texture, thickness and weight than commercial pasta, making it better able to absorb sauces and quicker to cook. Pasta makers should be carefully cleaned and maintained after use to prevent rusting and sticking.

Manual pasta maker

Sausage machines, meat grinders and mincers

These pieces of equipment can perform a variety of functions. You can use separate mincers and grinders to shape and form cuts of meat into mince, using interchangeable cutting plates depending on the texture of meat required: coarse, medium or fine texture. You can also use food processors and free-standing mixers with specialist attachments for grinding and mincing. Sausage fillers and stuffers can fill sausage casing, using extrusion techniques to shape and form the sausage.

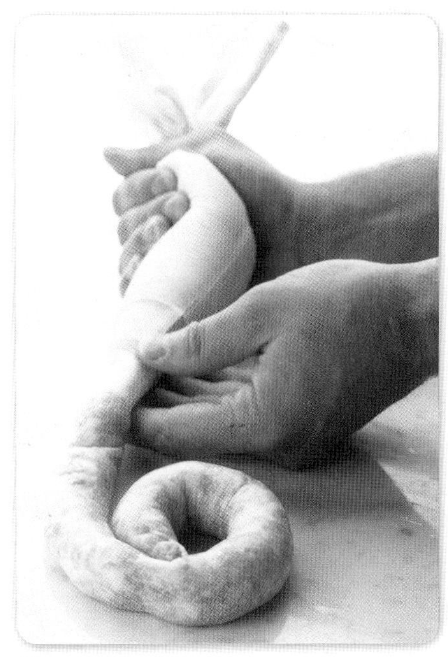

Manual sausage filler

Manual meat grinder

Burger press

You can produce shaped meat, fish or vegetables using a burger press or cutter and wax discs to create burgers of a consistent size and shape.

Burger press

Crimping tools, rolling pin and cutters

You can enhance the finish of a pastry or pasta product using a crimping tool to cut, seal and make a pattern on pastry and pasta edges.

You can use cutters for pastry, scones, biscuits, burgers and fishcakes to create crinkled or flat edges to products before baking.

Moulds and cake tins

A range of shapes, sizes and styles of mould and tin is available to create jellies, mousses, cakes, biscuits, bread and desserts. The choice of material depends on the use of the mould or tin and the ingredients being moulded and shaped. Food products with a high water content (mousses and jellies) require a material that will ensure the safety of the food product, and stay free from rust contamination. Aluminium, tin, stainless steel, glass, china and plastic may be used, often with additional finishes to create non-stick properties to allow for the easy removal of the food product (others require lining with baking paper and greasing). The success of the finished product is often affected by the quality of the tin or mould and how well it is prepared.

Cake tin

Pastry cutter

Piping equipment

Piping bags, syringes and nozzles create a high-quality decorative finish for a range of foods, including icing, cream, potato and choux pastry.

Piping bag and nozzle

Quick notes

Moist methods

- boiling
- poaching
- steaming
- braising
- stewing

Dry methods

- baking
- roasting
- grilling
- barbecuing

Other methods

- frying
- microwaving

Processing

- shaping
- forming

Industrial food preparation techniques

Objectives

- **Understand** food preparation techniques used in the food industry
- **Describe** the advantages, disadvantages and safety issues of these food preparation techniques
- **Know** the stages in the commercial manufacture of food products using machinery

ResultsPlus Build Better Answers

Describe the two cleaning processes used in the food industry. (4 marks)

Basic answers (0–2 marks)
At this level, answers gave one or no description of a cleaning process.

Good answers (3 marks)
At this level, answers named and described one type of cleaning process or named the two types of cleaning processes. For example:

1. Wet cleaning.
2. Dry cleaning food is sieved or screened to remove contamination.

Excellent answers (4 marks)
Answers named and described two types of cleaning process.
For example:

1. Wet cleaning: using clean water to free food from contamination and chemicals; muddy foods can be soaked in water, before further cleaning.
2. Dry cleaning: food is sieved or screened to remove contamination.

Manufacturers perform the handling and preparation of raw food materials through a number of different stages, depending on the quality, size and cleanliness of the raw food material and its intended use in the chain of food processing and manufacture. These may be dry or wet preparation techniques.

You can broadly classify food preparation techniques used in the food industry into the following groups:

- separation processes
- size reduction
- mixing and combining
- blanching.

Separation processes

Separation processes separate contamination from food. They include cleaning, sorting, peeling and grading.

Cleaning

Manufacturers can clean food with or without water, and it usually takes a number of different processes to ensure that the product is thoroughly clean.

In dry cleaning, done without water, food is sieved or screened to remove contamination. Screens separate large and small particles from the food depending on the size of the screen. This is a cheap and efficient method of cleaning, but can involve considerable dust from the food product, resulting in recontamination.

Continuous drum

Mechanical harvesting of crops has resulted in an increase in contamination from stones, soil, twigs, weeds, insects or small animals. These can be separated from the food product during screening. The continuous drum screen is a commercial machine used in the food industry to separate these contaminants; using this machine is more efficient and less labour-intensive.

Aspiration uses air blasts to remove lighter particles from food. This relies on the fact that the food product and contaminants have different weights and buoyancies in the air stream.

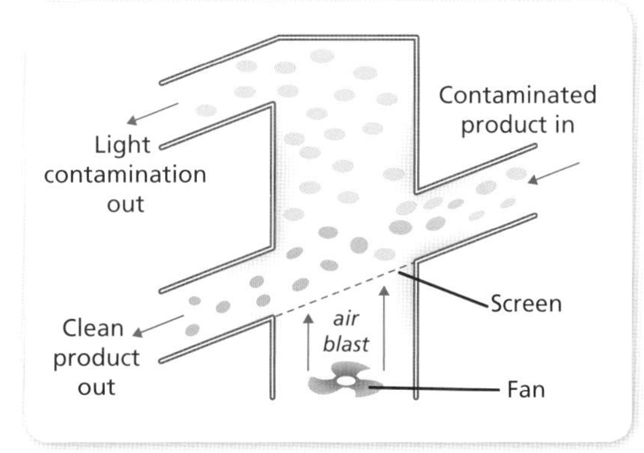

Aspiration

Wet cleaning uses clean water to free food from contamination and chemicals. Muddy foods can be soaked in water, before further cleaning. Agitation can improve the result of the soaking process further.

Spray washing is a common wet method of cleaning. A small volume of water is pressure-sprayed; the force of the spray cleans and washes the food product as the water runs over it.

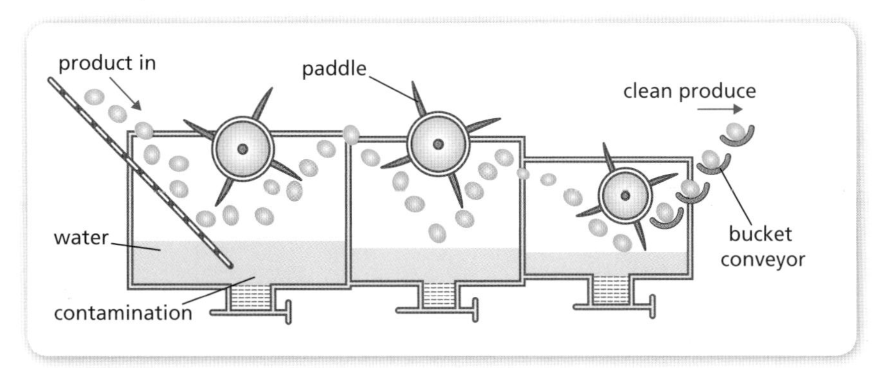

Floatation washing

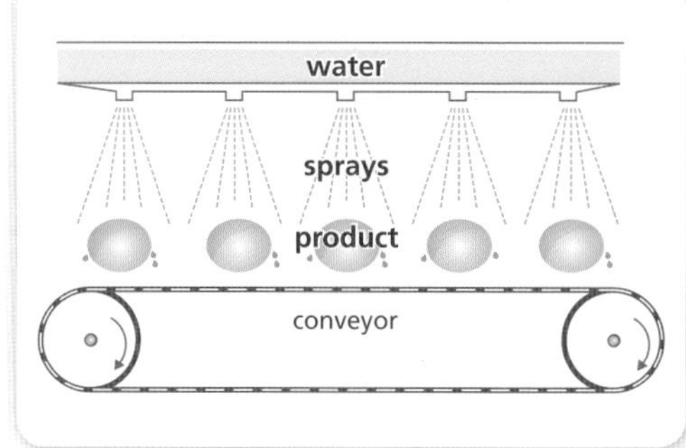

Spray washing

Flotation washing is a mechanical system used to push food through a number of different compartments or weirs, forcing the food under the water by slowly rotating paddles.

Peeling involves removing the outer skin, which can also remove contamination. Multi-functional machines designed to wash and peel vegetables using a range of peeling plates or spin salad leaves, with a flotation tank and waste disposal outlet to remove sludge.

Sorting

Manufacturers sort food according to a particular characteristic. This might be size, shape, weight or colour. This makes it much easier to pack, store and transport foods. However, fruit and vegetables must be handled carefully to avoid bruising.

Table 3.9 shows the main sorting characteristics.

Sorting characteristic	Examples of food products	Special points
size	fruits and vegetables	• if foods are to be mechanically prepared and processed, it is far more successful if the raw food is the same size (e.g. filleting fish, blanching and canning processes) • packing and storage of food is much easier • screens are used to sort according to size
weight	cuts of pre-packed meat, small vegetables, eggs, fruits and nuts	• many fresh items are sold according to weight, then packaged and labelled
shape	fruit and vegetables	• screens are used to sort according to shape • round is a much easier shape to sort than any other
colour	dried peas, rice, coffee, potatoes, onions and grain	• natural colour variation is acceptable • colour due to bruising, rotting and poor handling is unacceptable • labour-intensive if performed manually • an electronic system can be used with photoelectric cells to compare colour against a standard colour; rejected food is removed using a blast of air

Table 3.9: Features of sorting methods

Grading

With grading, food is separated according to quality. This can be according to people's preferences or because of the intended use of the end product. For example, 'class one' fruit and vegetables are sold in supermarkets, but 'class 2' would be acceptable for use in the catering trade, due to the separation systems available in commercial food manufacture; these fruits would be of the same eating quality, but might be dirty or misshapen, but not so as to affect the overall eating quality of the food.

Grade 1 and grade 2 vegetables

Size reduction

Many processed foods are not in their original size or shape because manufacturers have reduced or modified them into a different shape to allow for preparation, processing or preservation treatments. Size reduction is used for ready-prepared food products, such as fish fingers or sausages, and for preparing raw ingredients for other processes, such as juice extraction.

Table 3.10 shows the main types of size reduction processes.

Size reduction process	Example of foods	Special points
pulping	fruit for jams and sauces	• high-speed paddles pulp food to aid the extraction of juice or water before freezing
slicing chopping	meat, fruit and vegetables and other fibrous material	• **rotary cutting knives** are very sharp with a mechanical slicing action • safety guard prevents operation if machine is set up incorrectly
dicing	diced meat and vegetables for soups, dried products and ready meals	• **cross knives** used to dice food • safety guard prevents operation if machine is set up incorrectly
milling	wheat grain into flour	• **milling** separates the endosperm from the rest of the grain; these small, fine particles are used in the production of semolina, pasta and breakfast cereals • during milling, the nutritional content of the grain can be altered due to the extraction of different particles of the grain • the **extraction rate** (%) is the amount of the whole grain that is used
grinding	grain, sugar, nuts, pepper-corns, lumps of sea salt, spices	**hammer mill** • fragile material is shattered into small fragments **disc mill** • rotating discs with studs break the product **pin or ball disc** • rotating plates or balls with rods and pins break the product • cannot be used on fibrous, elastic or liquid foods as they rely on the fragility of the product
shredding	herbs	• food shredded before dehydration • large surface area increases moisture loss
grating	cheese, vegetables	• can be used on solid food items • increased surface area aids **mixing** and **combining** processes

Table 3.10: Size reduction processes, features and equipment

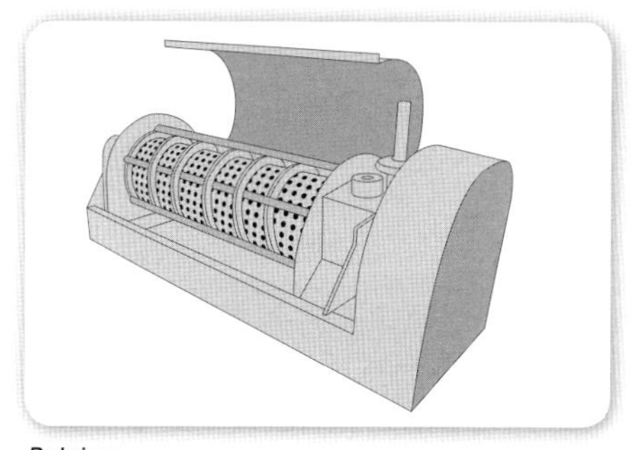

Pulping

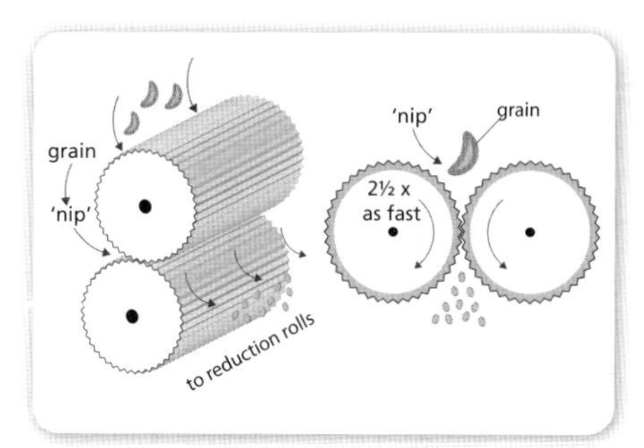

Milling

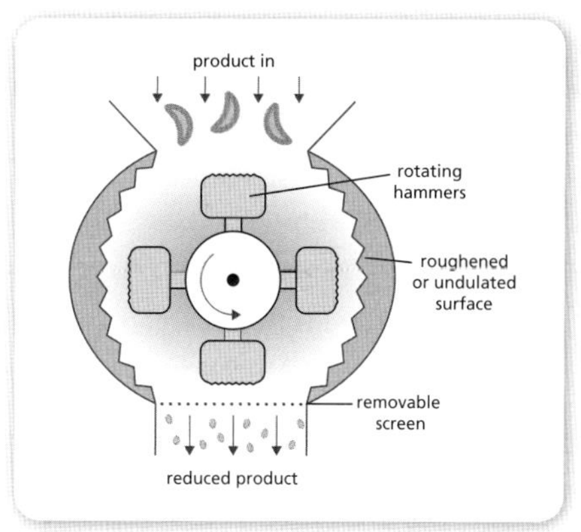

Hammer mill

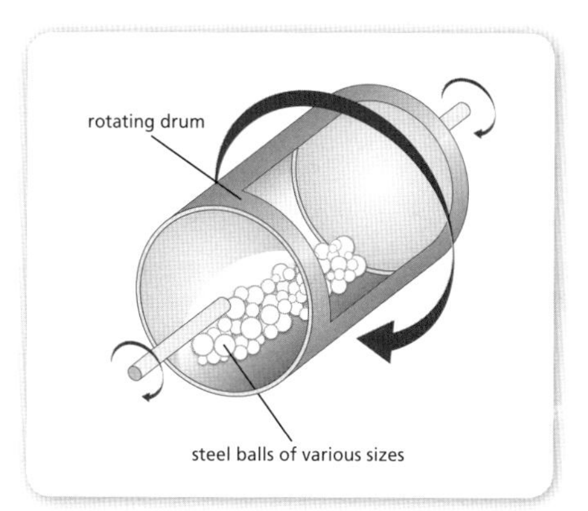

Ball mill

Mixing and combining

Manufacturers use these processes to blend a range of ingredients together to form a uniform mix. This can be very difficult with dry products because each ingredient particle might be a different size, shape, weight and consistency. The closer the particles are in size, the easier it is to mix and combine them.

Large particle variations can produce inconsistencies or demixing. This is where the blend of ingredients used to form a product becomes less uniform than it was in the first stages of the preparation process. The process of mixing and combining liquids does not encounter the problems associated with dry mixes because size of particle is not a factor to consider. However, some liquids separate out after mixing (for example oil and water) because they are immiscible; emulsification is necessary to combine the two immiscible liquids together.

Homogenisation is another mixing process, where particle size is also reduced to aid dispersal and uniform mixing. This is a common process applied to milk, where the dispersed fat droplets are reduced in size to create uniformly mixed milk, without a layer of cream on top.

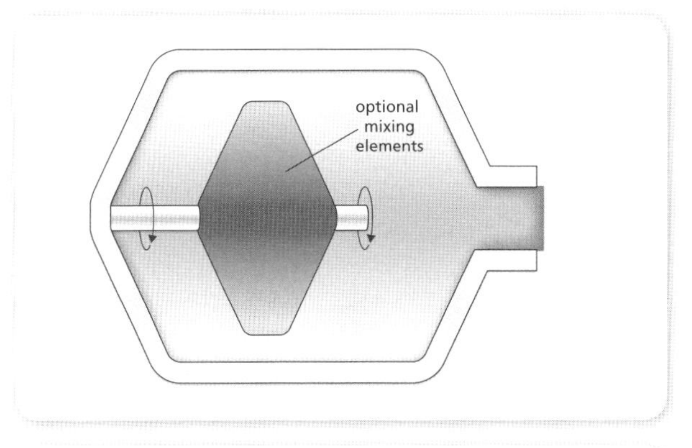

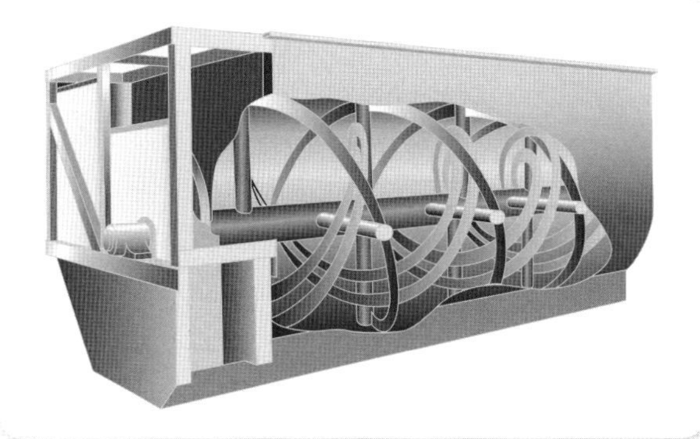

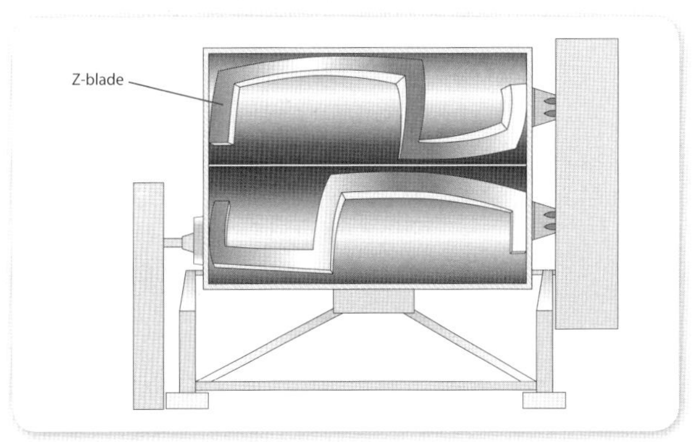

Tumbler, ribbon blender, Z-blade mixer

Support Activity

Research the quality of mixing and combining of ingredients in dry powder products, such as soups, stuffing, sauce and cake mixes. Comment on the uniformity of the mix by using the ingredients list and visual inspection of the powdered mixes.

ResultsPlus Exam Question Report

A small business specialises in making desserts.

(a) Give three ways in which the small business could use an electric mixer to prepare ingredients for the desserts. (3 marks, 2009 Higher)

How students answered

The majority of students were unable to suggest a single use.

60% got 0 marks

3% got 1–2 marks

26% got 3 marks

Whisking, creaming, liquidising, rubbing in and blending were common correct answers. It was not enough to simply state whisking – a context was needed for maximum marks.

Table 3.11 shows the main types of mixing machines.

Mixing machine	Example of foods	Special points
dough mixers	pastes and dough	• Z-blade mixers combine pastes to allow even blending of thick mixtures • dough is generally thick in texture and requires a powerful mixing element, capable of reaching all areas of the bowl
liquid mixers	batters, sauces and soups	• stir liquid in an irregular pattern to create better mixing and smooth texture
powder and particle mixers: • tumblers • ribbon blenders	powdered soups, sauce mixes, cake mixes	• mix ingredients using agitation to create uniform blend of ingredients • ribbon blenders use two propeller elements, mixing in opposite directions to create an even mix within a bowl (trough)

Table 3.11: Mixing machines

Blanching

This is a short heat treatment using water, steam or microwave blanching, carried out on vegetables before canning, freezing or drying. Foods are rapidly heated to temperatures of 100°C for the required time, and then quickly cooled or processed further. Time and temperature will depend on the food product to be blanched.

Functions of blanching include:

- inactivate enzymes before preservation treatments
- shrinking the product by removing some air and moisture from the product before preservation treatments
- cleaning and partial removal of surface bacteria (however, if the product is left warm and wet, bacterial growth will increase)
- improving taste and texture of some food products.

Water blanching uses a continuous blancher machine in which the food passes through boiling hot water for between 30 seconds and four minutes. Water blanching can cause loss of water-soluble Vitamins B and C. Sometimes, additives are added to the blanching water to improve the product.

Steam blanching uses a closed vessel with saturated steam, through which the food product is passed. Steam blanching does not cause soluble vitamin loss because leaching does not occur.

Stretch Activity

1. Evaluate the different methods of blanching for a range of fresh vegetables in a domestic (test) kitchen. Blanch each vegetable for three minutes using steam, water and a microwave. Comment on the appearance, weight, size and shape of the product before and after blanching.
2. Record your results in a table like this.

Food	50g mushrooms	50g broccoli	50g carrots
before blanching			
steamer			
boiling water in a saucepan			
microwave blanching			

Industrial food processing techniques

Objectives

- **Understand** the names, uses, advantages, disadvantages and safety issues of food processing techniques used in the food industry
- **Know** that food materials are processed on an industrial scale using large machinery
- **Understand** the concept of HACCP

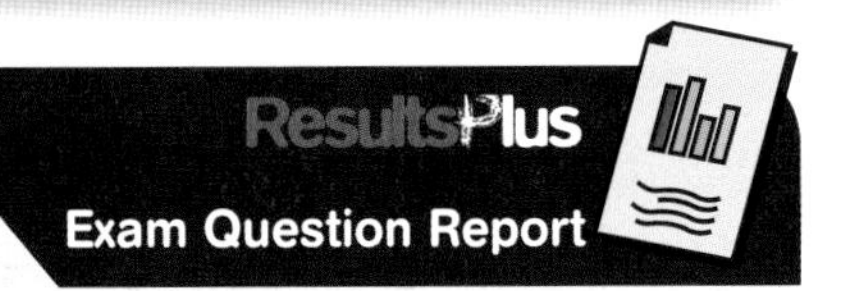

Name the tool/piece of equipment.
(1 mark, 2007 Foundation)

How students answered

Very few students were able to identify this tool.

88% got 0 marks

12% got 1 mark

Possible answers include:
industrial cutter, drum cutter, roller cutter

Give an example of a task that can be carried out using it. (1 mark, 2007 foundation)

How students answered

Far more students were able to suggest what it might be used for.

43% got 0 marks

57% got 1 mark

Good answers made relevant suggestions to industrial processing techniques for shaping/moulding or cutting dough (pastry, biscuit or bread).

Reasons for industrial food processing

Industrial food processing techniques are used to treat foods for a number of important reasons and advantages:

- Mass-production of food is much cheaper overall than individual production of meals from raw ingredients. Large profits can be made by manufacturers and suppliers of processed food products.
- Storage life is increased through preservation treatments and the removal or reduction of microbial growth. Processed foods are often less prone to early spoilage than fresh foods, and are better suited for long distance transportation from source to consumer. Fresh ingredients are more likely to harbour pathogenic microorganisms capable of causing serious illnesses.
- The sensory properties of foods are often increased or altered.
- The techniques aid the distribution and transportation of food from source to shop.
- Take advantage of seasonal gluts when food is in cheap and plentiful supply.
- The techniques maximise the availability of foods all year round through the use of temperature-controlled transportation systems or preservation treatments.
- Foods are produced as ready-prepared foods or pre-manufactured components. Consumers may enjoy the benefit of convenience foods, but will rarely save any money by using processed food rather than preparing food at home. Working patterns have changed eating habits, and some families have little time for food preparation using fresh ingredients.
- Modern food processing also improves the quality of life for people with allergies, diabeties, and for other people who cannot consume certain foods.
- Food processing can also add extra nutrients such as vitamins through fortification.
- The techniques used improve the safety of food through control systems to identify and eliminate potential risks and hazards (HACCP). For more on HACCP, see page 97.

Industrial food processing techniques

The following are common characteristics of the machinery used in industrial food processing.

- Industrial machinery used for large-scale production of food has a far greater size and capacity than domestic equipment.
- Machinery is powered by electricity to aid large-scale production of food. The safety of machinery is regularly checked, as part of the HACCP risk assessment, and annually inspected.
- The operating, maintenance and energy costs of industrial equipment are far greater than those of domestic equipment.

- Machinery is generally made from stainless steel to prevent contamination, eliminate corrosion and aid cleaning.
- Machinery must be robust, strong and easy to clean and maintain.
- Time and temperature controls operate with alarm systems to prevent cross-contamination and maintain the quality of the end product.
- Wet and dry ingredients are stored separately until they are mixed and combined, to prevent cross-contamination and food spoilage.
- Weighing scales are calibrated and checked to ensure accurate measurement and weighing of ingredients.
- Conveyor belts and pipes move ingredients around the factory.

Stretch Activity

Choose a food product. Compare the food processing techniques used to make the food product at home and in industry.

Storage

Equipment: silos and vats

Storage includes:

- large-scale storage of dry and wet raw ingredients using time, temperature and control to monitor safety of food product
- pressure-rated or atmospheric tanks
- 15 to 60,000 litre capacity depending on design and use.

Jacketed tanks include steam and water for heating and cooling.

Vats and silos

Preparation

Equipment: piped food system pipes food to food preparation areas

Preparation involves:

- fully automated using computer-integrated manufacture (CIM)
- made from stainless steel
- variety of sizes.

Dry ingredients can pose a problem with dust contamination.

Piped food system

Mixing and combining

Equipment: industrial mixer

Mixing and combining is fully automated using CAM and CIM. There are a variety of variety of sizes of mixer and attachments for different processing techniques.

Industrial mixer

Movement

Equipment: conveyor belts

The conveyor belts are:

- wire mesh belts or smooth surface bands
- fully automated – no manual intervention
- variety of sizes and widths
- used during all stages of food processing: drying, cleaning, baking, cooking, freezing and preservation techniques to direct products to wherever needed
- used at high and low temperatures.

They can withstand acid, alkaline, chemical corrosion, abrasion and impact.

Movement of food around a food processing factory

Depositor and injector

Rollers and cutters

Boiling vat

Blast chiller

Apply it!

Apply HACCP to your Design and Make activities to demonstrate high-level safety awareness throughout all aspects of food manufacture in Unit 1.

Dispensing materials

Equipment: depositors and injectors

The depositors and injectors are:

- fully automated using computer integrated manufacture (CIM)
- made from stainless steel
- a variety of sizes.

Shaping and forming

Equipment: industrial cutters and rollers, grinders, mincers, stuffers and fillers, extrusion machines

Adjustable cutters, discs and interchangeable moulds are used to achieve different shapes, texture, thickness and size. Often, these are multi-purpose machines that can perform a number of different tasks: automatic mixer, kneader, laminator and moulder.

Cooking

Equipment: travelling ovens, large kettles, boiling vat, industrial microwave

These are rapid heating systems that allow high temperatures to be achieved instantly. They use:

- CIM production and are fully automated
- time and temperature controls within computer aided manufacture (CAM).

Temperature control

Equipment: blast chillers, freezers

These may be benchtop, tunnel or chest freezers depending on the food to be frozen within the production system. They use:

- rapid cooling systems which allow low temperatures to be achieved instantly
- CIM production and are fully automated
- time and temperature controls within computer aided manufacture (CAM).

Transportation

Equipment: temperature-controlled transportation

The temperature-controlled transportation involves:

- a dedicated food transport system
- refrigeration, deep-freeze controlled vehicles using regulated temperatures at all times
- storage in both refrigerated and dry storage facilities
- ordinary or temperature controlled trailers
- logger to monitor and record temperature
- hygienic
- cooled to 0°C
- frozen to –25°C
- heated to +25°C.

Hazard Analysis and Critical Control Point (HACCP)

HACCP is the risk assessment system used for identifying potential hazards involved in food production.

Risk assessment means considering what harm could happen and when it might happen, and taking preventative action at critical control points to make sure it does not happen. Risk assessment methods ensure that food operations are designed to be safe by taking potential hazards into account.

Hazards

A hazard is anything that may cause harm to a consumer. It might be:

- biological (for example, salmonella in chicken)
- physical (for example, metal or glass in food)
- chemical (for example, cleaning chemicals in food).

A hazard could occur at any stage in food preparation, processing, production, manufacture or service.

Critical control points

Critical control points are the key points at which a control measure may need to be taken to prevent harm, at any stage in the food production process. These points cover a wide range of items: hygiene, storage, equipment, weight, consistency, temperature, time or foreign body control (biological, physical or chemical hazards).

Critical control points are categorised as:

- safety points
- quality points
- mandatory points (required by law: Food Hygiene Regulations 2006 and Food Safety Act 1990).

Developing HACCP helps companies to comply with legislation, supports 'due diligence' requirements and fulfils customer requirements for a food safety management system.

The seven principles of HACCP

1. Analyse hazards. Prepare a list of steps or a flow chart of the production process. Identify hazards associated with a food and describe the measures to control hazards.
2. Identify critical control points. Identify points during a food's production, from its raw state through processing and distribution to consumption, at which the potential hazard can be controlled or eliminated.
3. Establish preventative measures with critical limits for each control point. For cooked food, this might include setting a minimum cooking temperature and time to ensure harmful microbes are eliminated.
4. Establish procedures to monitor critical control points: for example, determining how and by whom cooking time and temperature should be monitored.
5. Establish corrective actions to be taken, for example, disposing of food if a metal has been detected.
6. Verify by checking that HACCP is working.
7. Establish effective record keeping. Documenting the HACCP system provides detailed records to use for traceability and accountability.

Apply it!

You can use ICT to produce a production plan, including HACCP procedures for your range of final products in your Design and Make activities.

Support Activity

1. Choose a food product. Make a list of one hazard that might occur during each stage of its production. Write your list in order of production.
2. Identify the critical control point for each hazard. This might be a safety, quality or mandatory point.

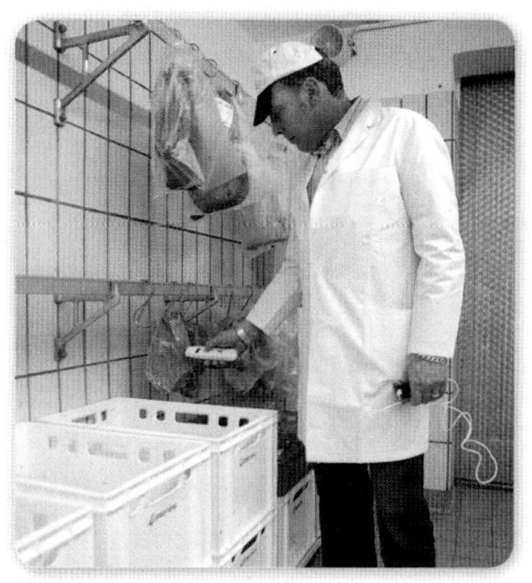

HACCP used in burger-making

Quick notes

The seven stages of HACCP are:

1. hazard analysis
2. critical control points
3. critical limits
4. monitoring
5. corrective action
6. verification
7. record keeping.

Additives

Objectives

- **Understand** that additives are used in both home and industry foods processing
- **Describe** the uses and functional properties of additives

What are additives?

Additives are substances added to food during processing to alter, improve or restore specific characteristics of food, characterised as:

- sensory
- physical
- storage
- nutritional
- processing.

Food additives originate from different sources, but may be classified into two groups:

1. natural – substances found naturally in plant or animal foods: for example, colours such as red (beetroot), green (chlorophyll)
2. artificial – substances created in a laboratory that are either artificial copies of natural ingredients or completely new chemical substances that can also give additional quality to processed foods.

For manufacturers, artificial additives are good to use because they are easy to control due to their purity and consistency.

Some additives have been used for centuries, such as vinegar in pickled products, salt in bacon, and pectin and sugar in jam-making. With the rapid development in food science and technology, the range of food and processing methods used to meet consumer demand has changed dramatically, resulting in greater use of chemicals in foods. This might be to restore flavours or colours lost during processing, to improve the nutritional value of foods, or to give a longer storage life.

Natural additives

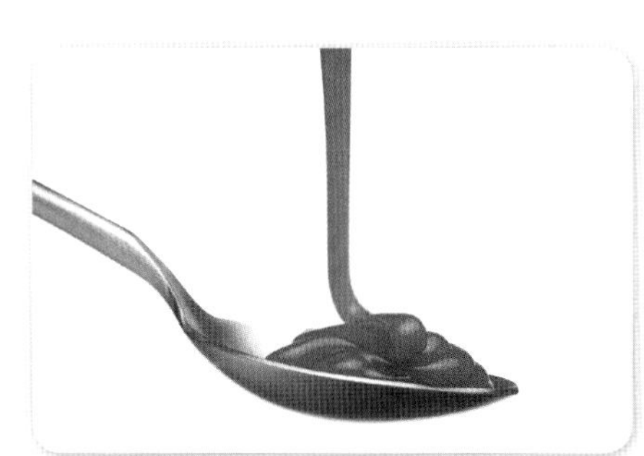

Artificial additives - caramel

Cutting down on additives

Food additives have a number of important functions, but despite this there is an increasing demand for foods without them, particularly those considered to cause allergic and intolerant reactions. Because of these concerns, some manufacturers are working towards producing foods with clean labels, trying to reduce the use of artificial additives by using natural substances to restore, enhance or improve the functional characteristics of food. Natural additives can be difficult for food manufacturers to use as they can be hard to control due to instability once extracted from their plant or animal origin.

There are thousands of natural and artificial additives that food manufacturers can use in the UK.

Permitted additives list

Additives affect the characteristics of foods in different ways.

Table 3.12 shows how they affect sensory characteristics.

Additive	Reasons for adding to food	Examples of use in food
colours	• replace or restore colours lost during processing • ensure consistency between batch productions • make food look more attractive by adding colour to colourless foods	• margarine • cheese • processed desserts, cakes and biscuits • drinks
flavours	• create a particular taste or smell • replace flavours lost during processing • enhance a food's existing flavour	• sauces • soups • processed meat products
artificial sweeteners	• add flavouring to foods • replace natural sugar with artificial sweeteners to reduce calories in a food or because of beneficial effects on the diet (countering tooth decay, obesity, diabetes mellitus) • **intense sweeteners**: aspartame and saccharin are very low in energy but difficult to use in food preparation due to lack of bulk • **bulk sweeteners**: sorbitol and sucralose have similar levels of sweetness to sugar, but an unpleasant aftertaste	• soft drinks • desserts • diabetic jams • canned drinks • bakery products • low-calorie drinks • diabetic products and sugar-free confectionary
herbs and spices	• enhance the flavour and colour of foods using minute quanitites of the leaves, stems, roots, flowers, seeds or barks of plants • used in minute quantities, so have minimal nutritional significance	• bouquet garni • pre-blended herbs and spices • sauces, soups, cakes, desserts, main meal dishes

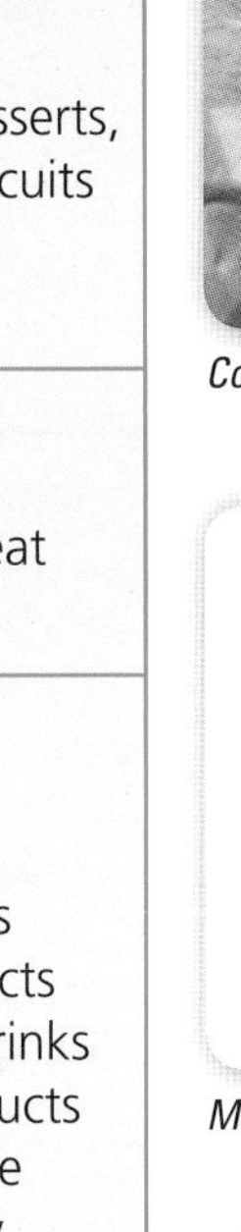

Table 3.12: Additives that affect sensory characteristics

Colours in food

Monosodium glutamate on a food label

Artificial sweeteners

Safety

The use of additives is controlled by the Food Safety Act 1990. The Food Standards Agency provides guidance and controlled checks on the use of additives in the UK. Additives accepted as safe are placed on the 'permitted additives list' and reviewed by the European Food Safety Authority. All additives must be included in the list. They may appear as E numbers - a category that means that the additive has been passed as safe by the European Union.

Tables 3.13–3.15 shows how additives affect physical, storage and nutritional characteristics of food.

Additive	Reasons for adding to food	Examples of use in food
emulsifiers	allow water and oils to remain mixed together in an emulsion	• mayonnaise • ice cream • homogenised milk
stabilisers	bind and absorb large quantities of water to create gels and thickening properties in jams and emulsions	• instant desserts • cake mixes • jams • ice cream
gelling, setting and thickening agents	increase the viscosity (thickness) of a mixture, to give a smooth, creamy texture	• sauces and soups • desserts • mousses
raising agents	make a product rise, to improve taste, texture and appearance	• baked products
preservatives	prevents the spoilage of food by the action of microorganisms, to improve the storage life of foods	• drinks • yogurts • processed cheese • pizza • cheesecake mixes • fruit pie fillings • dried fruit
anti-oxidants	prevents rancidity in foods with a high fat content	processed foods: • sausages • scotch eggs • vegetable oils • ready-prepared meals
food fortification	• improves the nutritional content of foods to ensure that minimum dietary requirements are met (this is a public health initiative) • restores the nutritional status of a product after food processing • improves the storage life of a product by using the benefits of a nutrient, but in an alternative way • many food manufacturers fortify foods and use this to promote their products to improve sales	• white flour (iron, calcium, B group Vitamins) • margarine (Vitamins A and D) • breakfast cereals (B group vitamins, iron) • Vitamin C used in bread-making can also enhance the storage life of the product • fruit drinks and squashes

Table 3.13–3.15: Additives that affect physical, storge and nutritional characteristics

ResultsPlus
Build Better Answers

Explain how additives may be used to change characteristics of a food product. (6 marks)

Basic answers (0–1 marks)
At this level, answers gave one or no methods.

Good answers (2–3 marks)
At this level, answers gave two methods and/or one reason.

Excellent answers (4–6 marks)
Answers gave three methods with at least one explanation. For example:

1. Stabilisers bind and absorb large quantities of water to create gels and thickening properties in jams and emulsions.
2. Gelling agents increase the viscosity (thickness) of a mixture, to give a smooth, creamy texture.
3. Raising agents make a product rise, to improve taste, texture and appearance in baked products such as cakes, muffins and breads.

Other additives

Anti-caking agents

Anti-caking agents prevent lumps in dry powder mixes, such as icing sugar, cocoa powder, instant desserts, powdered milk.

Icing sugar

Acidity regulators

These change or control the acidity or alkalinity of foods, for example, sauces and drinks.

Non-alcoholic carbonated drinks

Buffers

Buffers control and stabilise the ph of foods, for example, meat products, bread, processed cheese, canned vegetables.

Canned vegetables

Support Activity

Shortcrust pastry cases with a Bramley apple filling (48

INGREDIENTS

Wheat Flour, Bramley Apple, Sugar, Vegetable Oil, Glucose Syrup, Dextrose, Modified Maize Starch, Humectant (Vegetable Glycerine), Salt, Malic Acid, Flavouring, Raising Agents (Disodium Diphosphate, Sodium Bicarbonate), Preservatives (Potassium Sorbate, Sulphur Dioxide), Gelling Agent (Sodium Alginate), Adipic Acid, Milk Protein.

ALLERGY ADVICE

May Contain Nut Traces

Contains: Gluten (Wheat), Milk and Sulphites

NICE TO KNOW...

- Suitable for Vegetarians
- No Artificial Colours or Flavours
- No Hydrogenated Fat

Suitable for vegetarians

Ingredients

Tomato Purée (55%), Water, Reconstituted Whey Powder (from Milk), Sugar, Modified Maize Starch, Vegetable Oil, Salt, Ascorbic Acid, Acidity Regulator (Citric Acid), Mustard Flour, Natural Flavouring, Garlic Oil.

Nutrition

Typical Composition | Half of a can (200g) contains | 100g contain

Identify the food products above using the list of ingredients from the food labels.

Stretch Activity

Research three uses of additves that can change the sensory characteristics of food.

Additives on a food label

Standard components

Objectives

- **Understand** that standard components are used in both home and industry food processing
- **Describe** the uses and functional properties of standard components

Apply it!

Investigate how standard components can be used in the mass production of your food product in your Design and Make activities.

Support Activity

Discuss four uses of standard components in food production.

What are standard components?

Standard components may be pre-manufactured components (ready-made) used in the manufacture of commercial and domestic food products.

Table 3.16 shows types and uses of standard components.

Category of standard component	Pre-manufactured components	Primary or secondary foods
pastries and doughs	• flan cases • pizza bases • pasta	• flour • fat • yeast • water • egg
powdered mixes	• cakes • biscuits • bread • soup • sauces • gravies • desserts	• flour • fat • milk • egg • vegetables • sugar
other standard components	• stock cubes • baking powder • pre-blended spices • dried and tinned fruit	• herbs and spices • sodium bicarbonate + acid or cream of tartar + acid • spices • fruit • fruit juice or syrup

Table 3.16: Types and uses of standard components

Functional properties and uses of standard components

Standard components are **reliable** and **consistent quality**:

standard size or weight

standard form or shape

standard flavour

accurate proportion and ratio

Standard components save time in the processing, manufacturing or assembly of a food product.

The dangers of high-risk food processing may be reduced because they are carried out in a separate location by a different manufacturer. This can reduce the risk of cross-contamination, but it relies on the health and safety procedures and reputation of a different supplier (for example, using pre-washed vegetables or pre-cooked chicken).

Food product storage life may be improved because of the use of preservatives. This might be beneficial for use in the home or industry, but consumers may want to avoid the use of artificial additives due to worries about health and safety.

Manufacturers find it **quicker** and **cheaper** to use pre-manufactured components as this can reduce the cost and time of the processing and safety checks needed in the assembly of a composite food in their production line. At home the use of these pre-manufactured components in recipes can increase the cost of the food product, but does make it quicker to produce.

The sensory properties and quality of standard components may be different from the consumer's expectations. For example, a pre-manufactured sauce could contain flavour enhancers or colours while a homemade sauce uses simple, fresh, seasonal ingredients; a pre-manufactured pie filling might contain less meat and more sauce than a homemade one. Food manufacturers trial and test the use of standard components in their products during food product development to ensure that each standard component meets all the requirements for their product.

Sauce ingredients

The use of a pre-manufactured component might reduce the nutritional value of a food product. For example, in highly processed foods (ready-meals and desserts) food manufacturers often use components that are high in fat, salt and sugar to enhance the sensory properties and keeping qualities of a food product. This can reduce the nutritional value of a food product and make the product unhealthy.

Sometimes, the nutritional content of a food product can be improved by using pre-manufactured components (for example, the use of white flour in pastry fortified with iron, calcium and B group vitamins or margarine fortified with Vitamins A and D).

Stretch Activity

1. Research the range of standard components that could be used in a ready-made pizza.
2. Compare and contrast the method used to manufacture a homemade pizza with that used for a ready-made pizza.

ResultsPlus
Build Better Answers

Describe two advantages to the food manufacturer of using standard components in a food product. (4 marks)

Basic answers (0–1 marks)
At this level, answers gave one or no advantage.

Good answers (2–3 marks)
At this level, answers gave two advantages or one advantage and a description. For example:
1. Standard components can save a manufacturer time.
2. Standard components can ensure consistency of the final product.

Excellent answers (4 marks)
Answers gave two advantages and at least one description. For example:
1. Standard components can save a manufacturer time because they do not need any additional preparation.
2. Standard components can ensure consistency of the final product because they are of a uniform size, shape or flavour.

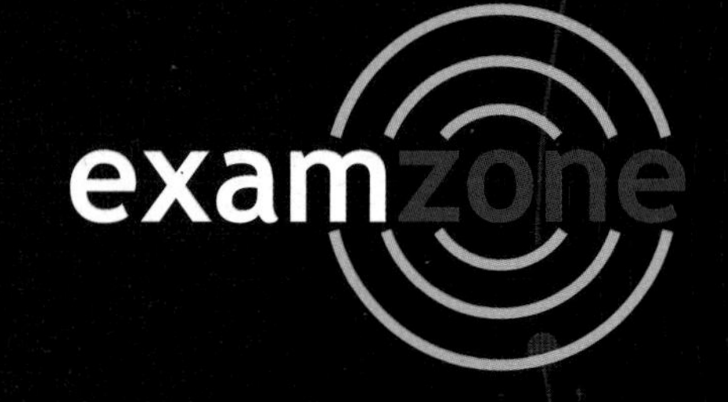

Know Zone
Chapter 3 Preservation and processing

For raw food materials to be used in food production, they need to be processed and/or preserved to make them suitable for further processing or immediate consumption. With knowledge of the principles of preservation, you will apply this understanding to how food is prepared and processed in the home and within industry, by considering the advantages, disadvantages and safety issues of each technique.

You should know...

☐ The main forms of preservation:
- food spoilage
- kitchen hygiene
- food poisoning
- personal hygiene
- food hygiene

☐ The Food Safety Act 1990 and Food Hygiene Regulations 2006.

☐ The main preservation methods:
- hot
- cold
- dry
- chemical
- packaging
- irradiation

☐ The main food preparation techniques – home:
- manual and electrical equipment
- cleaning
- peeling
- size reduction
- blanching
- mixing and combining

☐ The main food preservation techniques – home:
- freezing
- drying
- chemicals: acid, sugar, salt

☐ The main food preparation techniques – industry:
- separation processes: cleaning, peeling and sorting
- size reduction processes
- mixing and combining
- blanching

☐ The main food processing techniques – industry:
- industrial machinery and food processing techniques
- HACCP

☐ The main food preservation techniques – industry:
- hot: pasteurisation, sterilisation, UHT, canning
- cold: chilling, freezing, cook chill/freeze
- dry: sun, spray and AFD
- chemical: preservatives
- specialist packaging: MAP and vacuum packaging

☐ The ways that additives change the characteristics of food: sensory, physical, storage, nutritional and aid processing and production.

☐ About standard components and their functional properties and uses.

Key terms

microorganisms	food poisoning
cross-contamination	mould
perishable foods	pathogenic bacteria
high-risk foods	toxin
spoilage	yeast
bacteria	freezer star rating
danger zone	risk assessment
date mark	critical control point
food hygiene	standard components

Which of the key terms above matches each of the following definitions?

A Foods which spoil rapidly and usually have a high water content and good nutritional content.

B This may occur due to natural decay, microorganisms or enzyme action.

C Poison produced by a pathogen, such as moulds and bacteria.

D Bacteria that cause disease and illness, such as food poisoning.

To check your answers, look at the glossary on page 183.

Multiple choice questions

1 An anti caking agent is used in food products to:

A Prevent lumps in dry powder mixes.
B Prevent rancidity in foods with a high fat content.
C Improve the nutritional content of food.
D Make a product rise, therefore improving its texture.

4 Foods may be shaped and formed during food processing. Which food has been processed in this way?

A sausages and pasta
B milk and bread
C fats and oils
D sugar and syrups

3 What is HACCP?

A A food preparation technique.
B A method of cooking.
C An industrial preservation method.
D A system used for identifying potential hazards in food production.

2 Dry cleaning food might involve:

A sieving
B slicing
C pulping
D all the above

ResultsPlus
Maximise your marks

Microwave ovens are useful in the home for cooking food quickly.
Give three other uses of a microwave oven in the home. (3 marks)

Student answer	Examiner comments	Build a better answer
Student A Cooking (0 marks)	■ This answer does not answer the question.	△ Warming (1 mark)
Student B Making custard (0 marks)	■ The microwave does not make the custard; it warms the mixture and allows gelatinisation to occur.	△ Heating/reheating (1 mark)
Student C Melting (1/2 mark)	■ Correct, but could be more specific.	△ Melting butter (1 mark)

Overall comment: The students did not answer the question correctly. An explain question requires a correct statement and a relevant explanation.

Practice exam questions

1 Outline the difference between conduction, convection and radiation methods of cooking. (6 marks)
2 Give four safety rules to follow when using a microwave oven. (4 marks)
3 A food processor may be used to rub fat into flour. Give 3 other uses of a food processor. (3 marks)
4 A pasta bake product is sold as a cook-chilled product. Explain one way in which the cook-chill process makes the pasta bake safe to eat. (2 marks)
5 Evaluate the use of standard components in food production within the home and food industry. (6 marks)

Chapter 4: Product manufacture
Production methods

Objectives

- **Understand** production methods within the food industry

The term 'food processing' covers the methods and techniques used to transform raw ingredients into food for human consumption. Food processing takes clean, harvested or slaughtered and butchered components and uses them to produce marketable food products. Production methods fall into three main categories:

- one-off production
- batch production
- high-volume production.

The production method chosen depends on the:

- number of products to be made
- type of product
- type and cost of equipment available
- cost of the final product
- number of workers available
- level of skill of the workers.

High-volume production of soft drinks

One-off production

One-off production is used for specialist single items. A customer makes an order for something to be made to their own specifications, such as a wedding cake. Making this could take days depending on the complexity of the design and the ability of the chef.

Table 4.1 shows the advantages and disadvantages of one-off production.

Advantages	Disadvantages
• unique design • personalised message, image or decoration • ordered for a specific date • fresh • high-quality product • made to order and budget • caters for special diets • specific	• labour intensive • expensive to make; cost is passed onto the consumer • reduced profit margin for the manufacturer • slow process

Table 4.1: Advantages and disadvantages of one-off production

One-off production

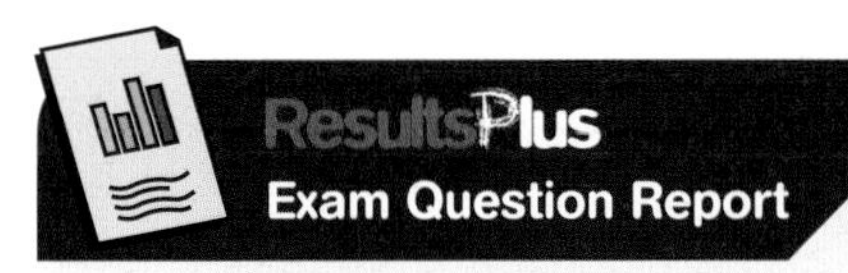

Give two advantages to the customer of having a celebration cake made to order. (2 marks, 2009 Higher).

How students answered

Only half the students were able to provide two advantages.

21% got 0 marks

Many students failed to make the link to one-off production.

21% got 1 mark

Students repeated the stem of the question (made to order) and restricted their chance of achieving two marks.

58% got 2 marks

Advantages include being able to add personalised messages and decoration, and ordering for a specific day.

Apply it!

The kitchen you use for your Design and Make activities in food technology lessons could be a test kitchen, where ideas are trialled and modelled using one-off production.

The school canteen kitchen is an example of batch production, where the same quantity of items are produced daily, with small variations.

Batch production

Manufacturers use batch production for fixed quantities of identical items. The size of the market for a product may not be known, but the manufacturer produces products either as stock or to order. There is usually a range within a product line. For example, a ready-prepared meal range might be: pasta bake, pasta and meatballs, spaghetti bolognese and macaroni cheese. A certain number of the same goods will be produced to make up a batch or run. This method involves estimating the number of customers who will want to buy the product. Batch-produced food products include biscuits, sandwiches, ready-prepared meals, desserts and carton soups.

Table 4.2 shows the advantages and disadvantages of batch production.

Advantages	Disadvantages
• quicker than one-off production, saving time and money in production costs • cheaper than one-off production • ingredients and components can be bought in **bulk** • fixed production costs are spread over a larger product range • quality product due to consistency of identical items • reduces energy costs due to fixed production costs • equipment and labour cost altered to meet seasonal demand, e.g. apple pie in summer and mince pie in winter • HACCP controls safe working practices	• a too big batch size can lead to goods remaining unsold, which wastes resources and money • estimating product demand can be high risk for food manufacturers – depends on consumer and product need • expensive to repair and maintain machinery • implementing HACCP can be expensive • initial outlay of money for the premises, machinery and skilled labour force is very expensive • one fault on the production line can lead to excessive food and energy waste • powercuts can shut down production line

Table 4.2: Advantages and disadvantages of batch production

Stretch Activity

1. Name the production method used to make the range of chocolates in a box.
2. Discuss the stages used to make the chocolates.
3. What makes this a high-quality product?

Batch production

High-volume production

Manufacturers use high-volume production when there is a mass market for a large number of identical products. The product passes from one stage of production to another along an assembly line. This production method relies on large, regular sales being made. Food products made using high-volume production might include bread, crisps and soft drinks.

Table 4.3 shows the advantages and disadvantages of high-volume production.

Advantages	Disadvantages
• fast, efficent production due to manufacturing process being split into tasks and sequenced into an assembly line using conveyor belts and other **automated** industrial machinery, saving time and money in production costs • cheaper to produce large quantites of the same product • ingredients and components can be purchased in bulk, reducing cost • production costs are spread over a larger product range, lowering cost of final product • operates **24/7** • consistent results • CAM and CIM can help to lower the unit costs, due to reduced labour costs of small work force • reduced energy costs due to fixed production costs for each stage of the production line • automatic **quality control** leading to high-quality product • small workforce required • HACCP controls safe working practices	• a batch size too big can lead to goods remaining unsold, wasting resources and money • regular, thorough maintenance control checks to avoid expensive repairs and loss of production • implementing HACCP can be expensive: for example, expenses of staff training, **controls**, monitoring systems and **good manufacturing practice (GMP)** • initial outlay of money for the premises, machinery and skilled labour force is very expensive • one fault on the production line can lead to excessive food and energy waste • repetitive/dull work restricts recruitment of workers

Table 4.3: Advantages and disadvantages of high-volume production

Support Activity

1. Name the production method used to make a ham sandwich in a domestic kitchen.
2. Draw a flowchart showing the method of production for this ham sandwich.
3. List the pieces of equipment that would be used to make this product in school.

High-volume production

Quick notes

- One-off production: producing a single item from start to finish.
- Batch production: producing fixed quantities of identical items.
- High-volume production: 24/7 production line to produce large quantities of identical items.
- Batch or run: an amount or quantity produced during production or processing.

Product and recipe development

Objectives

- **Understand** product and recipe development within the food industry

Products can be developed in two different ways:

- new, original products
- development of existing products.

The product development process

The development of new products is a long process of research and consultation between designers, manufacturers and consumers. Designers and manufacturers keep many aspects of this process secret within the food industry, including their research, specification, design, testing, trialling, manufacturing and marketing strategies.

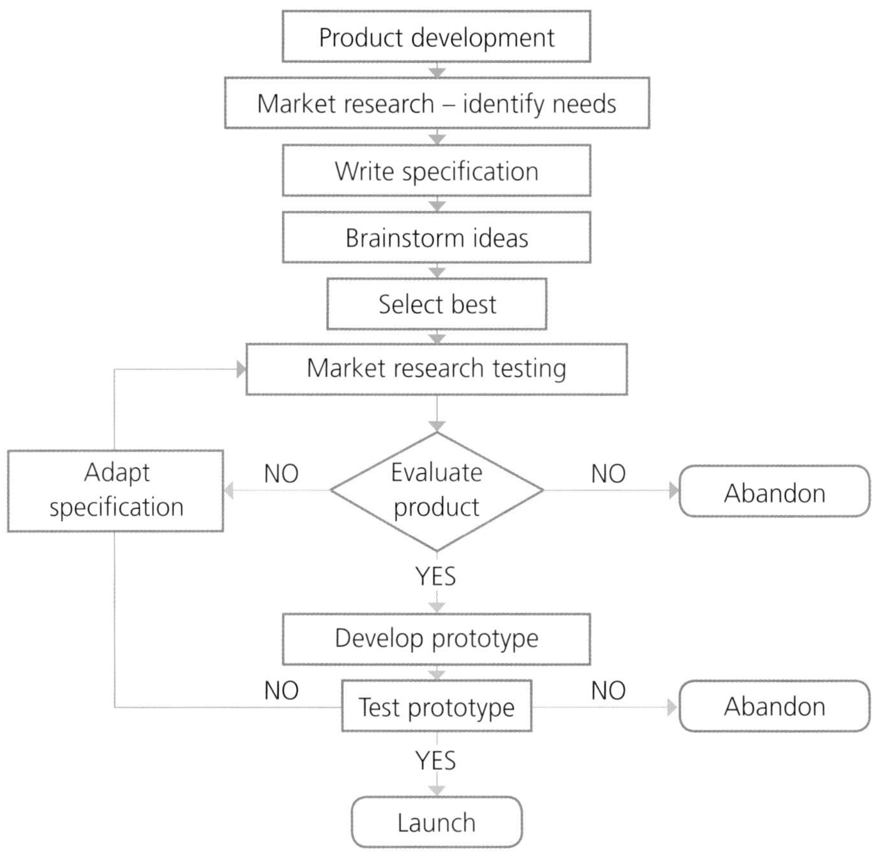

Flow diagram of product development process within the food industry

Group	Socio-economic groups
A	higher managerial, administrative or professional
B	intermediate managerial, administrative or professional
C1	supervisory or clerical, and junior managerial, administrative or professional
C2	skilled manual workers
D	semi-skilled and unskilled workers
E	state pensioners, casual workers, unemployed

Table 4.4: Socio-economic groups
(Source: Institute of Practitioners in Advertising)

Specification

The specification is a detailed description of the product. It includes technical and measurable details, collated from the research and consultation stages of the design process.

User requirements

Food designers identify people most likely to buy their product, in order to meet the needs and expectations of the target group, for example identifying specific age ranges or different-sized households with a range of ages, or using socio-economic groups to match income to the pricing of new foods, or catering for special diets and dietary restrictions.

Consumers have the power to determine the success or failure of a product. Consumer demand for new products is influenced by changing social, cultural, economic, technological, moral and environmental factors.

Table 4.5 shows the main factors affecting product development.

	Factors affecting product development
social	• ageing population due to increased life expectancy • increase in one-person households • increase in 'blended households' (where, for example, a couple may live together with children from previous relationships)
cultural	• convenience foods which save time and energy • lifestyle preferences motivated by health concerns, quality of life and leisure pursuits: e.g. low-calorie or sports foods • varied dietary customs for different ethnic groups, religious beliefs or traditional cooking practices
economic	• cost of the product: value, 'own label' and luxury branding of food products to meet the consumer's financial needs • meal deals, special offers and loyalty schemes, which all contribute to the consumer's choice and purchasing power
technology	• **functional foods** with specific health-promoting or disease-preventing properties beyond the basic function of supplying nutrients: for example, foods with the ability to lower cholesterol levels
environment	• **sustainability** to preserve the world's natural resources; supporting local producers and farmers helps appreciate the origin, season and source of food as well as ensuring that producers receive fair terms of trade and better prices • choice, design and production of packaging materials can affect the environment
moral	• farming practices such as GM, organic, **factory farming** and **free-range** motivate people to make choices about food they purchase; many people are vegetarian or vegan
medical	• diet-related medical problems including allergies, intolerances, coronary heart disease which create a market for new food products to meet the needs of consumers following special diets

Table 4.5: Factors affecting product development

Apply it!

The specification points in your Design and Make activities must contain more than just bare information, so that each statement is fully justified with reasons for the initial point. Write a specification for your product and include 'because...' after each point, justifying it with your research.

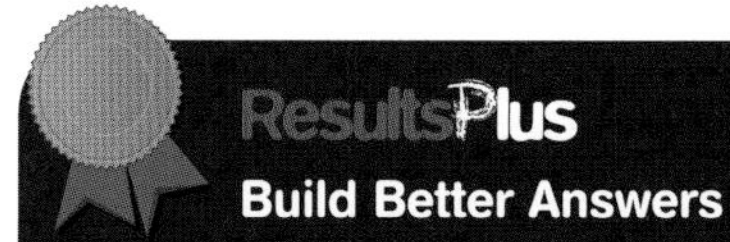

Describe two benefits to manufacturers of using recipe development. (4 marks)

Basic answers (0–1 marks)
At this level, answers gave one or no benefits.

Good answers (2 marks)
At this level, answers gave two benefits or one benefit and a description.

Excellent answers (3–4 marks)
Answers gave two benefits and at least one description. For example:

1. Using standard components instead of raw ingredients because of their consistent shape, size and flavour in quality control.
2. Creating a new image or concept for existing products because this can widen the appeal of the product and promote the brand name.

Quick notes

Recipe modification:

- budget
- special diet
- availability of ingredients
- times
- portion size
- bill of cook
- equipment available
- sensory properties
- nutrition profile

Stretch Activity

This recipe was used to produce a prototype cake.

100g self-raising flour

100g butter

100g caster sugar

2 eggs

30ml warm water

Describe two modifications that would make the cake suitable for a vegan diet.

Finishing processes

Recipe modification

Ingredients, processes and techniques are changed or adapted where there is an opportunity to create a variation of a product to fulfill a consumer's real or perceived needs.

Recipes may be modified for a range of reasons, including to:

- produce a product within a limited budget
- meet the needs of special diets, for example vegetarians, allergies and intolerances
- work when an ingredient is not available

See page 28 for more reasons recipes may be modified.

Nutritional analysis programs

Nutritional analysis programs offer students an opportunity to use computer-aided design (CAD) (see pages 130-1) to adapt, analyse or model recipes before trialling them. This is an important part of product development and recipe modification because it provides accurate, speedy results to allow the designer to compare recipes with existing products, alter specific nutritional characteristics, and calculate the nutritional values per 100g or per portion.

Finishing processes

The initial success of a product is judged first by appearance. 'We eat with our eyes' is a useful expression to describe the importance of the finish of a product. Table 4.6 shows the finishing processes and their uses.

Sensory analysis

You can use your sense organs to analyse, test and evaluate food. The qualities of food that affect sense organs are known as organoleptic qualities.

Tests include triangle test, paired preference test, hedonic scale test, duo-trio test, ranking test and rating test. For more on these tests and sensory analysis see Chapter 5, on pages 146–7.

Scaling-up of recipes

Once the recipe is judged to be acceptable, it is scaled up for factory production in a test kitchen. This involves changing the scale of production: for example, bulk buying, scaling up recipes from one-off production to batch or high-volume production. It involves a series of calculations to determine accurate weights, measures and proportions of ingredients to ensure that the recipe works for the new scale to create a high quality product.

Storage and distribution of commercial products

The storage and distribution of a commercial product is determined by:

- nature of the ingredients
- processing and preservation treatment
- destination of the finished product
- function of the product at the destination and how it will be used: perhaps as a final commercial product for sale to the public or as a food component used to create another food product.

Process	Examples	Uses
finishing	• crockery • tablecloth • doilies, napkins, cutlery or utensils	• complementing/contrasting colour for crockery can aid presentation and food photography • presentation of food can be greatly enhanced by the thought and care taken to serve food
garnishing	• sliced vegetables, fruit • breadcrumbs, cheese or gratin toppings	• to improve the colour, appearance, texture and flavour of a savoury dish
decorating	edible flowers and decorations: fruit, icing sugar, chocolate	to improve the colour, appearance, texture and flavour of a sweet dish
glazing	• egg wash • egg white • milk • sugar and water • arrowroot • jam	• pastry and scones • sweet pastry products • bread, pastry and scones • sweet bread products • fruit tarts and flans • fruit tarts
icing	glacé, butter, royal, fondant	cakes, biscuits, desserts
piping	• potato • choux pastry • mayonnaise • icing • creamed biscuit mixture	• cottage, fish or shepherd's pie • éclairs and profiteroles • salads and mousses • cakes, biscuits and desserts • biscuits
shaping and crimping	sweet and savoury dough mixtures	pastry, pizzas and calzones, pasta, bread
coating	• batters • breadcrumbs	• fish, meat and vegetables • scotch eggs, fish cakes

Table 4.6: Finishing processes and their uses

Support Activity

1. In groups, brainstorm a range of ideas in response to one of the following design briefs:
   - a seasonal soup for a farmers' market
   - a sports snack for a vending machine
   - a luxury food product for a picnic hamper.
2. Discuss the ideas and select one for product development, then write a specification for your product including:
   - form
   - function
   - ingredients
   - user group
   - sensory characteristics
   - production method
   - cost
   - packaging
   - sustainability issues.

Technological development

Objectives

- **Understand** technological development within the food industry:
  - man-made
  - functional
  - novel
  - specially developed
  - biotechnology
  - nanotechnology
- **Know** the advantages and disadvantages of genetically modified (GM) food

The food industry is dynamic and innovative, creating new technological developments to meet the needs of each user group. The user group might be producers, farmers, designers, manufacturers or consumers within the life cycle of a product.

In response to concerns about the use of modified ingredients or artificial additives in food, the food industry wants 'clean labels'. This means trying to reduce the use of chemicals by using natural substances to restore, enhance or improve the functional characteristics of food. Natural additives can be difficult for food manufacturers to use as they are often hard to control due to their instability once extracted from their plant or animal origin. They can also cause allergies and intolerances for some people.

Man-made

Smart food materials are raw ingredients that have one or more properties that can be significantly changed in a controlled fashion.

Modified starch is a synthetic or man-made food additive that is prepared by treating starch, causing it to be partially degraded. There are a number of different uses for modified starch.

- It is used as a thickening agent or stabiliser.
- It prevents sauces separating (synerisis) in ready meals. Commercial pizza toppings containing acid-treated modified starch allow ease of filling or pumping during production of topping.
- Pre-gelatinised starch thickens instant desserts, allowing food to thicken with the addition of cold water or milk, e.g. Angel Delight.
- It thickens instantly when hot water is added, so is used in instant sauces, soups and pot noodles.
- It is used to thicken low-fat desserts and salad dressings, acting as a stabiliser by binding excessive water within a product to prevent separation.

ResultsPlus Watch out!

The food industry is using 'clean labels' to create a positive image to consumers, by addressing consumers' concerns about the use of modified ingredients or artificial additives in food. 'E numbers' (see page 97) are becoming obsolete as designers and manufacturers are now reconsidering what is needed in an ingredient for it to function in a particular way.

Functional foods

Functional foods have specific health-promoting or disease-preventing properties beyond the basic function of supplying nutrients. Some manufacturers have developed products that they claim have specific benefits. These foods are also known as nutraceuticals.

The Food Safety Act 1990 requires all foods to be labelled, advertised and presented in a way that is not false or misleading. A manufacturer must support each claim with scientific evidence.

Apply it!

Consider whether the food product that you are designing and making might benefit from the use of a modified starch to aid your preparation and processing techniques.

Table 4.7 shows the main types of functional foods and their uses.

Functional food	Use
Nutraceuticals 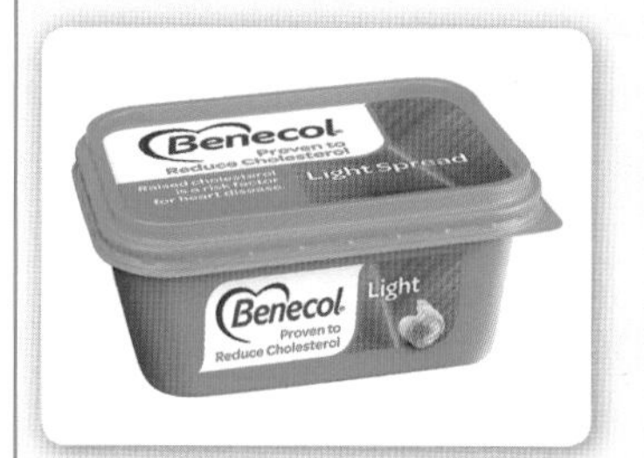	• **plant sterols** help block the uptake of cholesterol in the digestive system. Cholesterol is a natural fat found in food, and the body naturally produces cholesterol in the liver. Both these sources of cholesterol enter the bloodstream, and manufacturers claim that plant sterols can stop unhealthy LDL (low-density lipid) cholesterol entering the blood stream. These fats are called modified fats. Modifying fats replaces saturated fat with plant extracts, which reduces cholesterol levels in foods, making them a healthier alternative to foods high in saturated fats. • essential fatty acids cannot be made in the body, but are vital for the health and function of the body: – Omega 3 EFA helps protect the heart; found in oily fish, seeds, green leafy vegetables – Omega 6 EFA helps lower blood cholesterol; found in vegetables, grains, seeds and poultry
Prebiotics 	healthy, non-digestible food ingredients containing non-starch polysaccharide; used in foods including breakfast cereals, yoghurts and drinks
Probiotics 	biocultures contain living, helpful bacteria that help to maintain a healthy digestive system and immune system by maintaining the balance between helpful and harmful bacteria; found in yoghurts and milk products

Table 4.7: Functional foods and their uses

Stretch Activity

Create an information sheet about the uses of modified starch in food manufacture. Use scanned images and text as part of your ICT skills.

Support Activity

Investigate the range and type of foods containing plant sterols, by conducting some market research using either a visit to a supermarket or a supermarket website.

Quick notes

- **Plant sterols:** Chemicals that help to block the uptake of cholesterol in the digestive system.
- **Omega:** Essential fatty acids vital for the health and function of the body that can't be made in it.
- **Prebiotics:** Healthy, non-digestible food ingredients containing non-starch polysaccharide.
- **Probiotics:** Biocultures containing living, helpful bacteria that help to maintain a healthy digestive system and immune system.
- **Polysaccharide:** Simple or complex carbohydrate, formed from hundreds of glucose molecules.

Novel function

The properties and working characteristics of raw materials, ingredients and food components are determined by their nutritional structure and composition. Designers and manufacturers are now considering what is needed in an ingredient for it to function in a particular way and creating these ingredients for specific functions within products.

Sweeteners

Aspartame and sucralose are naturally occurring low-calorie substances, many hundred times sweeter than sugar.

Stabilisers

Celluloses are found naturally in foods as dietary fibre can be modified to make them easier to use as a novel ingredient.

Carboxymethyl cellulose (CMC) has many uses as a stabiliser to prevent oil or water separation, give smoothness and resist melting.

ResultsPlus
Watch out!

Stabilisers thicken and absorb a lot of water, and as a result help emulsifiers to stop separation of oil from water.

Support Activity

Investigate the use of lecithin within an emulsion. You will need:

1 jam jar with lid
100ml oil
25ml vinegar
1 egg yolk

1. Place the two immiscible liquids into the jam jar. Sketch what you can see.
2. Shake (agitate) the jar vigorously. Sketch your results.
3. Remove the lid and add an egg to the mixture. Record your results.
4. Shake vigorously. Record your results in a table like the one below.

	Before agitation	After agitation
oil and water		
oil, water and egg		

Products containing CMC

Emulsifiers

Lecithin, found in egg yolk, can be used to emulsify two liquids (oil and water) to prevent separation, as in mayonnaise.

Modified starches and proteins can be used together to improve bread dough and reduce staling. Modified fats can be used to stop fats separating by forming fat crystals.

Gelling agents (naturally occurring polysaccharides)

Alginates, extracted from brown seaweed, can thicken solutions, form gels and thin films, so are useful in sauces, syrups, soups, drinks, ice cream and jellies.

Xanthan gum, produced using biotechnology (see pages 118) on the outside of cells of the bacterium *Xanthomonas campestris*, is thixotropic - meaning that it becomes thinner when subjected to agitation, shaking or stirring, but thickens again on standing giving excellent mouthfeel to products and allowing rapid flavour release.

Carrageenan, obtained from seaweed, reacts with milk proteins to make a gel. This is useful in desserts to thicken products, retain foamy texture in instant cream or condition bread doughs.

Raw carrageenan used in desserts

Specially developed

A meat analogue is a meat substitute or extender that is similar in texture, flavour and appearance to meat. Meat analogues offer the consumer a variety of plant-based protein foods such as soya, TVP and Quorn™ that can complement a range of different dietary requirements. See Chapter 2 page 41 for more on this.

Biotechnology

This modern technological development is based on biology, medicine, agriculture and food. It uses technology to genetically engineer biological systems or living organisms to make or modify products or processes for specific uses. One example is chymosin, an enzyme found in rennet. Chymosin reacts with milk to produce curds and whey in cheese-making.

Genetic modification

This is a branch of biotechnology, with the potential to create change in the quality, variety and quantity of food available worldwide. Genetically modified (GM) foods are modified or engineered to alter specific characteristics. Examples of adaptions in foods due to GM are: shape of carrots, colour of tomatoes, size of cereal grain, use of an artificially produced chymosin in cheese-making, storage properties of cereals, tolerance of foods to adverse weather conditions, such as drought.

Table 4.8 shows the advantages and disadvantages of GM Foods.

Advantages	Disadvantages
• improved flavours, colours and textures	• long-term effects unknown
• improved nutritional content of foods, such as an increase in vitamin levels	• eliminates some wildlife species
• resistance to adverse weather conditions	• possible mutations to crops from cross-contamination and pollination of other crops
• improved yields	• irreversible changes to plants and animals
• delayed ripening of fruit and vegetables	• confusion regarding labelling of GM ingredients
• longer shelf life	• possible production of toxic substances
• reduced food costs	• allergic properties of crops transferred to others
• resistance to pests	• may transfer genes to bacteria, turning them into pathogenic bacteria
• resistance leads to less need for chemical pesticides	
• accuracy in selecting particular characteristics for food	
• reduced food wastage	

Table 4.8: Advantages and disadvantages of GM foods

Support Activity

1. Discuss the benefits of biotechnology for food manufacturers.
2. Outline the concerns that consumers may have regarding genetic modification of food.

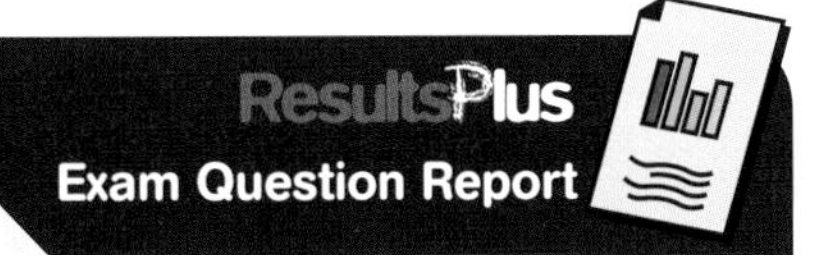

(e) Some foods have been altered by genetic modification (GM).

Give two benefits of genetically modified foods. (2 marks, 2009 Foundation)

How students answered

75% of students were unable to provide any benefits of genetically modified foods.

75% got 0 marks

Students did not understand the term genetically modified foods, referring incorrectly to additives, special diets or functional foods.

4% got 1 mark

Most of these students referred to drought resistant crops and increased yields but many students produced vague answers such as climate or yield, with no specific reference to GM foods.

21% got 2 marks

Benefits include improved flavour or nutritional content, resistance to weather, pests and disease, and improved yields.

Nanotechnology

Nanotechnology is an innovation in food science and technology that involves the manufacture and use of materials and structures at the nanometre scale (a nanometre is one millionth of a millimetre). The principle of nanotechnology is that materials at this small scale can have very different working characteristics from those at the larger scale, and are therefore potentially very useful. This is because these materials at a nano-level have a relatively larger surface area, which makes them chemically more reactive.

Approval for use is regulated under the Novel Foods Regulation, which is in force to ensure that products are safe when developing new foods and processes. The Food Standards Agency (FSA) is the UK body responsible for the assessment of novel foods. It is obliged to assess the food safety implications of any food product that will be entering the food chain.

Uses in 2010 include:

- nano-capsule protection, which can bind flavours or fortify nutrients, and allow controlled release into a food product: e.g. drinks
- nano-food synthesisers, which can create or alter food molecules
- nano-sensors that can detect the presence of pathogens, and changes in pH or temperature
- nano-bots, which are minute robots used to destroy bacteria to make food safe to eat
- nano-emulsions, creating double or triple emulsions to improve the texture of sauces.

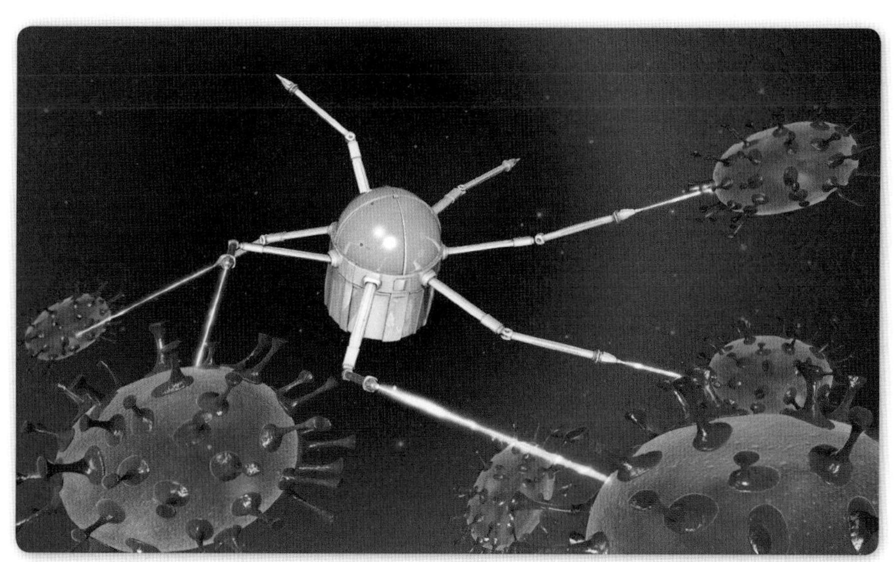

Concept art of nanotechnology in action

Stretch Activity

Evaluate the technological developments within the food industry.

ResultsPlus
Build Better Answers

Explain one way in which nanotechnology can be used in the food industry. (2 marks)

Basic answers (0–1 marks)
At this level, answers gave one or no way.

Good answers (2 marks)
At this level, answers gave a good explanation of one method. For example: Nanocapsule protection, which can bind flavours or fortifying nutrients, and allow controlled release into a food product: for example, drinks.

Quality

Objectives

- **Understand** quality issues within the food industry, covering assurance, control, design and manufacture

The safety of food and consistent quality are two customer expectations when purchasing food. The different stages in product design and manufacture need to meet these demands, to ensure that consumers are happy with their purchase and that the food industry is confident that it is safe and promises have been delivered.

Food industry standards are met and maintained through the application and use of quality control and quality assurance procedures. This is called good manufacturing practise (GMP), a term that covers the total manufacturing process and all the quality assurance procedures aimed at maintaining quality, ensuring that food products are produced to consistent standards.

Each area of the food industry plans, implements and monitors the different stages of preparation, production and manufacture for a food product. Each area needs to consider:

- understanding the customer's needs and expectations
- designing a food product to meet consumer demand
- accurate construction of the food product
- using consistent materials, ingredients and component parts from reputable suppliers
- clear labelling, advertising and presentation
- an integrated business where effective teamwork between the different departments (e.g. production, marketing, finance) fulfils consumers needs and exceeds their expectations
- safe and efficient storage and distribution (transport and delivery) systems
- good customer service.

Quick notes

The term quality can apply to:

- condition
- standard
- value
- characteristics
- features

Quality assurance

Quality assurance concerns the overall standard of a food product.

In addition to legislation and the guarantees offered by manufacturers, a number of codes of practice have been established. These are used to inform customers that work has been carried out to a set standard. Many countries use their own codes of practice and there are European and international standards as well. The International Quality System and British Standards Institute are two standards against which you can compare a company's quality system.

Table 4.9 shows the main quality assurance areas.

Quality assurance area	Measures
raw materials	detailed **technical specifications** of raw ingredients, considering source, **functionality** and sustainability
suppliers	using reputable suppliers, where food can be traced or tracked through the supply chain to the point of production and distribution (**traceability**)
specification	technical information, critical **dimensions** and **tolerance** levels that form part of quality control systems to create a consistent product
manufacture	• risk assessment procedures (HACCP) to ensure safety standards are met during production • the use of machinery, equipment and energy linked to safety, sustainability and environmental issues: carbon footprint, reducing energy, water and fuel consumption • monitoring waste
storage	risk assessment and hygiene procedures (HACCP) to ensure that safety standards are met during production
distribution and recall systems	• quick product recall and identification of all sourced components (traceability), which is vital to ensure food safety and maintain reputation of the business • bar coding, tagging systems and QA systems can track food through the supply chain • guaranteed standards for delivery and distribution systems to ensure that food is safe and of consistent quality throughout the food supply chain

Table 4.9: Quality assurance areas

Apply it!

Consider the quality assurances that you would give to consumers about the products you make in your Design and Make activities.

Apply it!

A critical dimension or tolerance level is a useful piece of technical information to include in your specification for your Design and Make activities. Use it to help you work out what you need to do to your product to make it a success.

Build Better Answers

Describe two benefits to manufacturers of using quality assurance schemes. (4 marks)

Basic answers (0–1 marks)
At this level, answers gave one or no benefits.

Good answers (2 marks)
At this level, answers gave two benefits or one benefit and a description.

Excellent answers (3–4 marks)
Answers gave two benefits and at least one description. For example:

- Food is tracked through the supply chain using a traceability scheme to ensure safety and quality of each raw ingredient.
- Risk assessment procedures (HACCP) ensure safety standards are met during processing, maintaining the reputation of the business.

ResultsPlus
Watch out!

Make sure you know the difference between:

- quality control: the way of checking the quality of a product throughout the food production system
- quality assurance: a guarantee to the customer about the quality standards of a food business
- good manufacturing practice (GMP): covers the total manufacturing process and all quality assurance procedures, aimed at maintaining quality, ensuring that food products are produced to consistent standards.

Stretch Activity

Quality control can be used for all scales of production. Produce a quality control checklist for each of the following:

- egg sandwich
- cheese and tomato pizza
- fruit trifle.

Quality control

Quality control is the way of checking the quality of a product throughout the food production system, from design, manufacture and distribution to the point of sale. It involves identifying critical quality control points to make sure that all aspects of the specification are met.

Table 4.10 details the quality control measures.

Quality control area	Examples of measures
visual inspections 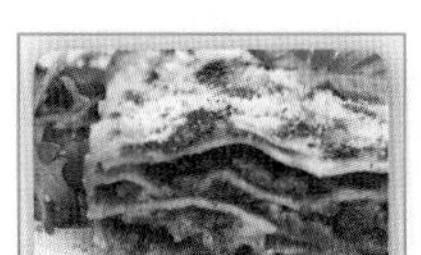	• preparation: cleaning, grading and sorting checks • physical characteristics: colour, size, shape, viscosity, thickness checks • storage: freshness (colour, texture, aroma), date marking system and stock rotation • layering and assembling: using critical dimensions and tolerances to achieve uniformity and consistency across product line • distribution: checking labelling system of foods for traceability and date marking system • reordering of stock (depending on scale of production)
weight 	• checking calibration of weighing scales and measuring equipment • recipe control for specific quantities of ingredients to ensure that correct proportions of ingredients will achieve consistency and quality • portion control through extruders, injectors or final weight checks for each component • counting and sorting food according to weight, into packages
random sampling 	• microbial sampling to check safety of food product • temperature controls for storage, cooking and chilling of high-risk foods • sensory testing to check organoleptic properties • moisture sensor to ensure correct crispness • colour sensor to ensure even cooking • mixing and combining checks to ensure correct consistency • stock rotation and safe storage of ingredients • monitoring rate of production for consistency and quantity
metal detector tests	tests at packaging stage to check for physical contamination

Table 4.10: Quality control measures

Quality of design

Quality of design is essential for a food product to be successful. About 1 per cent of ideas are developed into new product concepts. From this, only 5 per cent reach launch stage and, even then, might never reach the point of sale.

Quality of design is most likely to be successful if producers:

- understand the target group's needs and expectations through primary research: surveys, questionnaires, existing product analysis, disassembly and market research
- ensure that the product is easy to make
- have a clear specification with an effective recipe and trialling and testing
- have a clear production process, to ensure that consumers' needs and expectations are met.

New products are most likely to be successful when: a product is unique or superior to competing products; they have a good marketing strategy which promotes a strong image and a memorable advertising campaign; and the technical production is perfect.

A food product range

Quality of manufacture

The success of the quality of manufacture can be determined by:

- accurate weighing and measuring of raw ingredients, using quality component parts, and good layering, assembly and packaging
- use of critical dimensions and tolerances derived from the technical specification outlining specific characteristics during each stage of production.

Support Activity

1. In groups, discuss how you judge the quality of a product.
2. Choose one product you have made and check it against the quality criteria you have produced. How does it perform?

Quick notes

- **Quality control**: the way of checking the quality of a product throughout the food production system.
- **Quality assurance**: a guarantee to the customer about the quality standards of a food business.
- **Good manufacturing practice** (GMP): the total manufacturing process and all quality assurance procedures, aimed at maintaining quality, ensuring that food products are produced to consistent standards.
- **Critical control point**: where a control measure may need to be taken to prevent harm.

Food issues

Objectives

- **Know** the cultural, environmental and moral issues that relate to the food industry
- **Understand** the effects of these three types of issue

Apply it!

You could use multicultural and celebration foods as a starting point for a Design and Make activity.

Moral, environmental and cultural issues are often linked when looking at issues within the food industry. Try to consider the importance of each issue individually first, and then as part of food issues as a whole.

Food on the move

Food technologists try to meet the needs of their clients when designing and making food products, by considering the moral, cultural and environmental impact their products have on individuals and society. During the designing and making process, food manufacturers must consider these issues in order to meet the needs of consumers. These issues can affect health, safety, quality and well-being.

Cultural issues

Culture is the way people live, work and spend leisure time in a particular society or time. It is about beliefs, aspirations and how they interact with one another. These customs are part of what defines a group's unique identity.

The traditional skills, religious festivals and cultural knowledge can also affect the foods that people eat. Here are some questions worth considering.

- Where does the food that you eat originate from?
- How have existing products influenced the design of new products?
- How do cultures and beliefs affect the foods that people eat?
- How are foods linked with particular cultures prepared?

Every culture has its own traditional way of preparing, serving and eating foods. Some religions have dietary restrictions and all have foods that are associated with religious festivals, where food is shared amongst family and friends for pleasure and celebration. This is discussed in more detail on pages 30–1.

The United Kingdom is a multicultural society, reflecting a diverse range of cultures, customs, traditions and beliefs. In a multicultural society, there are a number of cultural values and influences.

Lifestyle

There has been an increase in less formal mealtimes and more individual control about what is eaten and when. More single portions are needed to meet the demands of individual people within a household. There has also been an increase in ready meals and microwaveable products, in grazing and eating on the move.

Novelty foods

Novelty foods can be seen as 'food for entertainment': string-type cheese, yogurt tubes, fruit and yogurt 'corners', stackable lunch packs. Product design, packaging and advertising are aimed at specific groups: e.g. cartoon characters for children, 'luxury' or 'finest' foods, value or economy product ranges for specific socio-economic groups.

Cultural foods

Culture is the shared customs, traditions and beliefs of a large group of people, such as a nation, race or religious group. In some cultures, sharing festivals and traditions with celebration food is very important: e.g. at Christmas, Diwali.

There has been a great increase in restaurant-style food available to take home: Indian, Thai, Chinese, Mexican, French, and so on. Some foods are eaten during a particular season: e.g. Brussel sprouts eaten with a Christmas meal. Equipment, utensils and recipe books are also available for people to experience and recreate foreign cuisine in their own homes. For example: chopsticks, woks, pizza ovens, pasta machines, tagine cook pots. In recent years, there has been fusion and hybrid cuisine from different cultures: for example, chicken tikka pizza, curried scotch eggs.

Other factors regarding cultural values include:

- cuisine meal deals and boxed meals for 'eating out, staying in'
- supporting local food producers and farmers
- helping to sustain local varieties of food (e.g. Wiltshire ham, Lincolnshire potatoes) or specific types of food (e.g. types of apple or regional cheese).

Pleasure and specialist foods

Pleasure foods are treats, indulgence and luxury items packaged and sold to aid convenience: for example, in-store delis, patisserie within supermarkets, vending machines with specialist food products such as sports snacks and speciality drinks.

Convenience foods

There are more pre-prepared, pre-packed, processed and added-value lines for immediate consumption at once or after microwaving, to reduce the preparation, cooking and clearing away of food. Developments include:

- ovenable and microwaveable packaging, disposable cups, bowls, knives spoons and forks
- energy-saving cooking methods
- time increase in processing and preservation treatments to increase storage life of foods and decrease shopping trips
- increase in internet shopping and home delivery to save time.

Cost

Budget or low-priced goods, own labels, mainstream everyday labels and luxury premium-quality ranges are linked to the taste and price value that consumers are willing to purchase.

Health foods

There has been an increase in low-fat, low-calorie, low-sugar, low-salt, high-fibre products to meet the needs of specific special diets (medical diets, allergies and intolerances). Governments and other agencies run healthy eating campaigns: for example 5 a day. Other phenomena include the rise of the 'super food' (garlic, olive oil, rice and pasta, fish and shellfish, red peppers, sun-dried tomatoes, blueberries) and functional foods: energy drinks, fortified foods and nutraceuticals.

Vegetarianism

There has been an increase in different types of vegetarianism due to health, moral or ethical concerns. Alternative protein foods (tofu, soya, mycoprotein) have been developed. See Chapter 1, pages 26–7.

Support Activity

In groups, discuss different countries and the foods associated with their cultures.

Stretch Activity

Choose one country or culture. Research how traditional skills, religious festivals and cultural knowledge can affect foods eaten.

ResultsPlus
Build Better Answers

Describe two ways in which retailers can promote a particular culture through their food. (4 marks)

■ Basic answers (0–1 marks)
At this level, answers gave one or no ways.

● Good answers (2 marks)
At this level, answers gave two ways or one way and a description.

▲ Excellent answers (3–4 marks)
Answers gave two ways and at least one description. For example:

- Restaurant-style cultural (Indian, Chinese, Thai) food available to take home to recreate holidays at home.
- Equipment, utensils and recipe books available for us to experience and recreate foreign cuisine in our own homes: for example, chopsticks, woks, pizza ovens, pasta machines and tagines.

Apply it!

Investigate the source of the food that you eat by looking at food labels to identify the origin of food.

Apply it!

Consider sustainability when writing your design specification for your Design and Make activities. What factors affect the sustainability of your design? How can you make your product more environmentally friendly?

Environmental issues

Sustainability

Sustainability is about preserving the world's natural resources for future generations. The last hundred years have seen a dramatic rise in innovative and powerful technology to capitalise on the earth's resources. As a result, natural resources (water, oil, minerals, coal) are likely to run out, unless people take action.

Feeding the world's population is increasingly challenging, with some areas suffering from starvation and others overeating and throwing away vast quantities of food. Food is the largest single factor affecting our carbon footprint. To achieve sustainable food production, the food industry must reduce waste, water consumption and energy inefficiency by using sustainable resources.

Pollution

The environment can be divided into three main elements: land, air and water. Table 4.11 shows how these three elements are polluted during food production.

Polluter	Polluting effect and counter measures
fuel	• using electricity within food processing and manufacture can affect the carbon footprint of food – producing electricity through the burning of **fossil fuels** (coal, oil or gas) pollutes the air with powerful **greenhouse gases** – using nuclear power to generate electricity threatens land, air and water by the possible escape of radioactivity • oil used in transportation releases carbon dioxide, contributing to global warming
industry	• the chemical and packaging industries may add to environmental pollution as water is polluted when chemicals escape • over-production of food leads to excessive food waste • food waste disposed into landfill sites leads to rotting food and production of **methane**, a powerful greenhouse gas contributing to climate change • raw food waste can be composted, but it is difficult to reuse processed foods and containers
agricultural chemicals	• the food most people in developed countries eat is made from intensively farmed crops with the help of agricultural chemicals: **fertilisers** and **pesticides**; these chemicals can end up in local food and water supplies • clearance of vegetation and overuse of soil leads to poorer soil quality and the need for more chemicals
contaminated water	many people get their water supply from underground sources, which can be contaminated by chemicals washed into the ground from farms, factories, etc
household waste	• buried household waste in landfill sites may contain chemicals that escape and pollute local water supplies • buried waste may not be **biodegradable** and increases landfill waste
packaging	• food packaging uses up natural resources and can cause air, land or water pollution • disposal of packaging materials varies depending on the local waste disposal facilities and recycling opportunities

Table 4.11: The polluting effects of food production

Food miles

'Food miles' refers to the distance food is transported from the time of its production until it reaches the consumer. Buying locally produced food supports local farmers, as well as helping to ensure that they receive fair terms and better prices. It also reduces food miles, pollution and CO_2 emissions. Many supermarkets actively source some food from British farmers or producers. This supports the UK farming industry, as well as reducing food miles and transport pollution. However, this is not yet common practice in all supermarkets.

In contrast, locally produced foods have limited food miles. Farmers' markets are run by farmers and food growers from the local area. They sell to local people, who can talk about the food to people who have grown or produced it. This increases trust between buyer and seller and encourages small-scale, environmentally friendly methods of farming and food production. It is also more profitable for the farmer, who can sell directly to the consumer without involving a shop or supermarket.

Organisations promoting environmental issues within the food industry, such as The Marine Stewardship, Farm Assured Scheme and Soil Association organisations raise the public's awareness and appreciation of managing natural resources.

Food miles

Remember that, in order to achieve sustainable food production, the food industry must find ways of reducing waste, water consumption and energy inefficiency by using sustainable resources.

Packaging

The choice, design and production of packaging materials affects the environment. Everyone should take responsibility for their use and disposal. Food packaging causes a number of problems such as:

- using up natural resources (oil, trees, metal)
- causing land, air and water pollution
- harming animals, birds and wildlife generally
- not being biodegradable or recyclable, so ending up in landfill sites
- generating litter and rubbish.

Stretch Activity

Which of the six Rs do you think are the most important in achieving a sustainable society?

Support Activity

In groups, consider these questions.

- Which environmental issue is the easiest to get people to act on?
- Which of these issues affect your life at present?
- What more can manufacturers do to help us?

Environmental challenges facing consumers and manufacturers

Consumers and manufacturers can improve their environmental practices and minimise the damage they cause to the environment through the 'six Rs': reuse, recycle, reduce, refuse, renew and respect.

Consumers should: **reuse** containers, carrier bags and left-over food; **recycle** waste; **reduce** waste by buying products with minimal packaging, and growing and making food at home, and reduce energy use in the home; **refuse** over-packaged foods and plastic bags; **renew** by composting organic waste; and show **respect** by disposing of waste responsibly, supporting local and moral producers and making informed purchases.

Manufacturers should: **reuse** by using paper or card from sustainable forests, and providing long-life bags and reusable packaging; avoid Tetrapak materials that cannot be **recycled** and use clear labelling and symbols; **reduce** the amount of packaging and processed food (which requires a lot of energy); **refuse** to supply plastic bags; avoid non-**renewable** plastic packaging and switch to **alternative energy sources**; avoid harmful processes that pollute, **respect** fair trade and ethical production, and labelling to promote recycling, identification and anti-litter symbols.

Labelling information symbols

Moral issues

Factory farming

Animals are often kept in disturbing living conditions, where intensive farming (factory farming) restricts their movement and eating patterns. This can lead to the spread of infection and disease.

The main purpose of selective breeding is to produce more food more quickly. It produces, for example, hens that lay more eggs, faster-growing chickens and cows that produce more milk. Through selective breeding within a factory farm, hens can produce up to 300 eggs per year. Most of the chicken meat we find in supermarkets and ready-prepared meals comes from broiler chickens, intensively confined on factory farms. A broiler chicken, reared for meat rather than eggs, is genetically selected for fast growth and is slaughtered when only six or seven weeks old. These chickens can suffer pain due to selective breeding, confinement, transportation and slaughter methods.

In contrast, free-range and organic animals live and grow in more natural surroundings with access to outdoor ranges and pasture: for example, chickens being reared in a chicken coop with an outside yard or field. This can be an expensive method of farming because it takes more time and resources than factory farming. As a result, free-range and oganic food can be slightly more expensive. However, the taste and quality are often far superior to factory farmed food.

The Red Tractor is an independent mark of quality. It guarantees that the food we buy comes from farms and food companies that meet high standards of food safety, hygiene, animal welfare and environmental protection.

Genetically modified (GM) foods

Genetically modified (GM) foods are foods that have been modified or engineered to alter specific characteristics within the food. This might include the benefits of:

- flavours, colours or textures
- higher yields
- longer shelf life
- delayed ripening of fruit
- improved nutritional content of foods
- resistance to adverse weather conditions.

Many foods can be genetically modified

ResultsPlus
Build Better Answers

Explain two moral issues arising from the use of factory farming. (4 marks)

Basic answers (0–1 marks)
At this level, answers gave one or no moral issues arising from the use of factory farming.

Good answers (2 marks)
At this level, answers gave either one moral issue and an explanation or two relevant moral issues, but they failed to provide the explanation.

Excellent answers (3–4 marks)
Answers give two moral issues and go on to describe their impact. For example: Animals may be kept in overcrowded conditions and this can lead to infection and disease. Animals may be force-fed to make them grow quickly, so that the cost of producing this meat is reduced.

ResultsPlus
Watch out!

Organic and free-range farming practices follow ethical and moral principles of good farming. However, they can be controversial due to the time and costs involved. Factory farming and selective breeding practices are controversial because of the intensive farming needed to produce food quickly and cheaply.

However, many people are concerned about possible problems with GM food, including:

- the loss of biodiversity and other negative effects on the environment
- eliminating some wildlife species
- mutations to crops due to cross-contamination
- permanent, irreversible changes to some plants and animals
- the long-term effects are unknown.

With a greater demand for food worldwide, others argue that GM food could help reduce the shortage of food in some areas.

Fairtrade

Fairtrade is about trade that offers better prices, decent working conditions, local sustainability and fairer terms of trade for farmers and workers in the developing world.

Fairtrade addresses the injustices of conventional trade, which traditionally discriminates against the poorest, weakest producers. By requiring companies to pay sustainable prices (which must never fall lower than the market price), it enables these producers to have more control over their lives.

The FAIRTRADE Mark

Traidcraft is an organisation that fights poverty through trade, helping people in developing countries to transform their lives.

Traidcraft logo

Organic farming

Organic farming is a low-carbon production system that works with nature-sustaining the health of the soil, ecosystems and people. It relies on ecological processes and biodiversity adapted to local conditions. Depending on where you buy it from, organic food can be more expensive than other foods. However, the taste, seasonability, safety and nutritional content is generally thought to be improved and it is scientifically proven to be better for wildlife and the environment.

The Soil Association

The Soil Association is a charity campaigning for good food and farming practices, by promoting the connection between soil, food, the health of people and the health of the planet.

Support Activity

Describe two concerns for the consumer of genetically modified (GM) foods.

Support Activity

Using market research, find out which Fairtrade or Traidcraft products are sold in your local supermarket.

Stretch Activity

1. Investigate the standards set by the Soil Association (www.soilassociation.org) for farms to achieve organic status.
2. Compare the cost of organic, free-range and value product ranges of a box of six eggs, 500g of chicken breast and 500g of beef mince. Write up your findings in a table like the one below.

Food product	Organic	Free-range	Value / economy
6 eggs			
500g of chicken breast			
500g of beef mince			

Quick notes

- Sustainability is about preserving the world's natural resources for future generations.
- Food miles are the distance food travels from field to plate.
- Sustainable design is about making something that will last without threatening the environment.

ICT

Objectives

- **Understand** the use of ICT within the food industry: CAD, CAM and CIM

Industrial kitchen design using CAD

ResultsPlus
Exam Question Report

(f) Food manufacturers use CAD/CAM processes to batch produce celebration cakes for supermarkets.

Give three advantages to the food manufacturer of using CAD/CAM to batch produce celebration cakes. (3 marks, 2009 higher)

How students answered

39% got 0 marks

Many students repeated the stem question in their answer or failed to write any answer at all.

5% got 1–2 marks

The most popular answers included time saving, labour saving and references to consistency and identical batches. Where answers were vague, marks were lost due to errors or repetitiveness, e.g speed, fast and quick - all these responses mean the same thing!

56% got 3 marks

Information and communication technology (ICT) is used extensively within the food industry, during all stages of design and manufacture and within different scales of production. It is used from the test kitchen at school for one-off or batch production, to the large-scale, high-volume production of mass-produced food products.

ICT can:

- communicate design intentions
- analyse the needs of user groups and research recipe databases
- compare products against design criteria and specifications
- aid product development and recipe modification
- monitor and control safety and quality within manufacturing, and control the flow of information during the whole design and make process.

This topic focuses on:

- computer-aided design (CAD)
- computer-aided manufacture (CAM)
- computer-integrated manufacture (CIM).

Computer-aided design (CAD)

Computer-aided design (CAD) is used to create, modify and communicate design intentions for a food product or components within a product. Here are some of the ways you can use CAD.

Adding pictures

Use digital photographs, scanned images and clipart to communicate design intentions and add pictures to text: digital camera to photograph food, clipart for mood boards, a scanner to process images from food labels and packaging.

Using CAD packages

- Develop product profiles, packaging nets, food labels and design ideas within product development and recipe modification: paint/draw programs to model packaging, food labels and design ideas; word processing to create questionnaires, sensory analysis charts.
- Present sensory analysis data using star diagrams, charts and spreadsheets: desktop publishing to design sensory analysis charts, questionnaires and interviews; spreadsheets/databases to collate and present results.

Using databases and modelling

- Use databases to source recipes.
- Calculate and analyse nutritional content using nutritional databases such as food focus programs.
- Use the internet to research user groups, existing products and recipes, or email to send photographs or documents/contact suppliers and producers.
- Design the physical profile of a product using paint/draw programs and nutritional databases.

Using spreadsheets

- Model the cost, portion size, weight, assembly of a single item or batch using databases and spreadsheets.
- Calculate the scale of production and scaled recipes, cost and stock control using spreadsheets.

Table 4.12 shows the advantages of using CAD.

Advantage	Examples
accuracy	• calculate and analyse nutritional data using a nutritional database; calculate scaling-up of recipes and costs using spreadsheets • reduce human error
finish	produce graphics and artwork on food packaging using paint/draw programs for professional finish to design work
quick	• analyse data quickly to produce graphs and results using spreadsheets • fast, efficient drawing process, with annotated detail using paint/draw programs
modification	information stored on database system or within a file, which can be retrieved and modified easily
modelling	• develop products and modify recipes designing the physical profile of a food product without the need to trial recipes • analyse results from sensory analysis, product analysis and testing (storage life, nutritional analysis, viscosity tests, etc.), which can be modelled within the design stages of a food product
research	• design questionnaires and interviews using desktop publishing • use images from clipart to produce mood boards and labelling symbols
records	use digital camera to photograph food components and products as a record of design and development work
communication	send designs via email
control	• stock control to monitor and reorder stock • quality control within the design stage: for example, calculate specific tolerances and critical dimensions within food products using spreadsheets/databases
cost-effectiveness	reduce design costs during product development and research stages (information is available immediately)

Table 4.12 Advantages of CAD

Computer-aided manufacture (CAM)

Computer-aided manufacture (CAM) is a system for monitoring and controlling the automatic production of food products based on set specifications and tolerances. CAM is used during the planning and manufacturing of a food product to check that the safety and quality of the product meet the requirements of the technical specification.

The scale of production determines the selection of CAM processes used for a product: e.g. breadmakers in single-item production or industrial mixers in batch or mass production.

Table 4.13 shows the advantages of using CAM.

Apply it!

CAD and CAM are two appropriate uses of ICT in your Design and Make activities in Unit 1.

Bread production using CAM

Advantage	Examples
accuracy	• electronic scales calibrated using weight tolerances • pre-programmed equipment and machinery used to control specific tolerances within the manufacturing process: e.g. thickness, shape, size and weight
consistency	in batch or high-volume production, every item within a batch is identical: e.g. sliced bread
quick	repetitive tasks carried out quickly: e.g. cutting, shaping, moulding
control	data-logging devices and sensors record and control specific tolerances: e.g. colour, temperature, pH levels; products falling below minimum standard are rejected from the production line
monitoring	• critical control points monitored on production line to eliminate risks: e.g. storage temperatures, cooking temperatures, time controls • HACCP control and monitoring systems (see page 67)
safety	automated processes carried out by industrial equipment and machines, which reduces hazardous tasks for workers: e.g. slicing, cutting, chopping
storage	automated process allows use of data to control stock systems and ordering, so no need to store vast quantities of ingredients or components for long
cost-effectiveness	automated process and less need for a skilled labour force reduces manufacturing costs
finish	high standard of finish achieved in manufacture, packaging and labelling due to automated controls: e.g. printing information onto labels, cutting of packaging nets
data	computer monitoring and control of complex production plans and stock
production	suitable for all scales of production, from automated industrial production (e.g. Chorleywood bread-making process) to one-off production using specialist single-item production (e.g. domestic breadmaker, edible icing printer, microwave oven, timers)

Table 4.13: Advantages of CAM

Single item production using CAM

Industrial vats, mixers and dispensers used in CAM

Support Activity

Choose a commercial food product. List the CAM processes involved its production.

Stretch Activity

You have been asked to produce a batch of 100 small cakes for a school fête. In groups, discuss how you will ensure that every cake is identical.

ResultsPlus
Build Better Answers

Describe two advantages to the manufacturer of using CAM. (4 marks)

Basic answers (0–1 marks)
At this level, answers gave one or no advantages.

Good answers (2 marks)
At this level, answers gave two advantages.

Excellent answers (3–4 marks)
Answers gave two ways and at least one description. For example:

- Automated process allows data to be used to control stock systems and ordering, preventing the need to store vast quantities of ingredients or components for lengthy periods of time.
- CAM reduces manufacturing costs due to automated process and less need for a skilled labour force.

ResultsPlus
Build Better Answers

Describe two advantages to the manufacturer of using CIM. (4 marks)

Basic answers (0–1 marks)
At this level, answers gave one or no advantage.

Good answers (2 marks)
At this level, answers gave two advantages.

Excellent answers (3–4 marks)
Answers gave at least three advantages. For example:

- Monitoring provides feedback to the system.
- Automatic adjustments can be made by computers at critical manufacturing points.
- Reduces wastage and rejection of products.

Sensors and quality control

Sensors are used to control and monitor quality control. For example, sensory properties, physical properties, safety, chemical hazards, production and processing operations.

Computer systems within the food process

Tolerances and dimensions

Temperature control system

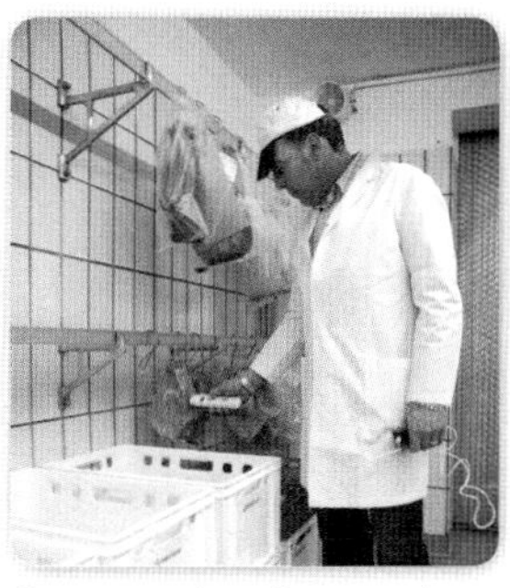

Sensors and quality control

CAM in one-off production

One-off production can also benefit from CAM technologies. Breadmakers, ice cream and yoghurt makers, food processors and microwave ovens are good examples of how CAM can be used to create single-item products within the home or school test kitchen. These appliances offer consistency, reliability, speed and quality in the manufacture of a wide range of food. The cook's skill and expertise often determine the success of the final product: accurate weighing and measuring, correct use and programming of the appliance and time, care and attention with equipment is vital to a product's successful outcome.

Computer-integrated manufacture (CIM)

Computer-integrated manufacture (CIM) is used in all stages of food production, to automatically control processes using computer systems. Computers are linked in a network to automatically adjust the machinery and the flow of information at critical manufacturing points. If these adjustments are not made, the product will not meet standards at strict critical control points and the product will be rejected.

It is necessary to control the ingredients, materials, components or activities as they move through the system. In the food industry, this is done using CIM.

Details of the controls are logged into the computer, which is attached to a sensor in the production process. Automatic adjustments may be made to:

- weight of ingredients
- rate at which a mixture or ingredients flow through the process
- temperature ranges at critical control points
- pressure levels for shaping and forming
- consistency of food components
- pH levels for storage, processing and preservation
- moisture content
- speed of conveyor belt
- production rate.

Computer systems within the food production process

Support Activity

Name three pieces of equipment found in a school kitchen that could be used to control the outcome of a food product.

Stretch Activity

Investigate the different stages of production used to make bread products. Identify the critical control points and consider how these could be controlled by computer.

Quick notes

- CIM is used in all stages of industrial food production, to automatically control the processes by computer systems.
- Computers are linked in a network to automatically adjust both the machinery and the flow of information at critical manufacturing points during the process.
- CIM can aid quality control.
- A system can be something as simple as a recipe.

Packaging

Objectives

- **Understand** packaging within the food industry, including functions, materials, uses and specialist packaging and reasons for use

ResultsPlus
Watch out!

Legislation states that food packaging must not cause food to deteriorate, be hazardous to human health or cause unacceptable changes in the substance or quality of the product. (Food Safety Act 1990)

Apply it!

Consider how manufacturers are trying to reduce the use of packaging to make it more eco-friendly by using sustainable design, when designing and making your food productions in Unit 1.

Support Activity

Investigate the different types of packaging available to food products and consider their advantages and disadvantages.

Stretch Activity

In groups, consider the environmental impact of each packaging material. Which is the most/least eco-friendly.

Functions of packaging

Most food items, raw ingredients or components of composite food need to be packaged to ensure that food remains in prime condition.

Packaging:

- protects food from damage and reduces food wastage, including physical damage such as bruising, deterioration through high or low humidity and temperature change causing over-ripening of fruit
- ensures safety and hygiene of foods by preventing contamination
- increases the storage life of food by maintaining it in the condition that consumers expect
- contains the food in a condition appropriate for consumption
- is needed in storage, transportation and retail of food to maintain food in the condition appropriate for consumption
- conveys information on the packaging label, which must include details about contents, weight, nutrition, price, date marks, storage and, where appropriate, cooking guidelines
- promotes the food product using advertising and marketing techniques, to attract and persuade consumers to purchase the food.

Food packaging materials and their uses

A range of materials are available to package foods, used either individually or as a combination to package food products. Table 4.14 shows the advantages and disadvantages of food packaging materials.

Specialist packaging materials

A range of specialist packaging materials is now available, to meet particular needs within the food industry.

- Modified atmosphere packaging (MAP) or controlled atmosphere packaging (CAP) are techniques used to prolong the storage life of many foods, by creating unfavourable conditions for bacterial growth. The food is placed in plastic trays with lids or bags. It is then 'gas flushed' with a mixture of gases designed to delay deterioration. The contents are then hermetically sealed by fusing the plastic together. Each food type needs a different proportion of the gases: carbon dioxide, oxygen and nitrogen. Chilled pre-packed meats, fish, ready meals, fruit and vegetables such as lettuce will undergo MAP to increase storage life or delay ripening.
- Manufacturers use tamper-evident seals to ensure that food has not been contaminated or misused by mistakenly opening and resealing foods. Seals can be:
  - plastic collars on bottles (e.g. for sauces and marmalades)
  - tear-away strips around the top of bottles (e.g. for milk)
  - tin-foil seals in pourable boxes (e.g. cartons of juice)
  - plastic film wraps on cardboard boxes (e.g. for biscuits)
  - plastic film on ready-meal trays.

Material	Advantage	Disadvantage
glass	• recyclable • cheap to produce • withstands high temperatures • transparent • can be moulded into different shapes and sizes • used with metal seal to create tamper-evident packaging	• heavy • breakable • unsuitable for use in freezer for foods with high water content
metals and foils	• recyclable • withstands high and low temperatures • lightweight • can be moulded into different shapes and thicknesses • easy to store • tin is cheap to produce • can put tamper-evident seals on tin cans • some foods cooked in metal, aiding heat transference • flexible wrapping for covering foods at home (foil)	• cannot be used in a microwave • cannot see food • aluminium is expensive to produce • safety issues during use to prevent cuts
paper and cardboard	• recyclable • biodegradable • cheap to produce • easy to print text/images onto material • may be laminated to make it moisture-proof • lightweight • easy to open • variety of shapes and thicknesses • flexible for wrapping • good insulator	• tears easily • must be laminated to be waterproof, this can restrict recycling options • product might be easily damaged • often used with another packaging material to aid storage life (breakfast cereals with plastic wrapping)
plastic 	• cheap to produce • withstands high and low temperatures • lightweight • can be moulded into different shapes and thicknesses • easy to store • used in the microwave • transparent • some are biodegradable, but they are expensive	• made from oil • many plastics are still not recyclable • disposal into landfill

Table 4.14: Advantages and disadvantages of food packaging materials

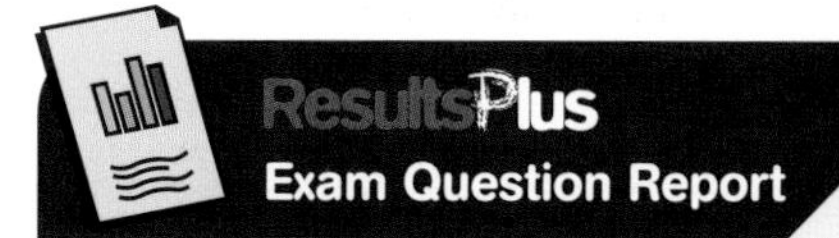

(d) When designing new food products, the effects of packaging on the environment must be considered.

(i) Give **three** advantages to the environment of using paper in food packaging. (3 marks, 2007 Foundation Paper)

How students answered

Over half of candidates failed to score in this question.

64% got 0 marks

This answer was often left blank.

33% got 1–2 mark

Students who could mention recycling, less pollution during manufacture of packaging material, less paper to landfill due to recycling and biodegradable, were awarded high marks.

3% got 3 marks

Labelling

Objectives

- **Understand** labelling within the food industry
- **Understand** the legal information available to consumers

Food labelling is regulated under the Food Safety Act 1990, where the main responsibilities of food businesses are to ensure that food is labelled, advertised and presented in a way that is not false or misleading.

Legally required labelling

The Food Labelling Regulations 1996 describe the following information that must in law be on a food label.

Name of the food

This must also include a description of the food product, if the name of the product does not make this clear. For instance, something labelled 'lasagne' could be referring to the lasagne sheets (dried or fresh) or ready-made lasagne, fully assembled and ready to eat. Additionally, if the product has been subjected to any special processing treatment, this must be clear on the label. For instance, smoking of meat, fish or cheese.

Ingredients listed in descending order of weight

This informs consumers about ingredients used to make the product, including any food additives and water.

Additives

These are usually named, and may also include an E number. Food additives have a number of important functions, but there is an increasing demand for foods without them, particularly without those considered to cause allergic and intolerant reactions. Manufacturers are working towards 'clean labels' as a result of concerns about the use of artificial chemicals in food. For more about additives, see Chapter 3, pages 98-9.

Instructions for use, cooking and storage

This tells consumers how to prevent spoilage. Temperature and time control guidelines help the consumer to ensure that food is safe to eat.

Net values

Manufacturers are required to show the net weight and volume of most pre-packed food. If food is not sold pre-packed, the quantity or volume must be shown. This allows consumers to compare the cost of products to determine value for money.

Name and address of the manufacturer

This allows consumers to contact the manufacturer in cases of faulty goods or to seek further advice.

Place of origin

This tells consumers where food has come from.

Under the Food Safety Act 1990, food businesses must ensure that food is labelled, advertised and presented in a way that is not false or misleading. This information is also in the Food Labelling regulations 1996.

Apply it!

Consider how labels are used to inform consumers, when designing and making your food products in Unit 1.

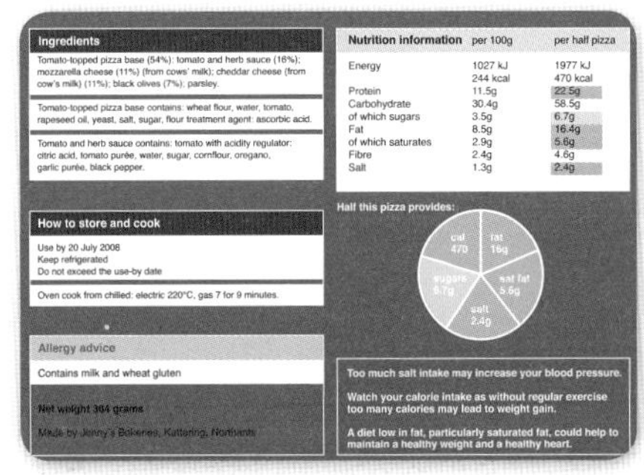

Food label elements

Special claims

These inform the consumer about the suitability of a food product for people with intolerances and allergies. Any specific nutritional claims must be supported with evidence to justify and substantiate the claim. GM and organic foods must also clearly labelled.

Processing treatments

The name of a food must include an indication of its physical condition or treatment, where it could be misleading if that information was not available. For example, UHT milk, smoked fish, unpasteurised cheese, frozen vegetables.

Date mark system

This tells consumers the length of time the product can be kept in optimum condition.

- 'Use by' date is for high-risk, perishable foods (raw and cooked meats, chilled foods, dairy products). The day and month is shown, as well as any storage conditions to be followed. After this date, the food may not look or taste different, but it will be unsafe to eat and should be thrown away.
- 'Best before' date is for low-risk foods (crisps, biscuits or foods that have undergone processing treatments to extend their shelf life e.g. UHT milk). The day, month and year will be shown. After this date, the sensory characteristics (taste, flavour, colour, smell, texture) will deteriorate.

Additional voluntary information

In addition to information that is legally required, the following may also be found on food labelling.

'Display until' or 'sell by' date

Is used by the food retailer to inform stock rotation as a critical control point. Food retailers will remove the product from shelves or chill/freezer cabinets when this date is reached. This date is usually a few days before the 'use by date'.

Nutritional information

This shows the nutritional content of foods and relevance to healthy eating guidelines. It allows consumers to choose food for specific nutritional characteristics, e.g. low in fat.

Further information

Serving instructions, disposal of packaging, special diets, opening instructions, barcodes, and advertising and marketing may also be found on food labels.

Support Activity

1. Choose a food label and stick it onto plain paper. Annotate your chosen label by identifying the details of legal information and voluntary information supplied by the food manufacturer.
2. Investigate the labelling schemes used by some manufacturers to promote healthy eating.

Stretch Activity

1. In groups, research the symbols used to identify the waste disposal for packaging materials.
2. Explain how sustainability information is conveyed to consumers through the use of food labels.

Give three advantages to the manufacturer of using barcodes. (3 marks)

Basic answers (0–1 marks)
At this level, answers gave one or no advantage.

Good answers (2 marks)
At this level, answers gave two advantages.

Excellent answers (3 marks)
Answers give at least three advantages.
For example:

- Aids stock control for the manufacturer by giving some product information, such as name and price.
- Traceability systems for food safety and product recall.
- Electronic data can be stored and communicated quickly from stock room to shop floor and vice versa.

Know Zone
Chapter 4 Product manufacture

There are many different aspects of product manufacture within the food industry and many factors determine use, choice, safety and quality within production, recipe development, technological changes and innovations, food issues, quality, ICT, packaging and labelling.

You should know...

- ☐ The main production methods:
  - one-off
  - batch
  - high volume production
- ☐ About product and recipe development within the food industry:
  - specifications
  - scaling up recipes
  - storage and distribution of commercial products
- ☐ The types of technological food development:
  - man-made
  - specially developed
  - functional
  - biotechnology
  - novel
  - nanotechnology
- ☐ What the quality issues are:
  - assurance
  - control
  - manufacture
  - design
- ☐ What the food issues are:
  - moral
  - environmental
  - cultural
- ☐ About ICT:
  - CAD
  - CAM
  - CIM within the food industry
- ☐ About packaging: materials, functions, uses and specialist packaging.
- ☐ About labelling: legal and voluntary information.

Key terms

one-off production
batch production
high-volume production
user requirements
traceability
tolerances
dimensions
factory farming
Fairtrade
sustainability
functional foods
meat analogue
biotechnology
nanotechnology
genetically modification (GM)
organic farming
selective breeding
CAM
CAD
biodegradable
'use by' date
'best before date'

Which of the key terms above matches each of the following definitions?

A Aids electronic stock control for the manufacturer by giving some product information: name and price. This can be used within traceability systems for food safety, product recall and quality control.

B A date mark for low risk foods (crisps, biscuits or foods that have undergone processing treatments to extend their shelf life, e.g. UHT milk). The day, month and year will be shown. After this date, the sensory characteristics (taste, flavour, colour, smell, texture) of the food will deteriorate.

C Used to create, modify and communicate design intentions for a food product or components within a product.

D A global communication system that links documents, organisations and people together by accessing websites or communicating via email, through the use of the internet.

E Treats, indulgence and luxury items packaged and sold to aid convenience. For example: in store deli, patisserie within supermarkets, vending machines with specialist food products: sports snacks, speciality drinks.

F This technology is based on science, biology, medicine, agriculture and food to genetically engineer biological systems or living organisms to make or modify products or processes for specific uses. Examples include Xanthan gum and chymosin.

Multiple choice questions

1 Batch production is a production method that is based on the following principles:

A A large scale method of production.
B Fixed quantities of items.
C Made for stock or to order.
D All the above.

2 A specification is a:

A shopping list
B detailed description for the chosen product
C nutritional database
D production method

3 Biotechnology is based upon:

A genetically modifying food for specific uses
B planning a special diet
C labelling food correctly
D using less packaging materials

4 CAM is:

A Computer-action Manufacture
B Control-aided Manufacture
C Computer-aided Manufacture
D Control-aided Making

ResultsPlus
Maximise your marks

Give two stages when CAM systems help to make each loaf of bread the same. (2 marks)

Student answer	Examiner comments	Build a better answer
Student A Using a draw programme to design each loaf of bread. (0 marks)	■ No! The question is about CAM not CAD.	▲ Weighing the ingredients prior to production. (1 mark)
Student B Cooking the bread. (0 marks)	■ CAM uses computers to regulate the time and temperature of the bread-making process. Student answer is too vague.	▲ To regulate the timing of cooking or proving. (1 mark)

Overall comment: Other acceptable answers would also include:

- Weighing/measuring/portion control of the finished product.
- Regulating/setting the correct cooking temperature.
- Timing of proving/cooking.
- Slicing/wrapping of finished bread product.

Practice exam questions

1 Describe the different types of legal information supplied by manufacturers on food labelling and its benefits to the consumer. (4 marks)

2 Explain the differences between one-off and batch production methods. (2 marks)

3 Evaluate the range of packaging materials available for food products by assessing their impact upon their environment. (4 marks)

Chapter 5: Analysing products

Importance of analysing products

Objectives

- **Understand** why product analysis is an important part of product development
- **Know** who uses product analysis and why

As the GCSE Food Technology exam paper is written to a template format, Question 12 will always be a design question and Question 13 will always be a product analysis question. These two activities are linked because of the need to work with specification points.

- In the design question, you will be given eight specification points. You need to design two different products that match these.
- In the product analysis question, you will be given a product as a starting point and will be asked to analyse parts of the product or the processes used to make it. You will also be asked to evaluate the product against certain specification points.

Specification points

All specification points are linked to the following areas.

- **Form** How should the product be shaped/styled? What size/weight will it be?
- **Function** What is the purpose of the product?
- **User requirements** What qualities would make the product attractive to potential users?
- **Performance requirements** What are the nutritional considerations to be achieved? See Unit 1 for more information.
- **Ingredient and component requirements** How should ingredients and components perform?
- **Scale of production and cost** How will the design allow for scale of production and what will determine cost?
- **Sustainability** How will the design allow for environmental considerations?

How do consumers choose a product?

Consumers have a huge choice of products in the supermarket and they make their choices considering many different criteria. There are many reasons why a consumer chooses one product over another. For example, it may be cost, as everyone has a budget to work within; or perhaps they might choose on flavour, for example, curries manufactured by different companies appear to be similar, but have different flavours. Some consumers have moral or religious considerations when buying meat products; some may use ready-made products for convenience.

Apply it!

Use the specification criteria headings (form, function, etc.), as the basis for your specification for your Unit 1: Creative Design and Make Activities.

Write a few points under each heading. The performance requirements (the technical considerations that must be achieved) are detailed in Unit 1, page 158, and consists of:

- nutritional content
- sensory characteristics
- cooling and/or heating requirements
- storage requirements
- cost
- special dietary considerations
- assembly and layering
- finishing processes
- sustainability issues related to the ingredients, materials, processes and techniques.

Understanding the market

In order to market and sell its products successfully, the manufacturing company must understand its place in the market and its consumers. Manufacturers need to ask themselves:

- Who uses our products?
- Why are the products used?

If a company understands its consumers and market share, it will be on the road to success.

Consumer choice

Consumers have different needs, so there is room for great variety within the market place. For people on a budget, price is the main consideration and supermarkets stock a series of 'value' lines to provide cheap food. For others, with higher budgets, health and quality may be more important than cost, and they may pay more for a product that they believe to be healthy or higher quality. For many, of course, there is a mix of needs, and people may buy food based on cost for some occasions, while for a special meal or treat, for example, they may be looking more for quality.

Some supermarkets aim their ranges more at the cost end of the market, and others more at the quality end, but there is an increasing need for greater variety in all sectors. Food shoppers demand quality and range when it comes to cuisine and ingredients. They also increasingly want value lines to deliver healthy choices and, for an increasing number of health-conscious consumers, the labelling of fat, calorie and salt content is also important.

What should the manufacturer consider?

The market place is highly competitive. A manufacturer needs to plan carefully when introducing new products, and when designing a new product will probably consider:

- **Form** size, weight, colour, appearance, ingredients, texture, flavour, aroma.
- **Function** whether the product is targeted at a specific dietary need, who it is for, where it might be eaten or the function of the ingredients.
- **User requirements** sweet, savoury, dietary requirements, portion size, nutritional requirements.
- **Target market** the type of consumer and the amount they are prepared to spend; whether they are families, single adults, households with no children, older people, people with dietary needs, students.
- **Budgetary constraints or costs** cost to manufacture, price to be sold for, profit margin, value for money for consumer.
- **Moral issues** animal welfare, GM foods, irradiated products, Fairtrade.
- **Cultural issues** use of meat, foods reflecting the region or country they come from (increased travel has resulted in consumers being more willing to try different types of food).
- **Environmental issues** food miles, packaging, pollution, sustainability.

Apply it!

As a student of Food Technology, you must understand how to analyse a product. This knowledge will help you to understand how food products are produced and you can then apply it when designing new products in the controlled assessment.

Ready meals provide UK consumers with quick, inexpensive meals

Support Activity

For each of the products pictured, answer these questions.

- Does the product contain a protein food?
- Does the product include a carbohydrate food?
- Is the product suitable for vegetarians?
- Is the product suitable for a consumer on a calorie-controlled diet?

Beef lasagne

Low-fat cottage cheese

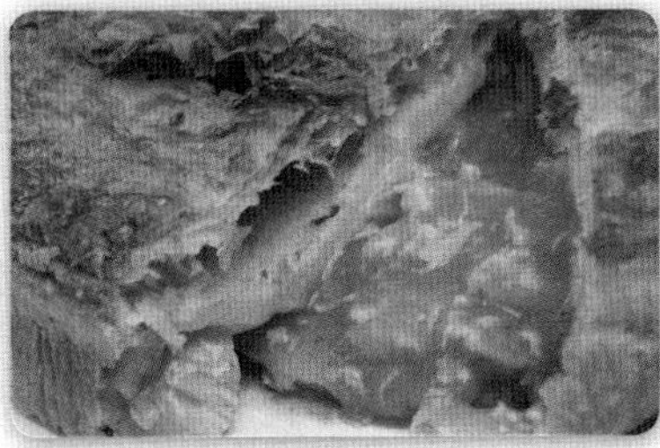

Chicken pie

Manufacturing decisions

Before any practical development work is done, the manufacturer will carry out market research to provide background information. Market research asks people a number of closed or open questions. Closed questions allow consumers to choose from the answers provided by the market researcher, and answers can be statistically analysed; open questions allow consumers to give opinions. These cannot be statistically analysed but provide important information.

When preparing a questionnaire for market research, a manufacturer should consider:

- **the sample** – who are they going to ask?
- **the method** – how are they going to ask them?
- **questions** – what are they going to ask?
- **results** – what will they do with the information?
- **timescale** – when will they need the information?

A good set of questions allows the manufacturer to make correct judgements about a new product and the requirements of the product for the target market.

Analysing products in the examination

Analysis of an individual fruit trifle

In the examination, you will be asked to look at information about a product and answer questions about it. You will need to consider all the products you have made and analysed during the course. In the examination you will be provided with a starting point, for example a picture, and then asked a series of questions. Think about the product – who is the target market; is it massed produced or batch produced; how many people will it serve; can it be eaten hot or cold. Thinking about a range of issues will help you to carefully consider the examination questions you are specifically being asked. You will be given a specification point and asked to answer a question regarding the product. The specification point may ask you to consider form, function (needs of the user), quality, market or environmental issues.

Analysing packaging

Manufacturers include information on the packaging to inform consumers. The packaging gives an idea of the product and how to serve it. The label allows the consumer to analyse the content.

How to analyse food products

Objectives

- **Understand** how to analyse a food product with regard to disassembly, quality of design and quality of manufacture

Analysing products

Everything you eat contributes to your daily intake of nutrients. If you look carefully at each product, you can understand how it contributes to your diet. You know you must eat a balanced diet, but how do you achieve this? By looking carefully at each part of a product or the information on packaging you can know exactly what you are eating – whether this is a snack product, a sandwich lunch or a main meal.

Companies analyse:

- similar products: for example a range of own-brand sandwiches
- different products: for example, ordinary sandwiches compared to low-fat sandwiches, or to the leading brand.

A cheese and tomato sandwich

Consider the simple cheese and tomato sandwich; its main components are bread, spread, cheese and tomato.

A manufacturer will carefully measure each of the ingredients to ensure a consistent product. The specification will include:

- type and thickness of bread
- type of spread (low-fat, butter, etc.)
- type of cheese
- how the cheese is prepared (sliced, grated, etc.)
- how the tomato is prepared.

All this information is available to the production line to ensure that the quality of each sandwich is the same. During production, the manufacturer will check the process to make sure that the specification is implemented. This process is called quality control (see page 122). If a problem is discovered, the production line is halted until the problem is resolved.

Mass-produced bread

Weighing and measuring

During the sandwich production, the manufacturer also considers the weight of each ingredient. All ingredients are carefully measured to make sure that each sandwich is identical. When making the bread, the proportion and type of ingredients must be exact in order for it to taste as the consumer expects.

Method of production

The manufacturer will also consider the method of production. Products such as bread are produced in high volume as it is a staple food that is eaten everyday in most households and is used by manufacturers to make products such as sandwiches. Therefore bread is in high demand and thousands of loaves are needed everyday, therefore it is produced day and night. Bread has a limited shelf life and is brought fresh into shops everyday. Cheese is produced in batches; although it is a popular ingredient the demand for it is moderate. Cheese has a reasonable shelf life and needs much care and attention during its production; therefore batches of cheese can be carefully monitored and it can be left to mature for different amounts of time.

Disassembly of products

Disassembly of products is a technique used by designers to investigate a current product and develop it into something more appealing that the consumer will want to buy. The designer may discover that a product is too high in fat, or not suitable for vegetarians, so they will use their knowledge and skills to adapt the for a different market. To help you understand a product, you can take it apart (disassemble it) and find out what is in it. Disassembly can also mean to take apart the other aspects of producing a product: for example, packaging, cultural issues, and so on.

However, other products can be difficult to take apart so you have to look at individual components. For example a ready-made pasta sauce or a shop bought sponge cake cannot be easily taken apart. The designer would consider the colour of the product; the texture; the flavour; the aesthetic qualities (what it looks like) and analyse each area individually. The designer would look at the label to see what ingredients had been used. This can provide vital information. The designer may compare several types of pasta sauce. These comparisons provide a basis for further development of a product.

With the cheese and tomato sandwich, this process is easy. You weigh the bread, cheese and tomato and look at the quality: for example, is the tomato fresh? You also taste the different parts of the sandwich and decide whether the best flavours and textures have been used to ensure an excellent product. However, other products can be difficult to take apart so that you can look at individual components.

Sensory analysis

As consumers' tastes change, there will be gaps in the market for new products. Food manufacturers employ development chefs who invent, design and adapt new products. A development chef has a design brief to work towards and a range of criteria agreed with the manufacturer. The chef will analyse products already on the market and develop a new product.

While developing a product, manufacturers conduct taste panels to help them gather information about the flavour of a food or product. You can test products by considering taste, texture, smell, appearance and flavour. These tests are often carried out by professional 'tasters', trained to be impartial in their views.

In the food industry, a group of people are used as a sensory profiling panel to analyse and evaluate food samples. They might be randomly selected from a consumer user group or a trained group of sensory analysts to identify particular sensory characteristics of food. A large vocabulary of words called sensory descriptors are created to describe the appearance, odour, flavour, mouthfeel and aftertaste of a food product. Sensory tests are then used to rate or rank a product based on particular characteristics. They are used throughout the design, development and manufacture of a food product, to ensure that the final product meets the technical specification. It can aid the development of a product by testing and trialing recipe modifications with user groups and the competition in the market place.

Stretch Activity

Conduct a simple food-tasting test in school using three natural yoghurts.

Display the yoghurts so that testers cannot identify the brand. Identify each yoghurt with a circle, a square and a triangle. Decide on your questions. Here are some examples.

- Describe the initial smell.
- Describe the initial taste.
- Describe the texture (help with prompt words such as smooth, lumpy, light, frothy, fluffy, heavy, thick, runny).
- One yoghurt costs £1.09 for 500g; one costs £1.19 for 500g; one costs £1.39 for 500g. Which do you think is which?

Apply it!

Attribute profiles may be used to help you analyse qualities in a product that you could design and make in Unit 1.

A taste panel may be used:

- by a company to ensure consistency
- by a manufacturer to develop a new product, considering the results in order to change or improve the product before it goes into production
- by a group trying to prove a point about the differences, or lack thereof, between two products.

Taste panels can be used to conduct a range of different tests.

- **Triangle test** Panellists receive three coded samples. They are told that two are the same and one is different, and are asked to identify the odd sample. This discriminatory testing method is often used as a tool in quality assurance programmes to ensure that samples from different production lots are the same. Triangle tests are also used in product development studies to determine whether various ingredient substitutions or changes in processes will result in problems.
- **Paired preference test** A pair of coded samples is presented for comparison on the basis of some specified characteristic (saltiness, sweetness, etc.). This method is similar to the triangle test, but fewer samples are required and there is less tasting. The statistical efficiency is not, however, as great.
- **Hedonic scale** 'Hedonic', from Greek, relates to the degree of like or dislike. Panellists rate products on a scale of like or dislike.
- **Duo-trio test** Three samples are presented: one sample is labelled 'R' (reference) and the other two are coded. One of the coded samples is identical to 'R' and the other coded sample is different. Panellists are asked to identify the correct sample, and their chance is always 50 per cent. Both triangle and duo-trio tests may be used to screen panellists for their ability to repeatedly select a specific trait when tasting products for flavour. The duo-trio test is often preferred because it involves less tasting.
- **Ranking test** This is an extension of the paired comparison test. Panellists receive three or more coded samples and are asked to rank samples for intensity of some specific characteristic. Ranking tests are often used to screen one or two 'best samples' from a group rather than thoroughly test all samples. However, this test gives no indication of the magnitude of difference between samples because samples are only evaluated in relationship to each other.
  - **Rank preference** When four or five samples are served in a ranking test, the difficulty for panellists to rank products is increased. More re-testing is generally done in order to assure the correct positioning of the rankings.
- **Rating test** Tasters rate food according to sensory qualities (attributes).
- Profiling A star diagram is used to plot the attributes of food and compare them to another taster's results or another product.
- Sensory profiling This offers a detailed, descriptive evaluation of the range of differences between products.

Support Activity

Look at the picture of the sandwich and consider the following questions.

- What type of bread has been used?
- What nutrient does bread provide in the diet?
- Why do we need this nutrient?
- How is CAM used in: production of the bread dough; weight control of the product; cooking of the bread; slicing of the bread?
- What textures does this sandwich provide?
- What nutrient does the cheese provide?
- Is this product suitable for a vegetarian? Or for a vegan?
- Is this product suitable for someone wanting a low-fat product?
- How could this product be changed to increase the intake of fibre?
- How does the use of tomato enhance this product?

Support Activity

If you look at a range of pizzas produced by different manufacturers you will notice each has a different function and appeals to a different target market. Each pizza has a dough base and a basic topping of tomato paste and cheese. However, the manufacturer has given the consumer a choice. The toppings have been changed, as have the size and the production method for the base.

Compare and contrast the thin-crust vegetable pizza with the thick cheese-filled crust meaty pizza.

- Which would be most filling? Why?
- Describe the textures that each pizza provides?
- Why would these products appeal to a wide age range of consumers?
- Which product would be the most time-consuming to produce? How would this affect the cost?
- How could CAM be used effectively to increase the speed of production?
- The dough is manufactured using CAM. Why would this be a suitable method of production?
- What quality control points would be considered during production?

Individual ingredients and their functions

Every ingredient used performs in a certain way as well as having a unique function. If the wrong ingredients are mixed, they will not combine in the way expected: for example, if you used plain flour to make bread, it would not rise and you would produce a bread brick, not a light, risen loaf of bread! See pages 56-9 for more.

Packaging

You looked at packaging in detail in Chapter 4 (pages 136-7). To help consumers understand what ingredients are included in the product, the manufacturer lists them on the packaging. The manufacturer must include the nutritional information and a range of other information required by the consumer, including environmental issues, shelf life and storage details. The packaging can also help a consumer with information on moral issues, such as:

- GM ingredients
- Fairtrade credentials
- whether the food is irradiated
- number of food miles involved in production.

Cultural issues are also often addressed through information on packaging. Where there is a specific cultural need related to food, the consumer should be able to check on the packaging whether certain foods have been included or animal welfare needs have been met.

On the examination paper you will be asked about producing products in industry. You will be asked about quality control and quality assurance. You will also be asked about the use of computer-aided manufacture (CAM) – see pages 120-3 and 130-5.

Quality of design

When designing new products, the manufacturer must consider the quality of the design and the needs of the target market. Manufacturers must think about:

- value for money – whether the consumer will think the product is worth the the price
- shelf life – how long it will last and remain at its best (after manufacture the product must be transported to the shop, then put on the shelf, then sold, then stored)
- safety – food hygiene and the health of the customer
- choice and proportion of ingredients and components – where the ingredients are sourced, their quality, and how sustainable the sources are
- manufacturer claims – whether the product does what is claimed: for example, if it claims to be low-fat, is it?

Packaging

When manufacturers arrange the design of the packaging, they must take into consideration:

- the suitability of the packaging for the product

- how the packaging is used to promote the product (eye-catching packaging may lead to a sale)
- the demands of quality of manufacture as they relate to packaging (see next section).

Quality of manufacture

When manufacturers produce an item, they must consider and test quality. They will think about a number of areas.

- **Organoleptic (sensory) qualities** Appearance, taste, texture, smell. Consumers 'buy' with their senses, even including sound (you expect crisps and some breakfast cereals to make a crunching noise).
- **Consistent quality** As a consumer, you expect the product to taste, look, smell and perform in the same way each time you buy it.
- **Legal requirements for safety** Consumers expect that products have been produced in a clean, safe environment where all aspects of law have been observed and implemented.
- **Quality of packaging construction** The manufacturer should test and evaluate the product to check that:
  - it is protected from any contamination
  - it is held secured – so it is not damaged when it arrives in the shop
  - it is a suitable shape and size for transportation
  - it has all the correct information on the packaging including ingredients; nutritional information; barcode and sell by date
  - if it has a picture, this is a true reflection of the product
  - it encourages consumers to consider the environment through recycling.

You have just analysed a product. You have considered the information given in the picture and the labels, as well as knowledge from your study. You can see how many questions can be considered for even a simple product. If a product has more ingredients or components, there will be even more possible questions. In the examination, you will always be asked to analyse a product. During your controlled task, you will also consider existing products available in supermarkets.

Homemade bread

Every product has a different function and properties. A simple product, like bread, can be very different depending on how it is made.

Mass-produced bread

Homemade bread is totally different from mass-produced bread. Bread can be made with different flours, which change the properties including the flavour. It can also be changed by adding other ingredients, such as garlic, dried tomatoes, onions, olives or cheese. Adding these can also change the texture and colour: for example, adding onion can give the bread a 'crunch', while adding olives or tomatoes can change its colour and add moisture.

Stretch Activity

Raspberry and chocolate roulade

Fruit crumble

Investigate the recipes used to make these desserts.

- List the ingredients used.
- Describe the textures that each dessert provides.
- Why would these products appeal to a wide age range of consumers?
- Which product would be the most time consuming to produce and how will this affect the cost?
- How could CAM be used effectively to increase the speed of production?
- What quality control points would be considered during production of the roulade?
- How could the fibre content be increased in each of these desserts?

Know Zone
Chapter 5 Analysing Products

This chapter focuses on the importance of analysing products for the user group and its intended purpose within design, development and manufacture. By using existing products for analysis, a comparison may be drawn between different food products. By understanding the work of a designer, it is possible to uncover and solve problems by making connections between existing products and one's own products within product development. This focus is on product analysis, disassembly, quality of design and quality of manufacture.

You should know...

- ☐ Why product analysis is an important part of product development and who uses it.
- ☐ How to analyse a product using existing products to compare and contrast differences and similarities.
- ☐ How to disassemble products using physical properties, production methods, sensory analysis, packaging, labelling and the working characteristics and functional properties of ingredients, components and products.
- ☐ What the moral, cultural and environmental issues are that would be considered when analysing products.
- ☐ Quality of design for target groups, packaging design.
- ☐ Quality of manufacture: sensory testing, quality, safety and packaging.

ResultsPlus
Design question

12 A manufacturer is developing a new range of hot dessert products that are suitable for the elderly. The specification for the hot dessert product is that it must:

- be suitable for elderly people
- be a single portion
- have a range of textures
- include one protein food
- be filling
- include one ingredient high in fibre
- be suitable to be reheated
- be fruit flavoured.

Use sketches and, where appropriate, brief notes to show **two different** design ideas for the hot dessert product that meet the specification points above.

ResultsPlus
Moderator comment

Design Idea 1.

Pear and Almond Bakewell Tart.

A traditional dessert enjoyed by elderly people.

Almonds are LBV protein

Shortcrust pastry containing wholemeal flour (high in fibre) and a crumbly texture.

Served as a single portion from a tray bake.

Soft pear (fruit & texture)

Sponge filling contains almonds and flour which would be filling

Reheat in an oven for 10mins at 180°C.

Design Idea 2.

Mincepie Crumble served with custard.

- Hand held mince pie 50g - single portion
- Reheat in microwave for 10 seconds (avoid soggy pastry!)
- Served with custard - milk is a HBV protein food.

Crumble topping high in carbohydrate (filling)

Made from oats (high in fibre)

Crunchy topping (texture)

Dried fruit for fruity texture and fruit content.

- Suitable for elderly people because it is easy to eat because pastry 'holds' filling and topping.

These two designs are named, carefully sketched and labelled, with annotation that is directly linked and justified to each point within the specification. This is an example of a high level response.

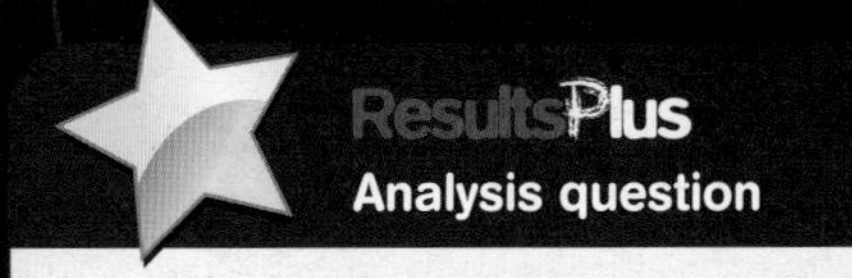

13(e) A food manufacturer produces a range of desserts. Below are two methods for making a trifle.

Recipe A (method only)	Recipe B (method only)
• Assemble and weigh ingredients. • Line serving container with sponge finger layer or sliced swiss roll pieces. • Wash and slice fresh strawberries. Place fruit onto sponge base. • Place two tablespoons of strawberry jam over the fruit. • Make custard using eggs, sugar and milk or instant custard powder, sugar and milk. Thicken over a low heat. • Pour cooled custard over fruit layer. Chill in fridge. • Whisk double cream until thick. • Using a piping bag, pipe cream over custard. • Sprinkle chocolate curls over top of trifle.	• Assemble pre-weighed ingredients. All ingredients checked for quality using control systems. • Automated assembly of sponge base (standard component), into plastic container. • Automated assembly of (standard component) sterilised fruit layer using depositor. • Automated assembly of (standard component) custard mixture, using depositor. • Cream layer piped onto custard layer using injector/ depositor equipment. • Conveyor belt to refrigeration tunnel – blast chilling. • Packaging and labelling of food product for distribution for retail.

Evaluate method A compared with method B for use by a food manufacturer.

Student answer	Examiner comments	Build a better answer
Method B uses ready-made ingredients whilst A does not.	■ The first sentence shows a basic, albeit correct, comparison of the two recipes. To access higher marks the student needs to show an understanding of that comparison.	△ Method B uses lots of standard components which help to save time and labour during the production line.
In method B, all the trifles would look the same.	■ This answer is a basic statement, but with no comparison to recipe A.	△ Method A could be individually decorated to create a unique product, whereas with method B all the trifles would look the same due to batch production.
Method A is made in a school kitchen.	■ The student must evaluate method A compared to B to achieve the marks for this answer.	△ Method A is made in a test kitchen at school using one-off production, whereas method B is batch produced on a large scale.
A conveyor belt is used in Method B.	■ This answer would benefit from a reason explaining why a conveyor belt is used in method B.	△ Method B uses a conveyor belt to transport the food products around the production line and this speeds up the process of making.
Recipe adaptation would be easy with method A.	■ This answer requires further detail to merit a mark.	△ In method A, it would be easy to change elements of this trifle (for example, by using seasonal ingredients), as only one product is being made and recipe adaptation is easier to control on a smaller scale.
Fresh fruit is used in method A but not in method B.	■ The comparison must show why fresh fruit is used in method A and sterilised fruit in method B.	△ Fresh fruit is a perishable food and has a short storage life, so is not suitable for batch production. In method B, fruit has been sterilised to prolong shelf life/storage life.

Overall comment:This question is an extended writing question and also marked using the QWC level descriptors.

Your controlled assessment

In this unit, you will complete a Design activity and a Make activity each based on one of a range of tasks provided by Edexcel, the exam board. This assessment will be worth 60% of the final GCSE Food Technology grade. There are two main options for delivery and assessment:

Combined design and make activities
The Design and Make activities can be linked, so you will design and then make a single range of products using the same task and design brief.

Separate design and make activities
You will design one range of products and make a different range of products. This could be for two different tasks (with different design briefs) or for two different types of food product from the same set task (such as savoury food products for the Design task and sweet food products for the Make task), using the same task and design brief.

Control

Controlled assessment means that your work will be carried out under 'controls', to ensure that the work you conduct for these tasks is all your own. There are two main types of control:

Task setting
Edexcel will provide five tasks or broad themes for you to choose from. You can choose your own projects providing they fit with one of the broad themes. Choosing to follow separate Design and Make activities will provide greater flexibility in the ingredients, components, skills, techniques, tools and equipment that you can use to design and make your food products.

Task taking
This has been established to ensure that the work carried out for the task is all your own.

Your assessment

<table>
<tr><td colspan="2">Design activity (50 marks)
You will undertake a Design activity covering the following three stages and eight assessment criteria:</td><td colspan="2">Make activity (50 marks)
You will undertake a Make activity covering the following three stages and five assessment criteria:</td></tr>
<tr><td colspan="2">Stage 1: Investigate (15 marks)</td><td colspan="2">Stage 4: Plan (6 marks)</td></tr>
<tr><td>1.1</td><td>Analysing the brief (3 marks)</td><td rowspan="3">4.1</td><td rowspan="3">Production plan (6 marks)</td></tr>
<tr><td>1.2</td><td>Research (6 marks)</td></tr>
<tr><td>1.3</td><td>Specification (6 marks)</td></tr>
<tr><td colspan="2">Stage 2: Design (20 marks)</td><td colspan="2">Stage 5: Make (38 marks)</td></tr>
<tr><td>2.1</td><td>Initial ideas (12 marks)</td><td>5.1</td><td>Quality of manufacture (24 marks)</td></tr>
<tr><td>2.2</td><td>Review (4 marks)</td><td>5.2</td><td>Quality of outcome (12 marks)</td></tr>
<tr><td>2.3</td><td>Communication (4 marks)</td><td>5.3</td><td>Health and safety (2 marks)</td></tr>
<tr><td colspan="2">Stage 3: Develop (15 marks)</td><td colspan="2">Stage 6: Test and evaluate (6 marks)</td></tr>
<tr><td>3.1</td><td>Development (9 marks)</td><td rowspan="2">6.1</td><td rowspan="2">Testing and evaluation (6 marks)</td></tr>
<tr><td>3.2</td><td>Final design (6 marks)</td></tr>
</table>

Task taking
Your teacher will mark your Design and Make activities and Edexcel will moderate the work across the suite of D&T subjects to ensure that marks for coursework are applied consistently and fairly for all students.

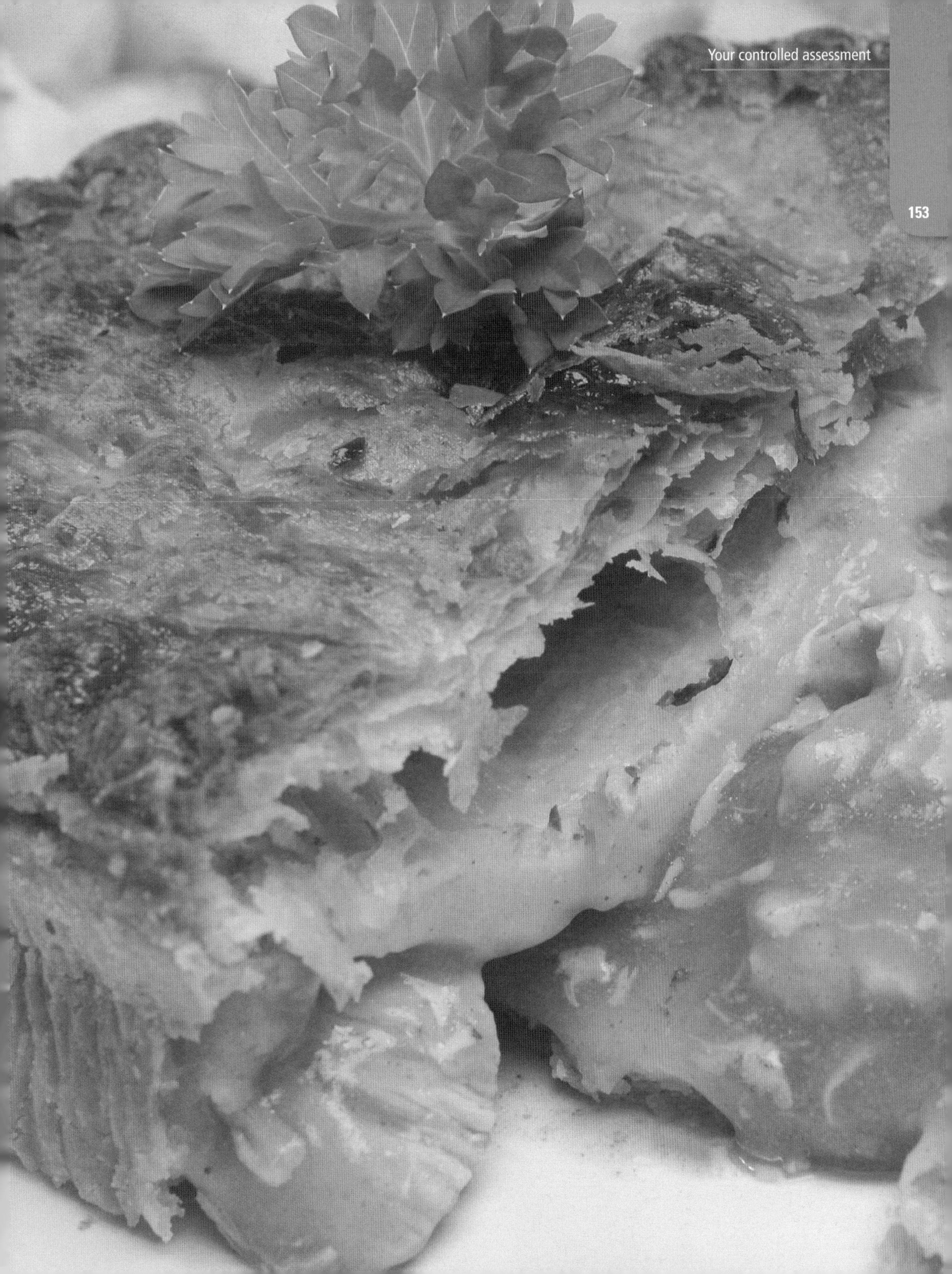

Analysing the brief

Objectives

- **Analyse** your design brief in enough detail to be able to clarify design needs
- **Analyse** the key words, terms and phrases that will help you to understand the issues related to your design brief

Celebration cake

ResultsPlus
Watch out!

Clear, concise analysis should fit onto a single sheet of A3 paper. Think about your presentation and avoid any unnecessary 'padding' information!

To get top marks you need to:
Write a clear statement of what you are going to design (and make) as a design brief. Analyse key words relating to your design brief.
Clarify design needs by providing enough detailed information to allow you to research your project in greater depth.

Design brief

Your design and make activities start with a design brief that fits with one of the Edexcel set task themes. The design brief should be a clear, precise statement of what you are going to design and/or make. You need to recognise a situation for design.

Separate design and make activities

Task: Celebration

Design brief: To design a luxury range of ready-made products suitable for a celebration. The range of food products should be individual portions, visually striking and aimed at working adults.

The separate design and make tasks allow for different products to be created in each of the two controlled assessment tasks. For example, the focus for the design task might be savoury foods and, for the make task, desserts.

Combined design and make activities

Task: Multicultural food products

Design brief: To design and make a multicultural range of food products suitable for sale in a local café.

User group feedback is useful at several stages of the design process, so by identifying a real client or target group for your project, you can then make design decisions based on their comments and feedback in both the design and make activities.

Pancakes

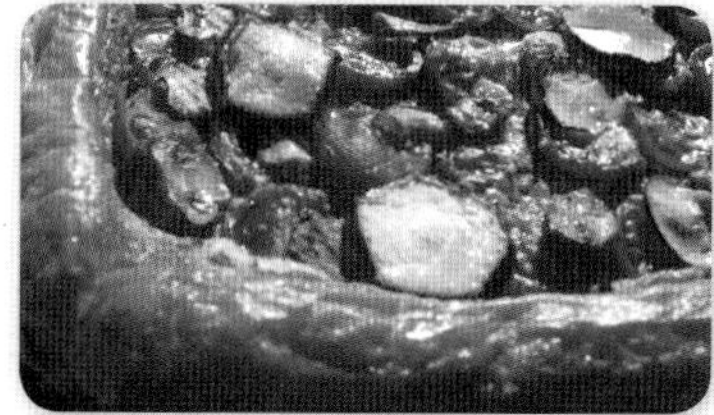

Mediterranean Tart

Analysis

Identifying the main issues for your design brief will help you to focus on exactly what needs to be done. Good starting points for inspiration are brainstorming and attribute analysis. This allows you to target a specific design need.

- Brainstorming or mind maps help to identify the important things that need to be considered before designing. Do this independently or as group work.
- Attribute analysis is used to clarify key features of the design brief, by identifying ingredients, properties and functions of food products for your target group.
- Mood boards or collages can also help to focus on the choice of food products, presentation, skills and techniques used to make the food products and also potential user groups or target markets. However, they must be kept focused and relevant.

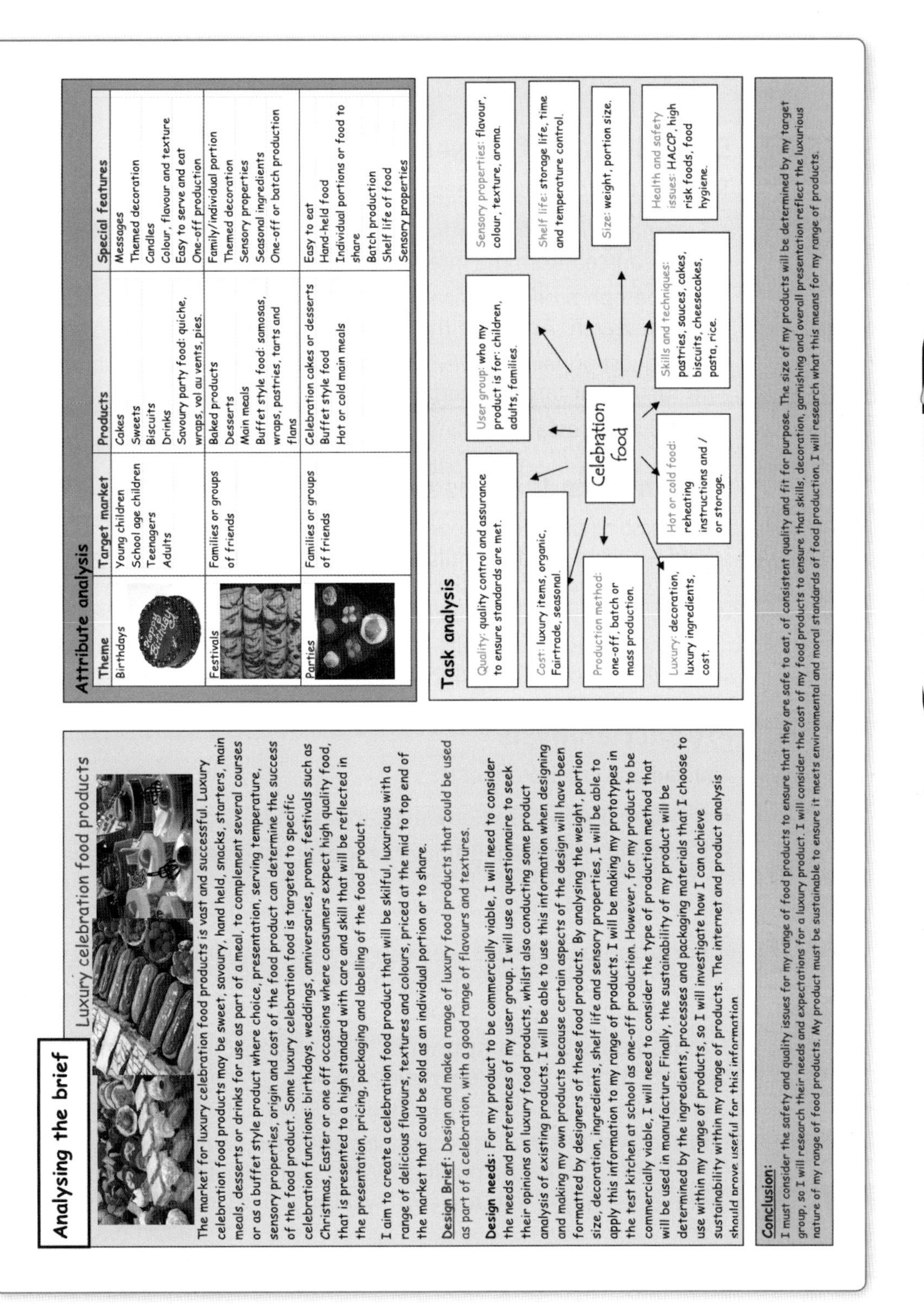

Analysing the brief

Luxury celebration food products

The market for luxury celebration food products is vast and successful. Luxury celebration food products may be sweet, savoury, hand held, snacks, starters, main meals, desserts or drinks for use as part of a meal, to complement several courses or as a buffet style product where choice, presentation, serving temperature, sensory properties, origin and cost of the food product can determine the success of the food product. Some luxury celebration food is targeted to specific celebration functions: birthdays, weddings, anniversaries, proms, festivals such as Christmas, Easter or one off occasions where consumers expect high quality food, that is presented to a high standard with care and skill that will be reflected in the presentation, pricing, packaging and labelling of the food product.

I aim to create a celebration food product that will be skilful, luxurious with a range of delicious flavours, textures and colours, priced at the mid to top end of the market that could be sold as an individual portion or to share.

Design Brief: Design and make a range of luxury food products that could be used as part of a celebration, with a good range of flavours and textures.

Design needs: For my product to be commercially viable, I will need to consider the needs and preferences of my user group. I will use a questionnaire to seek their opinions on luxury food products, whilst also conducting some product analysis of existing products. I will be able to use this information when designing and making my own products because certain aspects of the design will have been formatted by designers of these food products. By analysing the weight, portion size, decoration, ingredients, shelf life and sensory properties, I will be able to apply this information to my range of products. I will be making my prototypes in the test kitchen at school as one-off production. However, for my product to be commercially viable, I will need to consider the type of production method that will be used in manufacture. Finally, the sustainability of my product will be determined by the ingredients, processes and packaging materials that I choose to use within my range of products, so I will investigate how I can achieve sustainability within my range of products. The internet and product analysis should prove useful for this information

Attribute analysis

Theme	Target market	Products	Special features
Birthdays	Young children School age children Teenagers Adults	Cakes Sweets Biscuits Drinks Savoury party food: quiche, wraps, vol au vents, pies.	Messages Themed decoration Candles Colour, flavour and texture Easy to serve and eat One-off production
Festivals	Families or groups of friends	Baked products Desserts Main meals Buffet style food: samosas, wraps, pastries, tarts and flans	Family/individual portion Themed decoration Sensory properties Seasonal ingredients One-off or batch production
Parties	Families or groups of friends	Celebration cakes or desserts Buffet style food Hot or cold main meals	Easy to eat Hand-held food Individual portions or food to share Batch production Shelf life of food Sensory properties

Task analysis

Celebration food

Quality: quality control and assurance to ensure standards are met.

User group: who my product is for: children, adults, families.

Sensory properties: flavour, colour, texture, aroma.

Cost: luxury items, organic, Fairtrade, seasonal.

Shelf life: storage life, time and temperature control.

Production method: one-off, batch or mass production.

Size: weight, portion size.

Luxury: decoration, luxury ingredients, cost.

Hot or cold food: reheating instructions and / or storage.

Skills and techniques: pastries, sauces, cakes, biscuits, cheesecakes, pasta, rice.

Health and safety issues: HACCP, high risk foods, food hygiene.

Conclusion:
I must consider the safety and quality issues for my range of food products to ensure that they are safe to eat, of consistent quality and fit for purpose. The size of my products will be determined by my target group, so I will research their needs and expectations for a luxury product. I will consider the cost of my food products to ensure that skills, decoration, garnishing and overall presentation reflect the luxurious nature of my range of food products. My product must be sustainable to ensure it meets environmental and moral standards of food production. I will research what this means for my range of products.

Student exemplar: Analysing the brief

ResultsPlus
Watch out!

Analysis of the brief helps you plan a route through the task, deciding what information needs to be gathered and establishing the needs of the design brief.

Moderator comment

This is a good example of how students can successfully layout their analysis on a single A3 sheet of paper.

This student has presented their analysis in a logical and concise way. The introduction shows the thought process for the choice of analysis and clarifies design needs. The design brief is clearly stated on the page. Several methods of analysis identify key issues, including attribute analysis, mood board and brainstorming. The final conclusion shows that the student is making design decisions about possible research methods to gather further information from this analysis and move forward successfully into the rest of the project.

Research

Objectives

- **Present** selective and focused research that addresses the design needs or decisions
- **Analyse** relevant, existing products in terms of performance, ingredients, components, processes, quality and sustainability issues
- **Apply** the findings from your product analysis and research to inform the writing of your own specification criteria

To get top marks you need to:
Use selective and focused research.
Analyse at least two existing products and one in detail (product analysis) by focusing on performance, ingredients, components, processes, quality and sustainability issues.
Determine key factors from your product analysis that you will have to include in the specification of your own product.

Product analysis and existing product research must be the main focus of your research, not vague questionnaires or surveys.

Selective and focused research

Try these approaches to keep your research clear and succinct:

- Summarise in bullet points the key background information you have sourced from the internet/books.
- Photograph product analysis and disassembly to provide a record of your research. Annotate this with your main findings/observations.
- Plan questionnaires/surveys carefully using relevant closed questions to focus your target group on a particular issue.
- Avoid unnecessary padding.

Existing product research

Using existing products allows you to see how a professional designer solved a design need. Identify the main technical considerations, as well as any potential problems, and apply this to your design work. Work in small groups to make it easier to source food products and discuss issues. Record results independently (perhaps as a chart with a scanned image of the products and relevant research data).

Product analysis

You can analyse a product by:

- Disassembly of a food product, label and packaging.
- Comparison of existing similar products using common criteria.

Ask yourself:

- **Performance**: What is the purpose of this product? What technical considerations affect its performance? Consider size, weight, dimensions of layers/portions.
- **Ingredients and components**: What ingredients and components are used? Why? Consider their working characteristics and functions when combined with other ingredients/components within a product.
- **Processes**: What skills, techniques and manufacturing processes are used to make the product? Why? Consider specific preparation or processing techniques (e.g. layering or finishing), or practical skills needed to make specific components of a product (e.g. sauce, pastry, cake, bread or biscuit making skills).
- **Quality**: What issues of quality are involved in the design/manufacture of a product to make it fit for purpose, fully functional and free from defects?
- **Sustainability**: What are the sustainability issues throughout the product's lifecycle? Consider the source or origin of raw materials or ingredients (e.g. farming methods, seasonality, food miles or Fairtrade). Consider the implications of manufacturing processes: transportation, CO_2 emissions, use of water, fuel, agrichemicals, waste and packaging.

Research

Existing product research

Food product	Lemon meringue pie	Fruit flan
Cost	£4.99	£3.99
Weight/Size	500g Serves 5 people	500g Serves 4 people
User requirements	Individual or family portion size. Eat hot or cold.	Individual or family portion size. Eat cold.
Components and processes	Short crust pastry Blended lemon sauce Soft creamy meringue Served with fresh strawberries **Scale of production:** One-off or batch.	Sponge flan case Soft seasonal fruit with a fruity glaze **Scale of production:** One-off or batch.
Performance	Topping piped or forked to create luxurious appearance, with caramelised sugar. Lined pastry flan case is even thickness and golden brown.	Beautifully presented food with seasonal fruit and glazed to create a shiny, luxurious appearance.
Sustainability	Free range eggs Seasonal fruit	Free range eggs Seasonal fruit Leaf gelatine to ensure suitability for ovo lacto vegetarians
Safety/ Quality Issues	High risk food product. Ensure food product is cooked until set and golden brown. Balance of pasty/filling and topping crucial to luxurious product.	Layered food product requiring precision and accuracy to achieve even distribution of fillings to aid sensory properties and good quality finish.

Sustainability Issues

Sustainability is all about preserving the world's natural resources for future generations. If food miles are reduced, we cause less CO_2 pollution to the environment. Sourcing food locally by supporting local growers and farmers is a good way of trying to make a product sustainable. Many supermarkets are trying to do this already, so I will look out on food labels and at the weekly Devizes market to try to source food locally. Methods of farming can also affect sustainability. By choosing free range produce, home grown fruit and vegetables, seasonal produce and organic foods, I can try to be an ethical shopper! Organic food is often expensive, because of the way the food has been produced without any chemicals in the crops or soil. It is not an intensive farming practise unlike many other forms of agriculture, but I will consider this when purchasing my ingredients.

Sample from student exemplar: Research – existing products

Moderator comment

The sample shows two of the four products researched in this exemplar.

The presentation of this research is clear, logical and concise, focusing on the key issues for design: the performance, ingredients, components, processes, quality and sustainability issues of these products. The fact that some of the data is very similar (weight, sensory properties, quality issues) is a good way of identifying which issues are relevant to the process of design and also which features are more suitable for the food product than others. This is an example of good practise and should be used when designing your own product.

Research

Product analysis

Product	Summer Fruit Trifle
Weight	500g
Total cost	£6.99
Portions	4
Main ingredients	Fruit - sensory properties Jelly - moisture Sponge - bulking agent Custard - binding
Storage	2 days in fridge
Packaging	APET bowl, film lid Carton board sleeve
Target group	Families Adults Children
Processes	Batch production
Sustainability	Recyclable packaging Seasonal fruit Free-range eggs No waste Farm assured milk Food miles
Health and Safety	High risk foods Short shelf life Contains egg, milk, gluten

This product was delicious. It had a good range of textures, flavours and colours. The custard sauce, layered fruit and sponge fingers represented a good range of skills and would make it a suitable celebration food product for a family gathering because it could be created in individual portions or to share.

This product is expensive, but it is marketed as a luxury product and this is reflected in the presentation, skills and ingredients that have been chosen. This product could be adapted to suit the needs of my design brief.

Product	Tiramisu
Weight	500g
Total cost	£6.99
Portions	4
Main ingredients	Mascarpone – flavour + texture Marsala wine– flavour + texture Sponge - bulking agent Coffee sauce – flavour + colour Cocoa - decoration
Storage	2 days in fridge
Packaging	APET tray Carton board sleeve
Target group	Families Adults celebrations
Processes	Batch production
Sustainability	Recyclable packaging Fairtrade cocoa, coffee Free-range eggs No waste Farm assured milk Food miles
Health and Safety	High risk foods Short shelf life Contains egg, milk, gluten

This product was pleasing but it was very soft and soggy in places. The shelf life of this product would only be two days because it contains many high risk foods: cream and eggs. The layered product was well presented with an interesting dusting of cocoa on the top. The luxury ingredients make this product expensive and it would be limited to batch production due to the nature of the perishable foods.

This product could be adapted to suit the needs of my design brief by changing the base to provide a better range of textures. Sustainability issues could include the consideration of food miles and origin of food products.

Student exemplar: Research – product analysis comparison

Key: 0 = not very, 5 = very

From my star diagram I can see that both these products would be suitable for the task as they are luxurious products and could be used for celebration parties. I chose these descriptors based on the sensory properties that I would choose to have in my range of food products. I will use these descriptors to inform my specification.

Taste testing

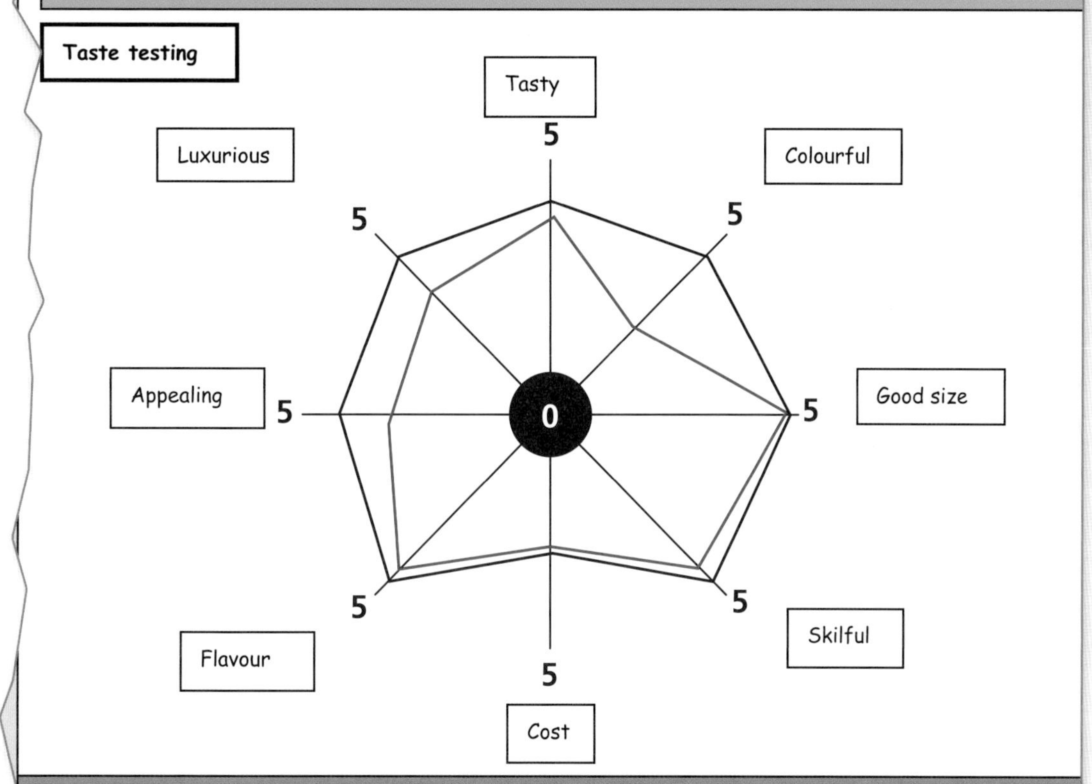

Conclusion:

Product analysis is very helpful to understand how a food product has been created by a designer. These products are luxury items that are branded for the ready meal market. They could be used by individuals or gatherings of people for celebration food. By choosing to use quality ingredients that are combined together using a variety of processes, a skilful food product can be created using a range of food preparation and processing techniques. I will try to address these issues in my design specification.

Key factors:

From my research I have found out that the portion size of a product is determined by the number of people it will serve. Many luxury items are served in bigger portions than value brands because, with value brands, the manufacturer is trying to reduce the cost of making the product so that this can be passed onto the consumer. By using seasonal ingredients in plentiful supply, I should be able to reduce the cost of my product whilst supporting sustainability issues for my product as this will reduce food miles. I have found out that most people are willing to pay £1.50 per portion of the luxury product and that they would like this product to be served either hot or cold. Many ingredients used in desserts are high risk foods, so I will need to ensure that I follow strict food hygiene, stock rotation and risk assessment procedures. Quality issues are important as they will help to determine the luxurious nature of my food product as well as the source of my ingredients. My product needs to be well flavoured with a good range of textures and colours to enhance the appeal of my product to my target group. I am going to target my range of luxury celebration desserts to adults.

Moderator comment

Two similar, relevant products have been analysed using the food product, label and packaging. A star diagram represents the main findings of the taste testing with relevant descriptors that have been identified from the attribute analysis. Observations in the form of analysis help to determine key factors from the product analysis that will have to be included in the specification and when designing their own food product.

Specification

Objectives

- **Produce** realistic, technical, measurable specification points for your own product
- **Produce** relevant issues of sustainability for your own product
- **Justify** your specification points using findings from your research

To get top marks you need to:
Write specification points under the seven headings outlined to the right.
Include issues of sustainability relating to your product in your specification. Justify each specification point.
Apply findings from your research to the specification criteria.

Your specification is one of the most important stages in your project. It is a detailed description of your finished range of products. It includes technical and measurable details, collated from the research and consultation stages of the design process, which are then used during design and development to help you evaluate objectively your work throughout the design and make process.

A specification could include:

- **Function**: What is the product's purpose?
- **Form**: How should your product be styled/shaped? Consider weight or volume, portion size, shape.
- **User requirements**: What qualities make your product attractive? Designers must identify people most likely to buy products, in order to meet needs and expectations. They might identify age ranges or different-sized households with a range of ages, use socio-economic groups to match income to pricing, or cater for special diets such as vegetarians or medical diets.
- **Performance requirements**: What technical considerations must be achieved? (e.g. critical tolerances, dimensions and quantities; the exact details of each performance requirement). This might include: nutritional content, sensory characteristics, cooking and/or heating requirements, shelf life or storage requirements, cost, special dietary considerations, assembly and layering, finishing processes, sustainability issues.
- **Materials and components/ingredients requirements**: How should the ingredients, components and materials perform? Consider the working characteristics of ingredients and their functions when used in combination with others.
- **Scale of production and cost**: How does your design allow for scale of production? What are the considerations in determining cost?
- **Sustainability**: How will your design allow for environmental considerations?

Realistic, technical and measurable

Your specification needs to include points that are realistic, technical and measurable.

Products should be visually striking.

Realistic

This specification point is realistic. Design and development practical work will determine 'visually striking' through sensory analysis by the target group.

Products must be an individually sized dessert: approximately 100g–150g weight.

Technical

This specification point is technical. It outlines a specific quantity of dessert for individual portions.

Product will have a shelf life of up to 3 days, stored in a fridge at 4°C or below.

Measurable

This specification point is measurable. It can be tested for quality after three days by making a visual comparison to a photograph when the food was first made. A taste test would be inappropriate!

Design Specification

- Form: A luxury celebration range of dessert food products.
- Function: Individual sized dessert, suitable for a single person. Approx 100g – 150g weight. 5cm x 10cm size.
- Target group: Young professionals (18-40 years).
- Materials and components: Good and varied flavour and texture throughout the desserts. It will contain fruit.
- User requirements: Easy to eat individual portion of luxury dessert, so it fits in with the luxury aspect of the specification required by the user group for celebrations and other special occasions.
- Performance requirements: A cold dessert. Products will be visually striking using a good range of skills and processes to demonstrate layering and assembly of the different components that will form the range of luxury dessert products.
- Cost: Research suggests no more than £2.00 for the individual portion.
- Storage requirements: Research suggests a shelf life of up to 3 days, stored in a fridge at 4°C or below.
- Scale of production: One-off production in the test kitchen, batch production within an industrial kitchen to allow for quantity of orders and stock rotation of high risk food products.
- Sustainability issues: Use local, seasonal food ingredients where possible to ensure products are both sustainable and relevant to environmental considerations and to support the needs of consumers within the target group.

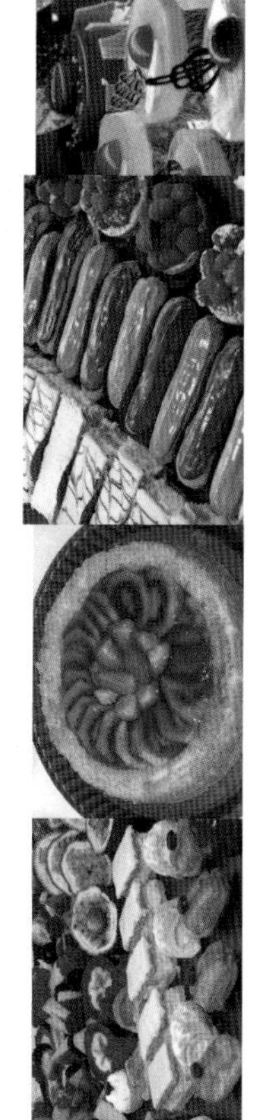

Reasons and discussion:

After analysing the brief and all of my research, I found that my target group has preferences when choosing and buying luxury desserts. For example, my user group identified the need for the range of desserts to contain fruit and to be priced within a particular branding range. I found from my product analysis that good texture and flavour are essential sensory properties for a dessert to be successful and commercially viable. Using seasonal ingredients, I can make use of foods when they are in plentiful and cheap supply. By sourcing these ingredients locally I hope to reduce the food miles of my range of products to meet the challenges of our environmental concerns in the 21st century.

Desserts are traditionally high in fat and sugar, so I have decided not to include any nutritional analysis for my dessert as luxury products often use ingredients that are unhealthy. By identifying the portion size and weight of my product, from the existing product research, I hope to achieve a good balance with the ingredients that I use with the skills and techniques used to create the luxury brand of desserts. The price of my food product is reflected from the research data. High risk foods such as cream, eggs and cheese have a short shelf life and need to handled and stored correctly to ensure they are kept in optimum condition for use as well as being safe to eat. For this reason, I will be making my one-off products in the school test kitchen, but they would be batch produced within an industrial setting to meet consumer demand and pre-ordering of goods by the leading supermarkets or other catering businesses.

Student exemplar: Specification

ResultsPlus
Watch out!

Each specification point must be fully justified and linked to findings from your research. Try using 'because'. For example: 'My product will weigh 100g **because** my product analysis research showed this was the average weight for an adult's individual portion of dessert. My tasters also agreed with this weight.' This response includes a statement and a justified reason.

Moderator comment

This student has decided to design a luxury celebration range of desserts. The specification is presented using the relevant headings, with a statement and fully justified reason. Take care that the specification does not become too complicated by trying to include too much information for one specification point. However, in this instance, the student demonstrates excellent use of the findings from the research with the reasons and discussion presented on the right-hand side of the page. This is an example of a very high level response.

Initial ideas

Objectives

- **Present** alternative initial design ideas that are realistic, workable and detailed
- **Demonstrate** your understanding of ingredients, components, materials, processes and techniques applied to your initial ideas
- **Apply** your research findings to your initial ideas
- **Address** specification points through your initial ideas

To get top marks you need to:
Present 4–6 different ideas for your 'range of food products'.
Identify the main ingredients, components, materials, processes and techniques that would be required to make the products.
Apply your research findings to your designs or include additional research where appropriate.
Annotate each design with reference to relevant specification criteria.

ResultsPlus
Watch out!

By using sensory testing with the practical work at the initial ideas stage, you will gain useful feedback from your user group about the sensory properties of the food products you have made. This will help you make design decisions.

Producing initial ideas is an important part of the design process. Create alternative ideas that fulfil your specification criteria by demonstrating imagination and creativity in the selection of initial ideas and the way that you communicate this information. Your ideas need to focus on key specification points. Your annotation should explain how these are met by demonstrating your understanding of different ingredients, components, materials, processes and techniques.

Presenting your ideas

There are many ways of presenting design ideas – use a combination of the following methods:

- Sketched or drawn images of your range of food products. This might include colour, rendering or shading of your cross section or plan views.
- Scanned images of ideas from recipe databases, magazines, cookery books or your own practical work.
- Practical work conducted for a smaller selection of ideas to help you to understand how your ingredients and components work within the process or technique you are using to construct your product.

Your ideas sheet should be full and detailed, with lots of images and annotation. In food technology lessons, create some of your initial ideas by using 'modelling' or practical work to help make decisions about what is successful about these ideas, using the specification criteria. This shows you exactly how your initial recipe ideas work and will lead you into the development stage. You do not need to make all your initial ideas.

Ingredients, materials, components, processes and techniques

Present this information as annotations with your images or as charts, sketches, diagrams or using CAD. A useful checklist might include:

- functions of ingredients
- explaining the skills and processes used within the making of the product
- identifying specialist equipment you need to help create the product
- where appropriate: nutritional analysis or costing using CAD.

Additional research

Research is ongoing – you might need to include short statements of relevant information where the understanding of a design idea requires a bit more detail. Keep this additional research concise and relevant to the design.

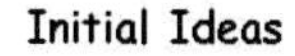

Design and make a range of ready made celebration desserts.

From my research and specification I have identified a possible range of initial ideas, based upon a cold fruit dessert that will serve one person. I have used recipe books, the internet, cooking shows and practical work at school for my inspiration of ideas. They are all linked to my specification.

Pastries and flans:
Jam tart
Fruit tart
Mince pies
Treacle tart
Profiteroles
Lemon meringue pie

A number of different types of pastries could be chosen to make the pastry case, this would hold the filling and provide good colour and texture with the different components.

Ices and iced puddings:
Sorbet
Syllabub
Fruit terrine
Ice cream

This could be difficult to make and store. It is a frozen dessert and may prove difficult to add a variety of textures to the dessert.

Cakes and biscuits:
Brownies
Cookies
Carrot cake
Gateau
Shortbread

These products are often used as accompaniments to desserts or as desserts in their own right. They could be adapted to contain fruit and different sensory properties.

Cheesecakes:
Baked and chilled cheesecakes
Tortes

These ideas would be great because they are cold desserts with a good range of sensory properties, which may be adapted for the task to include fruit. They can be made to look visually striking with finishing techniques such as piping or using a fluted tin.

Ready made celebration dessert ideas

- Individual portion
- 100-150g
- Adults
- Fruit
- Cold
- £2.00
- Visually striking
- 3 day shelf life
- Additive free
- One-off production
- Sustainable

Milk, custard and cream puddings:
Trifle
Crème caramel
Baked custard flan

These puddings are baked, but served cold, sometimes with fruit as a main ingredient or as an accompaniment. I could consider using free-range or organic ingredients to support non-intensive farming practises and make these products more sustainable.

Fruit Puddings:
Fruit flan
Pavlova
Summer pudding

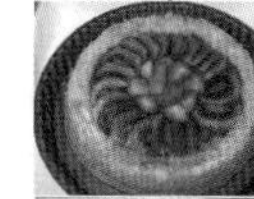

These desserts could contain seasonal fruit, sourced locally to reduce food miles. The different combinations of sensory properties would make these desserts very suitable for the brief.

Souffles and mousses:
These desserts are often sold as luxury items because they are skilful, and contain rich ingredients such as cream and soft fruit. I would need to make sure that I can meet my £2.00 ingredients budget. The textures are often soft and creamy, but they may have a limited shelf life due to these high risk foods.

Conclusion: From my initial ideas mood board, I am going to choose to make a cheesecake, a trifle, a fruit flan and a chocolate and orange mousse for my initial ideas. I have chosen these ideas because they match the specification points for my design brief. By making these four ideas, I will be able to understand how they relate to the task, explore the function of the ingredients and processes used to create these products, as well as asking some people from my target group their opinion of my products for the task. By sourcing the ingredients myself, I will be able to consider the impact of the environment on my choice of ingredients and whether they affect the final quality of my products.

Student exemplar: Initial ideas

- The presentation of your work is very important but, due to the time constraints of controlled assessment, it is far better to spend the time generating ideas than excessive decoration of your design sheets with borders, lettering or backgrounds.

Moderator comment

Good design sheets are 'busy' with annotated detail on images, sketches, drawings and photographs for a selection of different design intentions, linked to the research findings. The specification checklist helps to focus the student on the choice and selection of food products, whilst the annotation of scanned images, sketches and photographed practical work communicates a knowledge and understanding of the ingredients, components, processes and techniques for these initial ideas. It is clear that these ideas are workable and realistic as they have been made in a practical lesson with photographic evidence. The sensory testing using user group feedback will prove to be very useful for the review section.

Review

Objectives

- **Present** objective evaluative comments against your original specification criteria
- **Evaluate** your initial design ideas using user group feedback and issues of sustainability

This stage allows you to check the progress of your ideas against the specification, making objective comments that include both advantages and disadvantages about the suitability of each product for the design brief. With third party feedback and consideration of relevant sustainability issues, you can then make design decisions about which products you are going to take forward to the development stage.

User group feedback could include sensory testing, informal interview or simple comments from a client or short comments from a range of people that are recorded as written evidence in the review section. By using third party testing, you can gain valuable information or data that could influence further development of your product and ensure its success.

To get top marks you need to:
Test your ideas against relevant points in your specification.
Evaluate your ideas and identify what needs to be developed further.
Include user group feedback to help you to determine the best ideas to develop further for your range of food products.

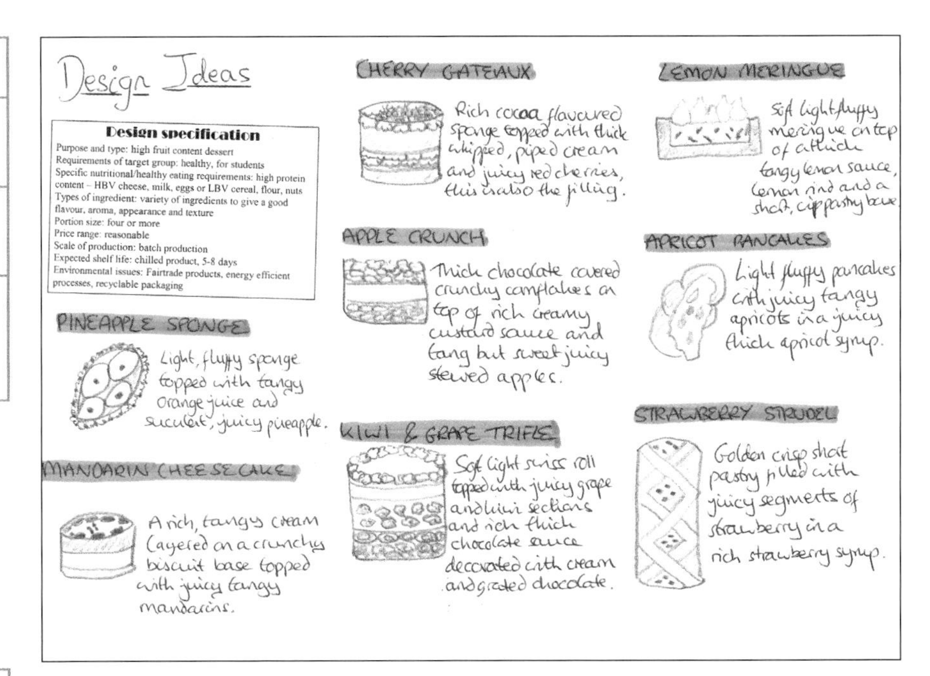

Student exemplar: Review

Communication

To get top marks you need to:
Present your ideas using a range of communication techniques and media, including ICT and CAD where appropriate, with precision and accuracy.

Moderator comment

Ongoing annotation of initial ideas relates back to the specification. The student has reviewed each idea as it has been drawn and included sensory testing for some of the ideas presented as practical work. This is clearly leading design decisions. Information is being communicated with precision and accuracy.

Review

Specification points		Lemon Cheesecake		Fruit Trifle
Individual portion 100-150g	★	This could be served as a slice or in a small mould. Wastage and portion control could be monitored in production linking to sustainability issues.	★	Lightweight and could be served in a small clear plastic container to allow consumer to see filling. Plastic container must be recyclable for sustainability.
Adults	★	User group reviews were positive and awarded 5 marks.	★	User group reviews were positive and awarded 5 marks.
Fruit	★	3 fresh lemons sourced from local farm shop provided flavour and colour to food product. High in vitamin C and contributed sharp tangy flavour.	★	Range of fresh seasonal fruit could be used in this dessert to decrease food miles and promote sustainability. Range of fresh fruit in winter months is low, so would need to consider tinned fruit for economical reasons.
Cold dessert	★	Served chilled from fridge.	★	Served chilled from fridge.
£2.00	✦	Fresh lemons and whipping cream were expensive ingredients, affecting final cost by 50p. I could consider using lemon juice and reducing the cream content as it was a very rich dessert.	✦	Fresh fruit is expensive and there was a lot of wastage from peel, pips and husks. I would consider using a combination of fresh and tinned fruit to reduce the cost.
Visually striking	★	Sliced lemons, fluted flan tin and piped cream enhanced the finish of my product. It could be adapted to a special occasion.	★	The layers to my trifle provide a good contrast in colour and texture. The sponge base supported the layers by absorbing the juices and creating a good combination of textures.
3 day shelf life	★	Cream is a high risk food product and susceptible to food poisoning bacteria. However, it would be fine in fridge for 3 days, as long as the initial ingredients are checked within date marks.	★	Fresh fruit can deteriorate quickly depending on the type and origin of the fruit. Fruit would need to be in perfect condition upon purchase.

Sample from student exemplar: Formal review sheet

If you have used sustainability as a heading in your specification criteria, you can review your ideas against this point also.

Moderator comment

This sample shows two of the four products featured in the exemplar.

The formal review sheet above is an excellent way of communicating design and review. It addresses the strengths and weaknesses of each design idea against the specification criteria, as well as summarising the findings of user group feedback.

Development

Objectives

- **Develop** your initial design ideas into a range of final design proposals
- **Use** modelling to test important aspects of your design idea as it progresses, against the specification
- **Evaluate** your ideas against relevant design criteria as you progress

To get top marks you need to:
Improve your chosen design ideas by developing technical details that are different and improved compared to any previous alternative ideas.
Use scale modelling to refine and test your ideas as they progress, using practical work with ingredients or components, 2D and / or 3D CAD software. Include user group/ third party feedback.
Review your designs against relevant specification criteria.

Each food product consists of a number of components. Use these components to focus development opportunities. For example: sauces, pastries, cake or biscuit-making methods, pasta, toppings, finishing techniques, mixing or combining techniques.

At the development stage, you use the review of your initial ideas to move forward to create something different or new. You need to develop, trial and test different aspects of your initial ideas to address points in your specification criteria.

'Develop' means changing and modifying your ideas, including refining features of previous design ideas, in order to present your range of final design proposals for the Design Task. These proposals for your 'range of products' should be significantly different to, and improve on, previous ideas. You should be able to demonstrate significant changes or improvements to your design proposals. There must be a point to developments and this should be explained: for example, to test proportions, change flavours/textures, nutritional content of ingredients or components of your product.

Design work is about people, their needs and views. User group feedback should provide valuable information about your developments, so that your design proposals satisfy user requirements.

Modelling

Practical work

Practical work plays an important part in modelling in the development of successful food products. For example, by trialing different types of sauces, you identify different working characteristics of ingredients and how they create pouring, coating or binding sauces. The final selection of a sauce might be because of its texture, flavour, colour or use with other ingredients. Another example might be that reviewing an idea leads you to explore different types of pastries and the proportions of ingredients used to create the sensory characteristics associated with each type. Use user groups in your practical work to provide valuable feedback about the sensory properties of your design proposals.

CAD software

Use CAD, where appropriate to the design brief, to model recipes and products.

- Design the physical profile of a product using **paint/draw programmes** and **nutritional databases**.
- Model the cost, portion size, weight, assembly of a single item or batch of food products using **databases and spreadsheets**.
- Calculate and analyse the nutritional content of a product using **nutritional databases** such as food focus programmes.
- Calculate the scale of production and scaled recipes, cost and stock control using **spreadsheets**.

Development

From my design ideas, I am going to develop the lemon cheesecake, fruit trifle and orange and chocolate mousse based upon the feedback from my user group in the rating test and also my practical work for these ideas. My challenge will be to meet all the points on my specification by improving these ideas. I will now conduct more practical work to see how these developments affect my products. Below, I have listed the main changes that will be taking place and I have linked the reasons to my understanding of the working characteristics of ingredients and processes. I will ask my user group to test my changes by using the same descriptors that I used for the design ideas. I can then compare my results to see if the changes have improved the food product.

Lemon Cheesecake Development

Original recipe	Development	Reasons
3 lemons	2 lemons and 3tbsp juice	Reduce cost but maintain flavour
150ml whipping cream	100ml whipping cream	Reduce richness but maintain flavour and texture
175ml condensed milk	No change	
150g Digestive biscuits	150g ginger biscuits	Alternative flavour and sweetness
50g butter	50g PUFA margarine	Unsaturated fat to reduce cholesterol levels

The lemon juice made the mixture quite runny, but it was easy to mix into the cream using a hand whisk. The zest of the lemons provided the colour for the cheesecake and I am pleased that I did not reduce the number of lemons further as this would have affected the final colour. The ginger biscuits were easy to use and I placed them in a plastic bag to crush them with a rolling pin. The soft margarine melted quickly and it was easy to combine the base ingredients together, to form a crunchy layer. The base was not as greasy this time and I am pleased that I tried using a different type of fat. The cost of this recipe was reduced by using one less lemon and reduced whipping cream. Therefore, I have met the requirements of my specification and user group.

skillful, luxurious, colourful, fruity, delicious, creamy, cold, flavour
0 = Not Very 5 = Very
fruit trifle, mousse, lemon cheesecake, fruit flan

Development Review
Individual portion – slice for one person
100-150g – 150g weight
Adults – yes
Fruit – lemons
Cold – chilled dessert
£2.00-£1.70 per portion
Visually striking – colour contrast
3 day shelf life – yes with date mark control
Additive free – yes
One-off production – yes and suitable for batch production in commercial setting
Sustainable – yes – used locally sourced ingredients, considered using lemon juice instead of fresh lemons, which worked really well

Fruit Trifle Development

Original recipe	Development	Reasons
Sponge fingers	Amaretto biscuits	Improve texture to create more flavour combinations.
2 eggs	No change	
50g caster sugar	No change	
150ml milk	No change	
75g seasonal fruit	Tinned and fresh fruit	Reduce cost and food miles, avoid fresh exotic fruit from far away.
100ml whipping cream	No change	

The Amaretto biscuits were easy to use and will definitely affect the final texture of my food product as they are crunchy rather than soft. It will be interesting to see if this affects the final product. The tinned raspberries were very soft and quite mushy when I opened them. There was a lot of juice, so I drained some of this away to prevent my trifle becoming too soft and sloppy! The fresh strawberries are seasonal fruit, and they were sourced from my local pick-your-own farm. The aroma and colour of these strawberries is great and I have reduced the food miles for this product by sourcing them locally. The custard remains unchanged, but I have sourced my eggs from the farm across the road where I live. They only cost me £1.00 for 6 eggs which is a better deal compared to the supermarkets. I am also supporting local farmers. When strawberries are not in season, I could consider using alternative tinned or fresh fruits, but this must not impact upon food miles.

skillful, luxurious, colourful, fruity, delicious, creamy, cold, flavour
0 = Not Very 5 = Very
fruit trifle, mousse, lemon cheesecake, fruit flan

Development Review
Individual portion – mini pot for one
100-150g – 150g weight
Adults – yes see star diagram results
Fruit – seasonal fruit and tinned fruit
Cold – yes chilled dessert
£2.00-£1.55 per pot
Visually striking – colourful layers in clear plastic container
3 day shelf life – with date mark control
Additive free – yes
One-off production – yes
Sustainable – used free-range eggs, local produce and seasonal fruit where possible

Orange and Chocolate Mousse Development

Original recipe	Development	Reasons
100g Fairtrade dark chocolate	Reduce dark Fairtrade chocolate and add white chocolate layer to add contrast in flavour and colour.	This would counterbalance the strong bitter chocolate and enable me to reduce the cost of the ingredients.
2 oranges	Use 1 orange for zest and juice and 3 tbsp concentrated juice.	Increase tangy orange with concentrated juice, but maintain zest with fresh orange.
2 eggs	No change	
150ml whipping cream	No change	

The colour contrast on this food product is really good and I am pleased that I have changed the proportion of chocolate, as well as reducing it by a quarter. The white chocolate is much sweeter than the dark chocolate because of the percentage cocoa bean used to make the chocolate bar. It also contains more sugar, however this compliments the other ingredients. As this is a luxury food product, I am not too worried about the sugar or fat content as these products are not eaten in great quantities. The concentrated orange juice has worked well, but it was quite expensive, so I am going to return to using the two oranges for their zest and juice. Oranges are imported to the UK from the Mediterranean and they are in abundance in January. Therefore, at other times of the year, I will seriously consider the use of concentrated juice as an alternative ingredient.

skillful, luxurious, colourful, fruity, delicious, creamy, cold, flavour
0 = Not Very 5 = Very
fruit trifle, mousse, lemon cheesecake, fruit flan

Development Review
Individual portion – mini pot for one
100-150g – 125g actual weight
Adults – yes chocolate is popular choice!
Fruit – oranges
Cold – yes chilled dessert
£2.00-£1.80 per pot due to Fairtrade chocolate
Visually striking – colour contrast and mini pot
3 day shelf life – yes with date mark control
Additive free – yes
One-off production – yes and suitable for batch production
Sustainable

User group feedback for development stage

User group	Lemon Cheesecake	Fruit Trifle	Orange and Chocolate Mousse
Tester 1	Delicious tangy filling on crunchy base 5/5	Seasonal fruity dessert 4/5	Rich tangy mousse 5/5
Tester 2	Delicious lemon dessert with good combination of flavour 4/5	Really liked new flavours in custard and exotic fruit 4/5	Luxurious taste and texture! 5/5
Tester 3	Juicy, tangy and improved filling 5/5	Colourful fruity layers. Good texture 5/5	Rich and delicious 5/5
Tester 4	Luxurious dessert with good textures 5/5	Delicious and colourful. Packaging is eco friendly 5/5	Fabulous rich dessert 5/5
Tester 5	Super lemon topping on crunchy base 5/5	Colourful layers and good textures 4/5	Best dessert ever! 5/5

The tasting shows that the developments worked really well and that I have successfully developed my range of ready made luxury celebration desserts. My tasters have all commented on the use of richness in flavour, well sourced ingredients that reflect the quality demanded by my design brief. These products meet the demands of sustainability by using locally sourced, seasonal ingredients where possible. The final packaging of these products would also include recyclable plastic trays/containers with cardboard sleeves to aid labelling for the manufacturer and the consumer.

Evaluation

These developments have been successful because I have met the points on my specification by adapting my recipes to meet the needs of my user group. The final cost of my food products has been reduced, although I feel that this was to the detriment of the mousse. Therefore, I feel that the luxurious nature of this product requires fresh oranges for the juice and zest. The alternative chocolate complimented my food product and this gave it an added quality with the contrast in colour and flavour. The fruit trifle was very successful and I am pleased that I changed the sponge layer to the biscuits as this improved the texture and flavour. The cost of this change was not significant and this product will still be able to meet the £2.00 price. Finally the lemon cheesecake was vastly improved by adding ginger biscuits and reducing cream. It made the cheesecake light and fluffy, with a well flavoured crunchy base. My tasters thought this was a very successful product. I will present these developments as final ideas for my range of luxury celebration desserts.

Student exemplar: Development

Moderator comment

In a separate design and make task, the student has taken forward three initial ideas after review, to the development stage. Good quality developments take place with trials to the filling and base of the cheesecake, the layers within the trifle and the use of alternative ingredients for the mousse including a Fairtrade chocolate trial compared to value branded chocolate and the use of concentrated juice to address cost and sensory issues with the availability of seasonal fruits. These are described in the text and images. Each development is recorded using photographic evidence, supporting written work for refinement and testing of developments, taste tests from the user group and a review of each development against the specification. This is a good example of high level development.

ResultsPlus
Watch out!

Remember that the enjoyment of food, and therefore its success, is judged by the sensory properties of the ingredients and components that are put together to create a food product. Practical work will play a significant part in the development of your final design proposals. It helps to inform decisions about the role of each ingredient or component within a food product.

Final design

Objectives

- **Present** your final range of design proposals in a format that communicates your design intentions
- **Present** technical details of ingredients, components, processes and techniques relating to your final range of design proposals

To get top marks you need to:
Clearly communicate your final range of design proposals using modelling, photographs or suitable drawing methods, with annotation.
Include technical information about the ingredients, components, skills and/or techniques to enable a third party to make your range of final design proposals.

You now present your final range (more than two) for the Design Task as a fully developed range of food products that meet the needs of the user group, and most of the specification criteria. For the six marks on offer for the Final Design section, you need to present these as working drawings, pictorial drawings, exploded drawings or photographic evidence, with detailed annotation. Link this to the functionality of ingredients, weights and proportions of ingredients, skills and techniques, dimensions and/or tolerances for each product within the range of final design proposals. Marks will be awarded for the communication of this information, which should allow a third party (another person) to be able to understand your design intentions.

In the separate Design and Make Tasks, the Design Task stops with this Final Design stage, with the communication of the final, fully developed range of design proposals. There is no expectation that the final range of design proposals are made, as they will have been fully developed in the previous section using modelling and/or practical work.

In the traditional combined Design and Make task, the final range of design proposals will be made now in the Make Task. In this approach, it is important to show a good range of different skills and techniques, tools and equipment in your making in order to gain access to the higher mark band.

Moderator comment

The three products presented as the range of final design proposals are presented on one sheet of A3 paper. The format and communication of this page is logical, clear and concise, with the technical information, necessary drawings and photographic evidence that allow another person to get a clear understanding of the products. Dimensions for thickness and consistencies for different components of the food products are in evidence, with critical control points that include relevant cooking and chilling times, date marking and storage requirements for high risk foods. The costing is relevant to the original specification criteria. The list of ingredients includes weights and measurements for each component, functionality of ingredients and a brief recipe method for each product, identifying the skills and techniques used to make the products.

Final design for range of luxury ready made desserts

Tangy lemon cheesecake with ginger nut base, Fruity Trifle, Orange and Chocolate Pots

Component	Ingredients	Functions	Technical details	Cost
Filling	2 lemons 3tbsp juice 100ml whipping cream 175ml condensed milk	Flavour, fruit component Whisked to create a foam Light and foamy Thick, sweet flavour and texture	Fresh, perfect condition Foam at soft peak stage to aid mixing Intense sweet flavour aids mixing and setting	40p 20p 67p 98p
Base	150g ginger biscuits 50g PUFA margarine	Crunchy texture, spicy flavour Binding agent	Crushed base Melted fat to aid binding	65p 35p
Decoration	Slice lemon Zest of lemon	Finishing technique	0.5cm thickness	20p
Total weight/ price	575g Per portion 143g	Sensory properties Binding Foams Finishing techniques	Slice cheesecake for portion control 20% base 80% filling	£3.45 Per portion 86p

Tangy Lemon cheesecake with ginger nut base

1. Crush biscuits in plastic bag with rolling pin until fine.
2. Melt fat.
3. Add crushed biscuits to fat and mix well. Place into flan tin. Press firmly.
4. Wash and prepare lemon juice and zest.
5. Whisk cream until light and fluffy.
6. Add milk, juice and zest. Mix well.
7. Place creamy filling into tin.
8. Chill 2 hours.
9. Decorate with lemon twist. Serve.

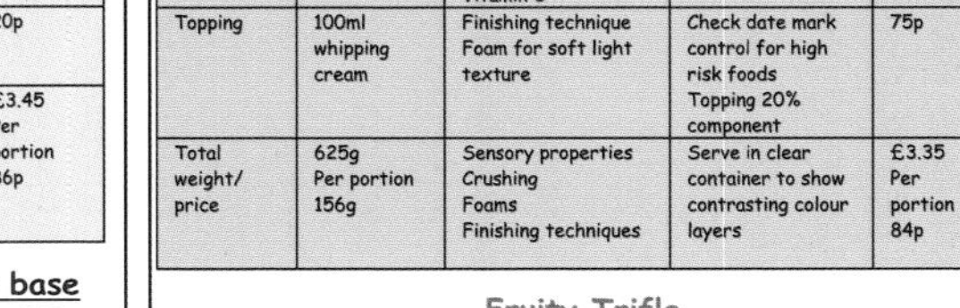

Component	Ingredients	Functions	Technical details	Cost
Custard filling	2 eggs 50g caster sugar 150ml milk	Setting agent for custard, colour Sweetness and flavour Binding agent for custard to thin consistency	Check date mark control for high risk foods Filling 20% component	40p 20p 50p
Base	150g Amaretto biscuits	Crunchy texture, spicy flavour	Layered biscuit Base 40% component	£1.30
Fruit	75g seasonal fruit 125g can raspberries	Fruit component Healthy Flavour Texture Vitamin C	Fresh, perfect condition Fruit 20% component	20p
Topping	100ml whipping cream	Finishing technique Foam for soft light texture	Check date mark control for high risk foods Topping 20% component	75p
Total weight/ price	625g Per portion 156g	Sensory properties Crushing Foams Finishing techniques	Serve in clear container to show contrasting colour layers	£3.35 Per portion 84p

Fruity Trifle

1. Line dish with biscuits.
2. Prepare fresh fruit (wash, slice) Place fruit on top of biscuits.
3. Make egg custard by heating milk over low heat.
4. Place eggs into mixing bowl with sugar. Mix well.
5. Pour warm milk onto egg mixture.
6. Mix well. Return to low heat in Bain Marie and thicken. Cool.
7. Once cool, pour custard onto fruit.
8. Whip cream until soft peaks.
9. Decorate trifle and serve.

Components	Ingredients	Functions	Technical details	Cost
Filling	75g Fair trade dark chocolate 25g white chocolate 2 oranges 2 eggs 150ml whipping cream	Bitter flavour, luxury item. Sweet flavour, luxury item and popular product! Fruit component Setting agent Texture and foam for soft light mouth feel 95% component	Check date mark control for high risk foods Fresh, perfect condition	£1.90 30p 40p 40p 65p
Decoration	Slice orange	Finishing technique 10% component	0.5cm thickness	20p
Total weight/ price	575 g Per portion 143g	Sensory properties Binding Foams Finishing techniques	Serve in small ramekin pot for luxury!	£3.85 Per portion £0.96

Orange and Chocolate Pots

1. Break or chop the chocolate into small pieces.
2. Set a heatproof bowl snugly over a pot of simmering water. Remove the pan from the heat and add the chocolate. Stir occasionally with a wooden spoon while the chocolate melts, then allow the chocolate to cool for 10 minutes.
3. Separate the eggs, placing yolks in one large bowl, and whites in another. Beat the egg yolks until well mixed.
4. Add orange juice and zest, mixing well. Scrape the melted chocolate into the egg yolks, beating well.
5. Whisk the egg whites until stiff and softly peaky, but not dry.
6. Whisk cream until light and foamy.
7. Add a large spoonful of egg whites to the chocolate mixture and mix well, then gently fold in the remaining egg whites.
8. Pour the mixture into a serving bowl, and chill for two or three hours until set.

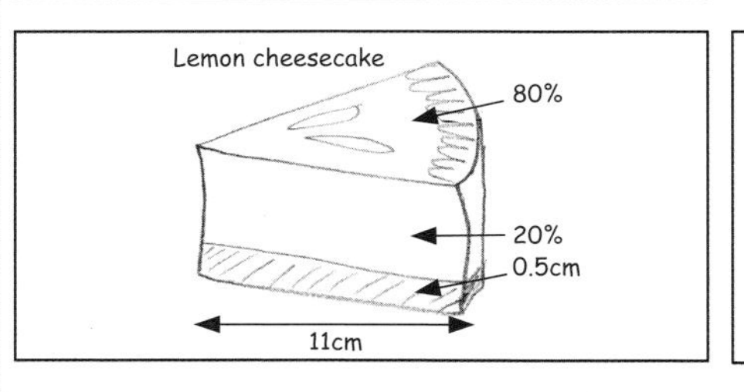

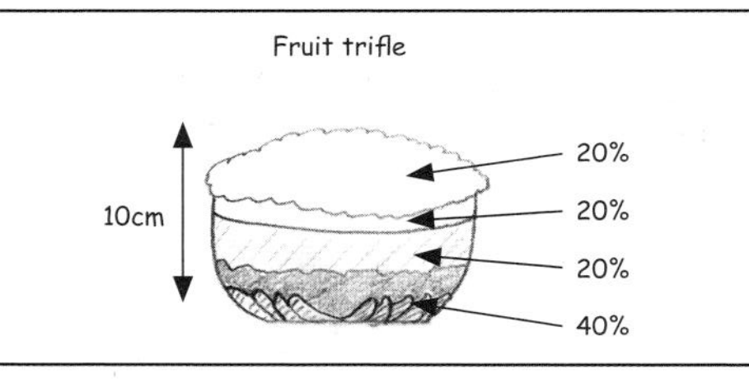

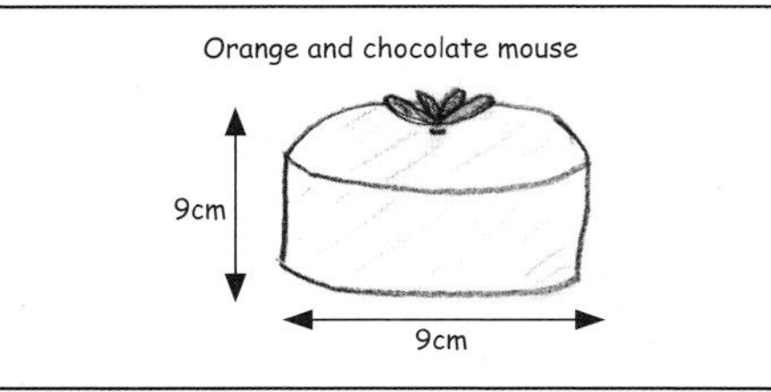

Student exemplar: Final design

Production plan

Objectives

- **Produce** a detailed production plan that considers the stages of manufacture for your products
- **Describe** the stages during making where specific quality control procedures should take place

To get top marks you need to:
Produce a production plan showing all the main stages in making your products, in the correct order.
Plan your making stages against time in order to meet deadlines.
Identify and describe where specific quality control (QC) procedures will take place.

ResultsPlus
Watch out!

■ Make sure you use only metric (or imperial) units when weighing or measuring, to avoid confusion and difficulties when making.

Before starting, you will need your detailed technical information (design brief, specification, recipe and working drawing from your final range of design proposals) in the Design activity. These can be given to you by your teacher if you are doing separate Design and Make activities.

You will be making your range of products in a 'test kitchen', using one-off production at school. Your production plan must be forward-looking and not a diary of how and what you have made. Careful planning prior to making your food products will help you to achieve success in your practical work.

The production plan could take the form of a flowchart, plan or chart showing the stages of manufacture in the correct sequence. Quality control (QC) points should also be clearly identified with relevant detail. For example: *Weighing and measuring ingredients using calibrated scales or following unit measurements consistently throughout a recipe* to ensure proportions of ingredients will be accurate. Mixing imperial or metric weights and measurements will not be a recipe for success!

In order to meet your deadlines, you should plan the stages of manufacture against the time you have allocated. Use 'real time' units such as minutes or hours which indicate measurable time in a practical lesson. Days, lessons or weeks are too vague.

Moderator comment

The production plan for the fish pie shows an excellent understanding of time, quality and safety issues throughout the manufacture of the product. The detailed understanding of the ingredients and their role within the recipe is exemplary. The supporting recipes and ingredients for the additional food dishes within the 'range of products' (not featured) showed a good understanding of how each product will be made and assembled. It is perfectly acceptable to have a detailed production plan for one of your food products, such as the one shown, and an ingredients list and brief method for the other dishes within the product range. You do not need to give this detail for all your products in the range.

The mark allocation for this section is 6 marks and this exemplar is worthy of good marks.

Production Plan: Fish Pie

Time	Step	Hazard	Control	Action
	Buying of ingredients	Contamination of ingredients from supplier.	Purchase from trustworthy supplier. Check date marks.	Reject purchasing poor quality ingredients or tampered packaging.
	Storage of ingredients	Bacterial growth and contamination could occur. High risk foods: fish, milk and cheese.	Stock rotation, check storage temperatures of fridge/freezer. Check date marks.	Reject if products are beyond date mark.
9.00	Prepare fish, place in saucepan and cover with milk. Poach for 10-15 minutes over a medium heat.	Physical and biological contamination. High risk food. Over/under cooking of fish.	Personal hygiene of food handler. Fish should be soft and flaky if cooked correctly.	Apron, wash hands, tie hair from face.
9.20	Remove fish from milk. Remove skin and bones. Place flaked fish into dish.	Physical contamination.	Visual check for bones and skin.	Remove bones and skin.
9.30	Place spinach in colander over pan of water. Allow to wilt. Place wilted spinach onto fish.	Physical contamination from soil.	Wash in running cold water.	Rewash or discard damaged leaves.
9.45	Peel and slice potatoes. Place in pan of boiling water. Cook until soft. (15-20 mins) Hard boil eggs in water.	Physical contamination from soil. Under/over cooking.	Wash in running cold water after peeling. Time control.	Rewash or discard bruised or damaged potatoes. Time control with alarm.
10.10	Drain potatoes in colander. Return to saucepan. Mash with butter and milk until soft.	Over/under cooked potatoes. Incorrect consistency of mash.	Insert knife into random potatoes to check softness after 15 minutes.	Continue to cook for further few minutes if undercooked.
10.15	Prepare roux sauce using melted butter and flour to form a roux. Add milk. Return to heat and allow thickening.	Incorrect proportions of sauce ingredients. Incorrect consistency of sauce or lumpy.	Calibrate scales and check recipe. Stir to remove lumps.	Weigh and measure ingredients using recipe. Remove lumps with either wooden spoon or hand balloon whisk.
10.25	Pour sauce over fish and spinach.	Uneven distribution of sauce.	Pour from saucepan or spread.	Use visual control and/ or spoon to redistribute sauce.
10.35	Place mashed potato onto fish mixture.	Uneven distribution of mashed potatoes.	Spread evenly or pipe with piping bag and nozzle.	Piping bag and nozzle or portion control using spoon.
10.40	Sprinkle grated parmesan cheese onto topping.	Uneven distribution of grated cheese.	Use tablespoon to sprinkle grated cheese.	Use fine grater to reduce size of cheese and aid distribution.
10.45	Bake 20-30 minutes until golden brown. Serve.	Oven/under cooking of fish pie.	Thermostat on oven. 200°C/Gas 6 20-30 minutes	Remove from oven and check internal temperature of pie. 72'C.

Recipe: Fish Pie

Ingredients	Function
500g potatoes	Bulking agent for topping of fish pie. Texture and flavour.
50ml milk	Binding agent for potato topping.
25g butter	Enriching agent for potato topping.
2 hard boiled eggs	Supplement protein content.
500g fresh white fish	HBV protein content. Flavour and texture.
200g spinach	Colour, flavour and texture. Iron and Vitamin C content.
25g butter	Enriching agent for sauce.
25g plain flour	Thickening agent for sauce: gelatinisation.

Student exemplar of one product

Quality of manufacture

Objectives

- **Attempt** a challenging making task involving the manufacture of several different dishes using a range of ingredients, equipment, techniques and processes
- **Select** tools, equipment and processes, including CAM where appropriate for specific uses (including full photographic records of the detailed stages of manufacture, showing relevant processes)
- **Demonstrate** a detailed understanding of the working properties of ingredients and components you have selected for specific use
- **Demonstrate** a wide range of making skills with precision and accuracy
- **Demonstrate** high level safety awareness throughout all stages of manufacture

To get top marks you need to:
Select the correct tools, equipment and processes for the food products with minimum guidance.
Use a wide range of tools, equipment and processes.
Make a range of different food products (more than two) with several different component parts in each.
Demonstrate high-level making skills with component parts made with precision and accuracy.
Use CAM where appropriate.

This stage is an opportunity to demonstrate your making skills. You will be making a 'range of food products'. This means you will make **more than two** food products. Choose products with several component parts to show the use of **different ingredients**, **skills**, **techniques**, **processes**, **tools** and **equipment** in their manufacture. You can discuss this with your teacher.

Using your production plan, make your food products to the best of your ability. You will gain marks for selecting the right tools, equipment or processes for making each component part of your products.

Finally, write up this stage by producing a full photographic record of the stages of manufacture, showing all the relevant skills, techniques and processes in detail. This step-by-step series of photographs should fully document all the tools, equipment and processes you used. (Bring either a cheap disposable camera or a digital camera to record the quality of manufacture for each of your food products.)

Annotate your photographs to support the decisions you made while making your products. For example, you could explain why you chose to 'bake blind' a pastry case or line a flan tin with greaseproof paper. Use short, concise statements for your annotations.

Your teacher will mark your health and safety working practises within the making activities. You do not need to keep a formal record of risk assessment. However, annotate your photographs to remind your teacher of your care and consideration to health and safety issues. For more on health and safety, risk assessment and HACCP, see page 95.

Note: The writing up of this stage will not form part of the time allocated for controlled assessment. Making time will be devoted to the actual making of your products and not their documentation.

Control

- The manufacture of your food products must be completed at school in a food technology kitchen.
- The moderators must be sure that all the practical work is your own, so take lots of photographs as you make your products.
- Your teacher can demonstrate specific tools, equipment and processes, but you must complete the actual work yourself.

Quality of Manufacture

Skills: Short crust pastry, lining tins, baking pastry blind, vegetable, meat and fish preparation, sautéing, poaching fish, steaming spinach to wilt vegetables, roux sauce, assembling and layering techniques, finishing techniques to improve appearance of food products, marinating for flavour development, cooking rice to al dente.

Savoury quiche tartlets: Short crust pasty base made using rubbing in method, cases lined with pastry using care and attention to ensure smooth with no holes! 'Baked blind' to improve texture of flan cases, savoury egg custard with sautéed seasonal vegetables and/or bacon for flavour, colour and texture. Lightly sautéing ingredients helps to develop flavour and colour of vegetables and bacon. Vegetables and bacon must be an even size to ensure even cooking. Each individual savoury quiche meets critical dimensions and tolerances for thickness of pastry, consistency of filling and proportion of each component.

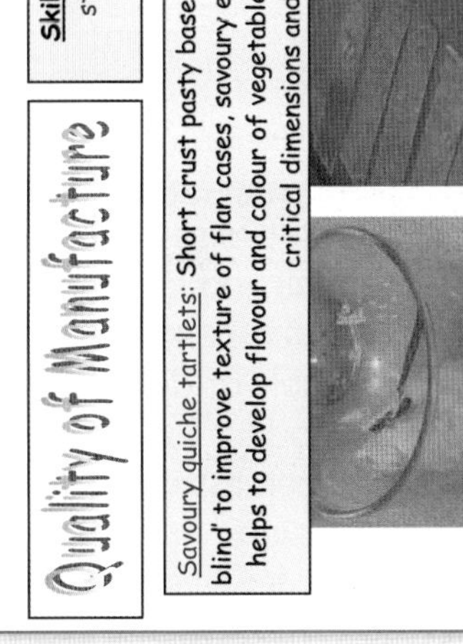

Fish pie: White fish poached in milk to develop flavour and texture. Potatoes cooked and mashed with masher to smooth consistency to aid piping with piping bag for portion control and even distribution. Spinach washed and wilted using steaming method with colander over saucepan. Roux sauce made using butter, flour and milk to produce a smooth, rich, glossy sauce of pouring consistency. This would hold the fish and spinach together to prevent them drying out, thus improving flavour and texture of fish mixture. Roux sauce well seasoned with pepper and salt. Hard boiled eggs added to supplement protein content. Fish pie assembled using layering techniques for consistency and dimension control. Gratin topping made with finely grated parmesan cheese to add colour, flavour and delicious texture to contrast well with other layers.

Chicken curry: Diced chicken pieces marinated in spicy yoghurt marinade. Chicken flash cooked with high heat to develop colour and flavour whilst cooking chicken. Marinade, herbs, spices and vegetables added to cooked chicken mixture. Simmer gently to develop flavour. Basmati rice cooked in boiling water to soften starch granules. Drained in colander and reserved rice. Assembled chicken curry product with rice and garnish.

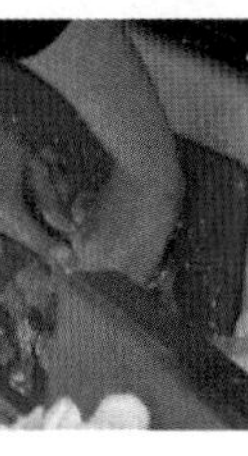

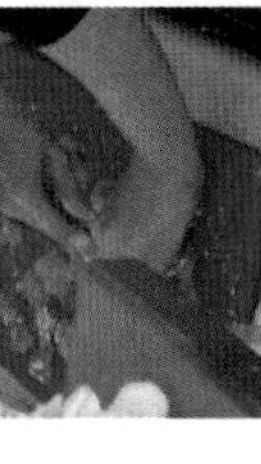

Tools and equipment: Chopping board, sharp and round bladed knives, wooden spoon, measuring equipment: spoons: tbsp, tsp, dsp; jug, weighing scales, variety of sized saucepans for cooking, poaching, steaming and frying: wok, frying pan. Mixing bowls for marinating, mixing and combining ingredients. Fork and grater, colander for draining wet ingredients, sieve for aerating dry ingredients, rolling pin and flour dredger, serving containers, baking tray and cutters for shaping and baking.

Student exemplar: Quality of manufacture

Moderator comment

The student has clearly documented the main stages in the manufacture of the 'range of savoury food products'. The photographs are presented in sequence, with annotations explaining each making stage, which makes it easy for a moderator to see how much work has gone into making these food products. The understanding of these processes is evident in the annotations, with references to skills and techniques, tools and equipment.

ResultsPlus Watch out!

Within the food industry, risk assessment methods ensure that food operations are designed to be safe by taking potential hazards into account. HACCP is a risk assessment used in the food industry.

ResultsPlus Watch out!

If you are following separate Design and Make activities, you will design and make different food products for each task. If you are following the combined Design and Make activities, your design work will follow straight into your make work. You will need to demonstrate a good range of different practical skills in these tasks for both modes of delivery.

Quality of outcome

Objectives

- **Produce** high quality dishes that are accurately assembled and well finished to produce a high-quality product overall
- **Produce** a complete 'range of products' (more than two) that is fully functional as a 'range of products'
- **Demonstrate** high-level safety awareness throughout all stages of manufacture

To get top marks you need to:
Make your 'range of food products' (more than two) to a high standard.
Ensure that each component of each food product is well finished.
Assemble all your component parts together accurately.
Produce a 'complete range of food products' that are fully functional, fit for purpose and meet the requirements of the design brief and design criteria, **with photographic evidence**.

ResultsPlus
Watch out!

In Food Technology, 'fully functional' means that it is fit for the purpose intended and meets the requirements of the Design/Make brief and Design/Make specification.

If you are taking the combined Design and Make tasks, the design criteria that you use in the Make Task might be the original specification points from the Design Task. If you are doing a separate Make Task, you will need to make sure that you have a brief and manufacturing specification as your starting point. Your teacher will be able to help you with this.

A manufacturing specification is a detailed list of criteria that your range of products must fulfill. It will include technical, measurable and realistic points which you can use to test and evaluate your products.

Remember that 12 out of the 36 marks available for your Make Task are for 'quality of outcome' rather than 'quality of manufacture' (worth 24 marks). It is the actual quality of your final 'range of food products' that is being assessed here. This will include the manufacture of all the different component parts, assembling these parts together and your final finished range of products. Your range should be fit for the purpose and should meet the requirements of your Make specification.

Your coursework folder will be marked and sent to Edexcel for moderation, but your actual final range of food products will not. Therefore you must make sure that you have a good selection of photographs of your range of food products, so that the moderator can see their quality. The food products can be photographed separately, but must include a label with your name and candidate number.

Moderator comment

The text and photos on the right are examples of how to present this section of the coursework. Students need to present a range of food products (at least two). Each food product uses a range of ingredients, components, skills and techniques, tools and equipment. The ingredients have been mixed and combined together to create different component parts. The technical practical skill and quality of finish is good, with pleasing sensory properties that can be judged from the photographic evidence: layering and assembly of different component parts to create a fully functional food product for different design briefs. It is clear that the components have been assembled correctly with care and attention, accuracy and precision.

Examples of 'Quality of Outcame'

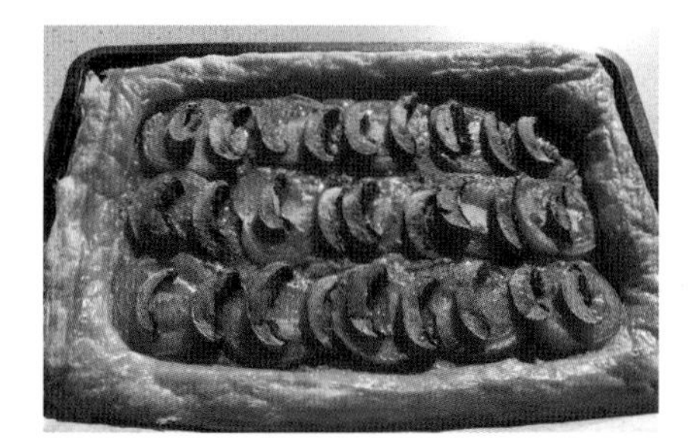

Flaky pastry Mediterranean tart for a vegetarian picnic hamper design brief

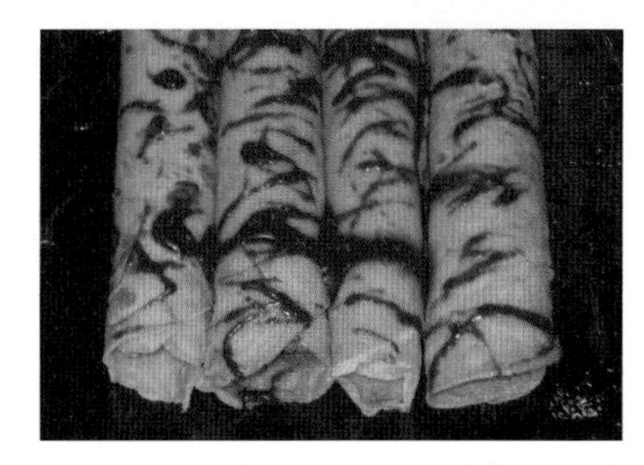

Pancakes with orange and ginger fruit compote and chocolate sauce for celebration dessert design brief

Garlic cheese filled choux buns with poached chicken breast and hollandaise sauce for a luxury celebration range of savoury main meals

Chocolate torte with vanilla cream for a multicultural range of dessert products

French patisserie pastry with crème anglaise, seasonal fruit and fruit glaze for celebration dessert range of products

Short crust pastry with sautéed vegetables in a savoury roux sauce Pastry baked blind prior to assembly to improve sensory properties of food product

- Your teacher will award marks for health and safety, based upon their observations of you during the Make activities. You do not need to record risk assessments during your Make activities.

Health and Safety

To get top marks you need to:
Take into account the risk assessment of relevant tools and equipment prior to using them.
Follow teacher instructions carefully when using tools and equipment.
Use tools and equipment with great care and attention.

Test and evaluate

Objectives

- **Devise** and carry out a range of suitable tests to check the performance and quality of the final range of products
- **Evaluate** your final range of products objectively with reference to the specification points, user group feedback and sustainability issues

To get top marks you need to:
Test your final range of products against your specification.
Write a balanced evaluation, including both positive and negative aspects of your final range of food products.
Obtain feedback from your user group regarding quality and performance issues. Include relevant sustainability issues in your evaluation.

Control

- Obtain user group feedback outside the classroom and bring your findings into class.
- Write up your testing and evaluation in the classroom.
- Your teacher can provide you with feedback to make sure that you have sufficiently tested and evaluated your final range of products.

Testing

Once you have completed making your final products, you are ready to test them against your specification to ensure that they are fit for purpose. Quantitative information is easy to test because dimensions, weight and form have measurable information that determine success. For example: weight of final product 100-125g. If the weight of the product is within this range, then it has achieved this purpose. Other specification points will require you to devise tests about the specific characteristics of a food product or views of the user group: storage life, nutritional analysis, transportation of food, survey, sensory testing.

Test questions

Start by writing out your specification points and using them as questions. For example:

Specification point: Must be an easy-to-eat individual portion of luxury dessert.

Question: How was my individual portion easy to eat?

Consider the components you used to make your product and what you did to ensure that it was easy to eat. This might include comments regarding the structure of the product and how a filling is held inside an outer layer to minimise breakage or waste. This answer is directly related to the performance of food components and the quality of manufacture. A user group tasting panel could also confirm this.

Specification point: Will have a shelf life of up to three days, when stored in a fridge.

Question: Does my product have a shelf life of three days when stored in a fridge?

It is not sufficient to say 'yes' to this question without further detail. You might decide that your knowledge of high risk foods and the date mark system allows you to make a judgement about the storage life of the food product. Or you will need to test this specification point by conducting a storage test of your product and photographing the results after three days storage in a fridge. At this point it would not be appropriate to test taste for results!

Evaluation

Evaluation is an on-going process that must be evident throughout the Design and Make tasks. The final evaluation considers all these comments and offers a truthful opinion of the final products. By discussing the positive and negative aspects of your products, your evaluation will be well-balanced (objective). By uncovering weaknesses, you open up new areas for development if the design were to be taken further. This is the work of a designer – to discover product weaknesses and solve problems!

Celebrate and highlight the many positive aspects of your project as well. Explain why things went well, and what you are most proud of, to demonstrate your knowledge, skills and understanding.

Sustainability

Relevant sustainability issues must also be addressed in order to access the highest marks. Include issues throughout the manufacture of your food products. For example: seasonality of ingredients, origin and source of food, food miles, carbon footprint, transportation issues. This topic is explored in greater detail on page 126.

Test and Evaluate

Make Task: To make a range of savoury products that are: visually striking, 150-200g in weight per portion, good range of flavours and textures, with a shelf life of three days.

Test 1: I am going to use sensory testing to consider texture, flavour, aroma and appearance. By using a rating chart with sensory descriptors that are used in my specification, I can see whether my food products have met the requirements of my specification. I am going to ask 3 people from my user group to taste and evaluate my food products. They will have to rate each food product on a scale of 0-5. 0 = not very good. 5 = very good.

	Fish Pie	Savoury Quiche	Chicken Curry
Tester 1	4/5 Delicious layers with good flavour and texture.	5/5 Crumbly rich pastry with light tasty filling.	4/5 Tasty curry sauce with soft chicken and rice.
Tester 2	5/5 Crunchy topping with soft layers inside the pie.	3/5 Well seasoned savoury custard with crumbly pastry.	3/5 Soft textures with rice and chicken. Needs more texture.
Tester 3	5/5 Delicious, rich sauce and tasty fish and potato layers.	4/5 Individual portions are great with good proportions of pastry and filling.	4/5 Spicy soft curry with nutty rice.

I can see that my user group thought the fish pie was the best product because the ratings were high. The combination of layers and textures helped to give the pie a good range of flavours. I am pleased I put the wilted spinach into the pie because this gave it good colour compared to the creamy whiteness of the other ingredients. The wilted spinach was not too watery because of the steaming prior to assembling the pie. However, this will have reduced the vitamin C content. I am pleased I added this ingredient also because it adds a strong colour and flavour to the food product. The chicken curry needed an additional texture to improve the dish. I would consider making naan bread as an accompaniment to this dish or serve poppadoms to give some crunchy texture to the dish. Alternatively, I could consider baking the chicken with the marinade to give it a tikka style flavour with more chewiness. However, I did not want my meat to dry out, which is why I chose to sauté the meat in oil in a frying pan. The mini quiches were visually striking and skilful food products to make. I was worried that the pastry cases might leak, so I lined my flan rings carefully and baked the pastry blind prior to assembling the filling. This helped to improve the texture of the dish, with a crumbly base and soft tasty filling.

Test 2: My food products must weigh between 150-200g per portion.

The total weight of each of my products divided between the number of portions shows that the fish pie and chicken curry met this specification point. However, the mini quiches did not because they were out by 32g! I think this would be acceptable because manufacturers work to tolerances with the average weight system and this would be within their critical tolerance. I could add more vegetables or bacon to my quiches or make the pastry thicker, but this would affect the overall results of my tasting and I am happy to keep the portion size at 118g because the feedback from my user group tells me that the combination of pastry and filling is just right.

Fish pie (serves 8)	Mini savoury quiche (serves 5)	Chicken curry (serves 2)
500g potatoes	200g plain flour	50g Basmati rice
50ml milk	50g white fat	75g diced chicken breast
25g butter	50g butter	5g oil
500g fresh white fish	3 eggs	Curry powder, cumin, coriander, black pepper
200g spinach	100ml milk	2 tomatoes
25g butter	50g cheese	100ml yoghurt
25g plain flour	100g seasonal vegetables	50g chick peas
150ml milk		
75g parmesan cheese		
1549g	589g	350g
193g per portion	118g per portion	175g per portion

The sustainability issues that I have addressed during the manufacture of my products include the purchase of white fish from a supermarket that promotes careful fishing management to prevent fish stocks becoming too low, free-range eggs that are produced from outdoor reared chickens and non intensively farmed, chicken breasts that are sourced from UK farms, to reduce food miles and to support local farmers and finally seasonal vegetables in my mini quiches which are available in cheap and plentiful supply in the summer.

Sample from student exemplar: Test and evaluate

ResultsPlus
Watch out!

- You do not need to make any suggestions for further improvement.

Moderator comment

This student has followed separate Design and Make activities and therefore has a manufacturing specification for the Make task. The two tests displayed on this A3 page are justified, with good explanation linked to choice and suitability. The sustainability issues are relevant and appropriate for the three food products and it is clear that, with a well balanced discussion, the student has applied knowledge and understanding from Unit 2 to this section.

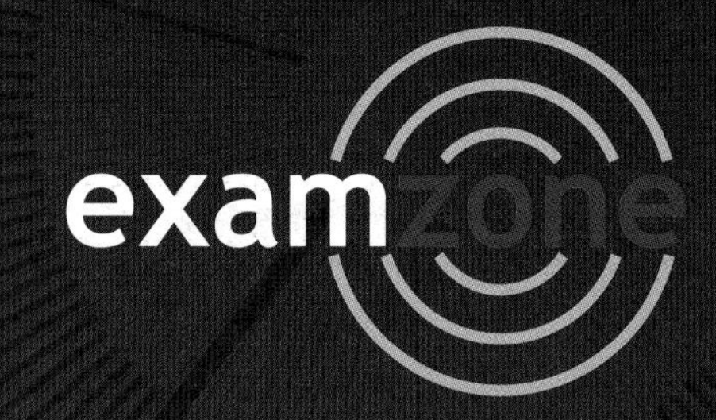

Welcome to ExamZone! Revising for your exams can be a daunting prospect. In this section of the book we'll take you through the best way of revising for your exams, step-by-step, to ensure you get the best results that you can achieve.

Zone In!

Well done, you have finished your exam. So, what now? This section provides answers to the most common questions students have about what happens after they complete their exams.

UNDERSTAND IT

Understand the exam process and what revision you need to do. This will give you confidence but also help you to put things into proportion. These pages are a good place to find some starting pointers for performing well at exams.

DEAL WITH DISTRACTIONS

Think about the issues in your life that may interfere with revision. Write them all down. Think about how you can deal with each so they don't affect your revision. For example, revise in a room without a television, but plan breaks in your revision so that you can watch your favourite programmes. Be really honest with yourself about this – lots of students confuse time spent in their room with time revising. It's not at all the same thing if you've taken a look at Facebook every few minutes or taken mini-breaks to send that vital text message.

GET ORGANISED

If your notes, papers and books are in a mess you will find it difficult to start your revision. It is well worth spending a day organising your file notes with section dividers and ensuring that everything is in the right place. When you have a neat set of papers, turn your attention to organising your revision location. If this is your bedroom, make sure that you have a clean and organised area to revise in.

BUILD CONFIDENCE

Use your revision time, not just to revise the information you need to know, but also to practise the skills you need for the examination. Try answering questions in timed conditions so that you're more prepared for writing answers in the exam. The more prepared you are, the more confident you will feel on exam day.

FRIENDS AND FAMILY

Make sure that they know when you want to revise and even share your revision plan with them. Help them to understand that you must not get distracted. Set aside quality time with them, when you aren't revising or worrying about what you should be doing.

KEEP HEALTHY

During revision and exam time, make sure you eat well and exercise, and get enough sleep. If your body is not in the right state, your mind won't be either – and staying up late to cram the night before the exam is likely to leave you too tired to do your best.

Planning Zone

The key to success in exams and revision often lies in the right planning. Knowing what you need to do and when you need to do it is your best path to a stress-free experience. Here are some top tips in creating a great personal revision plan:

JUNE

1. Know when your exam is

Find out your exam dates. Go to www.edexcel.com/iwantto/Pages/dates.aspx to find all final exam dates, and check with your teacher. This will enable you to start planning your revision with the end date in mind.

2. Know your strengths and weaknesses

At the end of the chapter that you are studying, complete the 'You should know' checklist. Highlight the areas that you feel less confident on and allocate extra time to spend revising them.

3. Personalise your revision

This will help you to plan your personal revision effectively by putting a little more time into your weaker areas. Use your mock examination results and/or any further tests that are available to you as a check on your self-assessment.

4. Set your goals

Once you know your areas of strength and weakness you will be ready to set your daily and weekly goals.

5. Divide up your time and plan ahead

Draw up a calendar, or list all the dates, from when you can start your revision through to your exams.

6. Know what you're doing

Break your revision down into smaller sections. This will make it more manageable and less daunting. You might do this by referring to the Edexcel GCSE Food Technology specification, or by the chapter objectives, or by headings within the chapter.

7. Link it together

Also make time for considering how topics interrelate. For example, when you are revising the design process for the Unit 1 controlled assessment, it would be sensible to cross-reference with other parts of your work. Chapter 5 Analysing products can be directly linked to the research that you conducted at the start of your controlled assessment project. This is linked to the product analysis question on the exam paper. You could draw up a mind-map of the design process and your controlled assessment, showing how and where they link together.

8. Break it up

Revise one small selection at a time, but ensure you give more time to topics that you have identified weaknesses in.

9. Be realistic

Be realistic in how much time you can devote to your revision, but also make sure you put in enough time. Give yourself regular breaks or different activities to give your life some variety. Revision need not be a prison sentence!

10. Check your progress

Make sure you allow time for assessing progress against your initial self-assessment. Measuring progress will allow you to see and celebrate your improvement, and these little victories will build your confidence for the final exam.

Finally – stick to your plan!

Know Zone

Remember that different people learn in different ways – some remember visually and therefore might want to think about using diagrams and other drawings for their revision, whereas others remember better through sound or through writing things out. Think about what works best for you by trying out some of the techniques below.

REVISION TECHNIQUES

Highlighting: work through your notes and highlight the important terms, ideas and explanations so that you start to filter out what you need to revise.

Key terms: look at the key terms highlighted in **blue/bold** in each chapter. Try to write down a concise definition for this term. Now check your definition against the glossary definition on page 184.

Summaries: writing a summary of the information in a chapter can be a useful way of making sure you've understood it. But don't just copy it all out. Try to reduce each paragraph to a couple of sentences. Then try to reduce the couple of sentences to a few words!

Concept maps: if you're a visual learner, you may find it easier to take in information by representing it visually. Draw mind maps or other diagrams. These are particularly good at showing links. For example, you could create a concept map which shows how to learn about sustainability.

Raw material extraction → Material production → Production of parts → Assembly → Use → Disposal/recycling

Mnemonics: this is when you take the first letter of a series of words you want to remember and then make a new word or sentence. An example of this is Controlled Atmosphere Packaging - or CAP!

Index cards: Write important events, definitions and processes on index cards and then test yourself.

Quizzes: Learning facts can be dull. Why not make a quiz out of it? Set a friend 20 questions to answer. Make up multiple-choice questions. You might even make up your own exam questions and see if your friend can answer them!

And then when you are ready:

Practice questions: go back through all the ResultsPlus features with questions to see if you can answer them (without cheating!). Try writing out some of your answers in timed conditions so that you're used to the amount of time you'll have to answer each type of question in the exam. Then, check the guidance for each one and try to mark your answer.

Use the list below to find all the ResultsPlus questions.

Chapter 1: p11, 13, 15, 17, 21, 22, 25, 29 and 31

Chapter 2: p35, 36, 39, 43, 46, 49, 50, 55 and 59

Chapter 3: p63, 71, 72, 73, 77, 81, 83, 88, 92, 94, 100 and 103

Chapter 4: p107, 108, 111, 118, 119, 121, 122, 125, 128, 130, 134, 135, 137 and 139

Don't Panic Zone

Once you have completed the revision in your plan, you'll be coming closer and closer to the big day. Many students find this the most stressful time and tend to go into panic-mode, either working long hours without really giving their brain a chance to absorb information, or giving up and staring blankly at the wall. Follow these tips to ensure that you don't panic at the last minute.

TOP TIPS

1. Test yourself by relating your knowledge to food and nutrition issues that arise in the news – can you explain what is happening in these issues and why?
2. Look over past exam papers and their mark schemes. Look carefully at what the mark schemes are expecting of candidates in relation to the question.
3. Do as many practice questions as you can to improve your technique, help manage your time and build confidence in dealing with different questions.
4. Write down a handful of the most difficult bits of information for each chapter that you have studied. At the last minute focus on learning these.
5. Relax the night before your exam – last-minute revision for several hours rarely has much additional benefit. Your brain needs to be rested and relaxed to perform at its best.
6. Remember the purpose of the exam – it's for you to show the examiner what you have learnt.

LAST MINUTE LEARNING TIPS

- Tell your teacher of any problem areas and ask them to give you some past paper questions to do on them. Use the Student Book to help you if you need to. Then get a copy of the mark scheme so that you can see what the examiner was looking for. Go over the problem areas and answer past paper questions on them, then look at the answers to these questions too.

ASSESSMENT OBJECTIVES

The questions that you will be asked are designed to examine the following aspects of Food Technology (Assessment Objectives).

AO1	Recall, select and communicate knowledge and understanding in design and technology including its wider effects.
AO2	Apply knowledge, understanding and skills in a variety of contexts and in designing and making products.
AO3	Analyse and evaluate products, including their design and production.

TYPES OF QUESTION YOU CAN EXPECT

The examination papers are designed so that the opening part of each question is the easiest part. The difficulty becomes progressively harder as you move through the question. The level of difficulty is controlled by the command word and content required in your answer. The exam papers have questions which have more 'scaffolding' (helping you to structure and develop your answer) to make these papers more accessible.

There are four different types of question:

- Multiple-choice questions where you select the correct response from a choice of four.
- Structured short-answer questions which ask you to give/describe/explain your responses.
- A design question where you will have to respond to a given brief.
- Extended-writing questions where you will have to evaluate/discuss/compare with longer responses.

UNDERSTANDING THE LANGUAGE

It is vital that you know what 'command' words ask you to do.

Common errors are: confusing describe with *explain*, and adding explanation when you are only asked to *describe*.

Command word	Marks awarded	Description
Give/State/Name	(1 mark)	These types of question will usually appear at the beginning of the paper or question part and are designed to ease students into the question with a simple statement or short phrase.
Describe/Outline	(2+ marks)	These types of question are quite straightforward. They ask students to simply describe something in detail. Some questions may also ask students to use notes and sketches, therefore they can gain marks with the use of a clearly labelled sketch.
Explain/Justify	(2+ marks)	These types of question will be commonplace in this exam. They are asking students to respond in detail to the question – no short phrases will be acceptable here. Instead, students will have to make a valid point and justify it.
Evaluate/Discuss/Compare	(4+ marks)	These types of question will appear towards the end of the paper and are designed to stretch and challenge the more able students. They will always be worth the highest marks because they require students to make a well-balanced argument, usually involving both advantages and disadvantages.

Identify/State/Name...	Name an ingredient, component, food, nutrient, process or technique.
Complete...	Finish off a task that has already been partly done.
Describe...	Give the main characteristics of a topic or issue.
Explain/Justify...	Give reasons why something is as it is.
Examine...	Describe something with some detail.
Outline...	Give the main features of something.
Define...	Say what something means.
Suggest/Give reasons...	Say why something might have happened or occurred.
Comment on...	Give some reasons why or how something is as it is.
Compare/Discuss/ Evaluate...	Give advantages and disadvantages for a well-balanced argument.

Your exam paper will be marked using an online system of marking, where your exam paper is scanned into the computer and marked by a number of different examiners. It is important that you write legibly and clearly in the spaces provided for your answers. For the design question, do not use coloured pencils or pens. Good, relevant annotated labelling will be rewarded with good marks for this question!

Pay attention to any text highlighted in bold. It is highlighted to alert you to important information, so be sure to read it and take note!

11 (a) The table below shows some tools and equipment.

Complete the table below by giving the missing names and uses: (4)

Tools/Equipment	Name	Use
	Rolling pin	
	Scales	
		To scrape mixture from bottom of mixing bowl
		To drain vegetables

(b) Sugar is one of the basic ingredients used when making sweet baked goods.

(i) Name **one** type of sugar that can be used in cake production. (1)

(ii) Give the functional use of sugar in the diet. (1)

(iii) Give **two** reasons for using sugar in a cake recipe. (2)

1 ....

2 ....

Edexcel GCSE in Design and Technology: Food Technology   Sample Assessment Materials   © Edexcel Limited 2008   17

Read the instructions each time – they are there to provide guidance.

The marks for each question are shown on the right-hand side of the page. Make sure that you note how many marks a question is worth as this will give you an idea of how long to spend on that question.

Zone Out

Food Technology links to all other subjects of the curriculum, so a GCSE in Food Technology is a stepping stone to a whole range of opportunities. A good grade will help you move on to further study. You may want to continue your study of Food Technology or take a course such as a BTEC or GNVQ with a more work-related approach.

The skills that you develop can lead you into: the food industry, catering, product development, teaching, nursing and medicine, retail, food safety, environmental health, scientific research, child care, farming and agriculture, advertising and media, food photography and styling, travel and tourism, journalism, ICT and many other careers.

Food Technologists are everywhere!

A

accelerated freeze drying (AFD) a process where food is quickly frozen and then placed in a vacuum under reduced pressure, which vaporises the ice, turning it to steam and leaving the food dry

aeration when raising agents are added to cake and bread mixtures to give lightness to a food product

agitation stirring something up

alginates substances extracted from brown seaweed that can thicken solutions, form gels and thin films

allergies where the skin itches and develops a rash, together with more serious symptoms such as severe stomach cramp, fever, nausea, swelling of the tongue and trachea (windpipe)

alternative energy sources non-conventional ways of getting energy, such as wind, solar or tidal power

amino acid a small unit that combines to form protein

anaemia iron deficiency due to insufficient oxygen being carried around the body by haemoglobin, causing extreme fatigue, paleness, weakness, poor health

antioxidants prevent rancidity in foods with a high fat content

artificial additive created in a laboratory, are either artificial copies of natural ingredients or completely new chemical substances that can also give additional quality to processed foods

aspartame naturally occurring low-calorie substances, many hundred times sweeter than sugar

aspiration a cleaning technique, using air blasts to remove lighter particles from food

attribute a quality or feature that is characteristic of something

automated done by machinery, usually controlled by computer

B

bacteria microscopic organisms, which may be useful or harmful

ball disc rotating plates or balls with rods and pins used in size reduction to break the product

Basic Metabolic Rate (BMR) the number of kilocalories you use to stay alive each day

batch an amount or quantity produced during one production or processing

batch production method used for producing fixed quantities of identical items

beriberi a condition of the nervous system, caused by a lack of thiamin

'best before' date recommended date by which to eat low-risk foods (crisps, biscuits or foods that have undergone processing treatments to extend their shelf life e.g. UHT milk); after this date, the sensory characteristics (taste, flavour, colour, smell, texture) of the food will deteriorate

binding using the coagulation of proteins to mix and hold ingredients together

biodegradable something that naturally decays and breaks down over time

biotechnology technology based on science, biology, medicine, agriculture and food to genetically engineer biological systems or living organisms to make or modify products or processes for specific uses

blanching a short heat treatment using water or steam; carried out on vegetables before canning, freezing or drying to inactivate enzymes and to shrink the product

British Standards Institute an organisation that produces exacting standards for management systems, including quality, environmental, information security, integrated management and occupational health and safety

broiler chicken a chicken reared for meat rather than eggs, genetically selected for fast growth, and slaughtered when only 6 or 7 weeks old

bulk ingredients or food products purchased in large quantities to reduce the unit cost of the product

bulk sweeteners sorbitol and sucralose have similar levels of sweetness to sugar, but an unpleasant aftertaste. They retain the bulk/weight/composition needed in some recipes to aid mixing and combining of ingredients

C

canning when food is packed in cans and sterilised or sterilised and then packed in aseptic (sterilised) cans

caramelisation when sugar (crystal or syrup) is heated and decomposes to produce a range of brown products

carbohydrate a macronutrient consisting of the elements carbon, hydrogen and oxygen

carbon footprint a measurement of all the greenhouse gases we individually produce through the burning of fossil fuels for electricity, transport, food production etc, expressed as tonnes or kg of carbon dioxide equivalent

carboxymethyl cellulose (CMC) a cellulose used as a stabiliser to prevent oil or water separation

carrageenan extract from seaweed that can react with milk proteins to make a gel

celebration food created for special occasions, such as festivals or birthdays

celluloses substances found naturally in foods as dietary fibre that can be modified to make them easier to use

cereals cultivated for the edible components of their seeds (grains)

chemical energy needed for chemical reactions in the body, such as respiration

chilling using low temperature (1-8°C, ideally 4°C) to slow down enzyme action and reduce microbial growth

cholesterol a natural fat manufactured in the liver and transported by the blood around our bodies

chymosin an enzyme found in rennet that reacts with milk to produce curds and whey in cheese-making

clean labels reducing the use of artificial additives by using natural substances to restore, enhance or improve the functional characteristics of food

climacteric ripening rapidly and quick to deteriorate after harvesting

coagulate set, gel

coating forming a protective layer around foods, using other foods

coeliac disease an autoimmune disease, where the body's immune system attacks its own tissues, triggered by gluten

collagen a soluble protein found around muscle bundles, forming a layer of connective tissue

combining blending a range of ingredients together to form a uniform mix

complementary proteins mixes of protein that contain all the essential amino acids that the body needs, created by combining LBV foods

composite food a food made of different component parts

computer-aided design (CAD) used to create, modify and communicate design intentions

computer-aided manufacture (CAM) the monitoring and controlling of the automatic production of food products based on set specifications and tolerances

computer-integrated manufacture (CIM) process where computers linked in a network automatically adjust both the machinery and the flow of information at critical manufacturing points

conduction where heat energy passes through molecules in vibrations

constituent an ingredient, something that goes to make up something else

contamination infection of food that may occur due to natural decay, microorganisms or enzyme action

continuous drum screen a commercial machine used in the food industry to separate contaminants from food

controlled atmosphere packaging (CAP) where the atmosphere inside is altered by decreasing oxygen and increasing carbon dioxide or nitrogen levels

controls (within systems) automatic adjustments made to such things as weight of ingredients, rate at which a mixture or ingredients flow through a system

convection transfer of heat that takes place in gases and liquids as molecules are heated, they expand and become lighter - hot air rises and cool, heavy air sinks to replace the hot air

convenience foods more prepared, pre-packed, processed and added value lines for immediate consumption at once or after microwaving, to reduce the preparation, cooking and clearing away time

coronary heart disease (CHD) build up of fatty deposits in the arteries, causing a restriction in the blood flow, leading to stroke, heart attack or death

criteria principles or standards by which something is judged

critical control point at which a control measure may need to be taken to prevent harm, can be at any stage in food production

cross-contamination when food has been infected with harmful microorganisms and is therefore not safe to eat, via food, the handler, pests, rodents, equipment or pets

cross knives special knives used to dice food

cryogenic freezing using liquid gases (CO_2 or nitrogen) at very low temperatures

culture the shared customs, traditions and beliefs of a large group of people, such as a nation, race or religious group; the way people live, work and spend their leisure time; their beliefs, aspirations and how they interact with each other

D

danger zone temperature ranges within which multiplication of pathogenic bacteria is possible (5-63°C)

date mark a 'use by' or 'best before' mark that food labels must carry to show the storage life of a food product

demixing where the blend of ingredients to form a product becomes less uniform than it was in the first stages of the preparation process

denature make irreversible changes to the chemical structure of a substance

design brief set of instructions for a design task, including purpose, target audience, etc

detergents products that remove dirt, grime and dissolve grease

dextrinisation the browning of food containing starch with dry heat

diabetes mellitus an illness where production of the hormone insulin in the body is ineffective at controlling the blood sugar level

dietary reference values (DRVs) a series of estimates of the amount of energy and nutrients needed by different groups of healthy people in the UK population (includes EARs and RNIs)

dimensions limits set to aspects of a product (e.g. size, shape, consistency, finishing processes, thickness) to ensure consistent quality

disaccharide a double sugar, made up of two monosaccharide units, such as sucrose, maltose and lactose

disassembly taking something to pieces, breaking something down into its component parts or ingredients

disc mill mill using rotating discs with studs to break the product; used in the grinding process

disinfectants products that reduce levels of bacteria

'display until' date used by the food retailer to inform stock rotation as a critical control point

diverticular disease distortion and inflammation of the digestive tract

dry cleaning separating contamination from food without using water, as in sieving or screening

duo-trio test where three samples are presented to the taster: one labelled as a reference sample and the other two made up of another reference sample and a different sample

E

E number E in front of a number means that the additive has been passed as safe by the European Community

Eatwell Plate shows balance of foods based on the Government's eight guidelines for a healthy diet

electrical energy energy used by the nervous system

emulsification the mixing of water and oils to remain mixed together in an emulsion

energy balance the relationship between food and drink intake and physical activity

enriching adding additional protein and fat to a recipe

essential fatty acids cannot be made in the body, but are vital for the health and function of the body

Estimated Average Requirements (EARs) average estimate of the requirement for energy for a group of people

extraction rate the percentage of the whole grain that is used in flour

extrinsic sugars visible, processed sugars used in food manufacture

F

factory farming intensive farming, especially of animals

Fairtrade a system of trade, and a consumer and industry movement, that aims to achieve better prices, decent working conditions, local sustainability, and fairer terms of trade for farmers and workers in the developing world

farmers' markets local markets run by farmers and food growers from the local area

fat a macronutrient composed of the elements carbon, hydrogen and oxygen

fat soluble vitamins can dissolve in fat and can be stored in minute quantities in the body

fermentation the series of chemical reactions that take place when yeast in a food product is given suitable conditions for growth

fertilisers chemicals added to the soil to promote plant growth

fibre a simple polysaccharide found in plant foods

flotation washing a mechanical system used to push food through a number of different compartments or weirs and forcing the food under the water by slowly rotating paddles

food components individual ingredients within a more processed product

food hygiene a process of working cleanly and hygienically to make sure the food is safe to eat after preparation, cooking and storage

food miles the distance food is transported from the time of its production until it reaches the consumer

food poisoning illness caused by bacteria, chemicals or poisons in food

food probe a thermometer that can be inserted into food to check the internal temperature of food

fortification improves the nutritional content of foods to ensure that minimum dietary requirements are met

fossil fuels oil, coal and gas

free-range animals that live in open spaces on a farm, rather than in confined sheds

freezer star rating number of stars found on the packaging of all frozen food, indicating temperature range and storage life needed to maintain quality

functional foods foods with specific health-promoting or disease-preventing properties beyond the basic function of supplying nutrients

functionality how fit for purpose a product is

G

gas flushing where the atmosphere in a package is altered to extend the shelf life of perishable foods, while maintaining or improving the quality

gel when starch is moistened and heated, it thickens into a gel

gelatinisation (gelation) the thickening properties of starch, with moist heat, to create a viscous product

gelling agents increase the viscosity (thickness) of a mixture

genetic modification (GM) altering the genetic make-up of a substance such as food crops to achieve specific characteristics

glazing improving the appearance of a food product by making it shiny/glossy

glycemic index (GI) describes this difference by ranking carbohydrates according to their effect on our blood glucose levels

good manufacturing practice (GMP) an all-embracing management operation that ensures food products are manufactured to consistent quality standards

grazing eating food on the move and/or at frequent intervals

greenhouse gases water vapour, carbon dioxide, ozone, methane and nitrous oxide - gases in an atmosphere that absorb and emit radiation and can greatly affect the temperature of the Earth

H

hammer mill where fragile material is shattered into small fragments; used in the grinding process

hazard anything that may cause harm to a consumer

heat energy produced when your body breaks down the chemicals from the food you eat

hedonic scale where tasters place food in order of preference

hermetically sealed where plastic is fused together using heat to form a strong seal

high biological value (HBV) foods containing all the essential amino acids

high-risk foods with a high protein and moisture content that could lead to food poisoning: examples include raw and cooked meat, poultry and fish, cheese, milk and dairy products, eggs and cooked rice

high-volume production method used to produce a large number of identical products for a mass market

homogenisation a mixing process, used with emulsification, whereby particle size is reduced to aid dispersal and uniform mixing

hydrogenation the chemical reaction that results from the addition of hydrogen (H_2) to unsaturated fat, changing it from liquid to a soft/semi-hard state, from unsaturated to saturated fats

hydrolytic rancidity when, in the presence of water, butter, cream and margarine are attacked by enzymes which alter the chemical structure of these foods, resulting in intense odours

I

immersion freezing using liquids

immiscible unable to be mixed together, e.g. oil and water

insoluble fibre found in the outer skins of fruit and vegetables, cereals and whole grain food products

intense sweeteners aspartame and saccharin are very low in energy but difficult to use in food preparation due to the lack of bulk needed in some recipes

International Quality System sets standards against which a company's quality system can be compared; companies are checked, tested and monitored by inspectors

intrinsic sugars invisible sugars found naturally in the cells of fruits and vegetables

K

kilocalories units of energy

kilojoules units of energy

kwashiorkor a protein energy malnutrition disease

L

lacto vegetarian eats dairy products but not eggs

lactose intolerance the body's inability to break down and use lactose, a sugar found in milk and other dairy products

leaching loss of water-soluble vitamins, colour, flavour or taste of foods during moist methods of cooking

lecithin substance found in egg yolk that can be used to stabilise two liquids (oil and water) to prevent separation

lipid a term used for fats and oils

low biological value (LBV) foods that are deficient in one or more of the essential amino acids

Lower Reference Nutrient Intake (LRNI) the amount of a nutrient that is enough for a small number of people who have low energy needs

M

macronutrients the main parts of our diet, found in foods and needed by the body in relatively large quantities

Maillard reaction in dry heat, where sugars are mixed with protein in baked products, producing browning and a pleasant, baked aroma

meat analogue a meat substitute or extender that is similar in texture, flavour and appearance to meat

mechanical energy the energy muscles need to perform basic body functions such as heart beat, digestion, movement, etc

mechanical harvesting use of machines to harvest

metabolic rate the rate at which the chemical reactions involved in metabolism take place in the body

metabolism system of chemical reactions that take place in the body to support growth, repair, maintenance and energy of the body

methane powerful greenhouse gas emitted during the production and transport of coal, natural gas and oil, and produced during the decomposition of organic waste (uneaten food) in landfill

microorganisms small organisms responsible for contamination of food; they can be classified into yeasts, moulds and bacteria

micronutrients nutrients found in food and vital to health, but required in very small quantities, such as vitamins and minerals

milling making grain into flour, by separating the endosperm from the rest of the grain

mixing *see combining*

modified atmosphere packaging (MAP) uses a mixture of nitrogen, oxygen and carbon dioxide to prolong the storage life of many different foods, by creating unfavourable conditions for bacterial growth

modified fats altered fat that can be used to stops fats separating by forming fat crystals

modified protein altered food chemicals that can be used together to improve bread dough and reduce staling

modified starch a synthetic or man-made food additive prepared by treating starch, causing it to be partially degraded

monosaccharide a simple sugar, such as glucose, fructose and galactose

monounsaturated fat contains only one pair of carbon atoms with one hydrogen atom

mould a form of fungus

mouthfeel the sensations of touch experienced when food is put in the mouth

myofribrils proteins responsible for the contraction of muscle

myoglobin a protein that carries oxygen to the muscles, giving meat its characteristic colour

N

nanotechnology the manufacture and use of materials and structures at the nanometre scale (a nanometre is one millionth of a millimetre)

natural additive additives found naturally in plant or animal foods, for example colours such as red (beetroot), green (chlorophyll)

natural resources water, oil, minerals, coal

net values weight or volume of just the product, excluding any packaging

neural birth defect defects of the brain and spinal cord that arise before a baby is born

non-climacteric ripening slowly and often improving after harvesting

nut allergy a condition which means that eating nuts can cause anaphylactic shock

nutraceuticals have specific health promoting or disease preventing properties beyond the basic function of supplying nutrients

novelty foods new foods created for specific occasions or eating habits

O

obesity a condition where excess body fat has accumulated to the extent that it may have an adverse effect on health, leading to reduced life expectancy and/or increased health problems

offal the less desirable parts of an animal for eating, such as intestines and internal organs

one-off production when a customer makes an order for something to be made to their own specifications

organic farming a production system that sustains the health of soils, ecosystems and people, relying on ecological processes, biodiversity and cycles adapted to local conditions

organoleptic concerning the sensory properties of a food product - taste, appearance, smell and feel

orthodox strict

osteomalacia a condition in adults where the bones soften, caused by a lack of vitamin D

ovo vegetarian eats eggs but not dairy

oxidative rancidity when, in the presence of oxygen, unsaturated fats are attacked by highly reactive particles called free radicals, producing undesirable odours and a change in colour and texture

P

paired preference test where tasters are given two samples of food and have to indicate which sample they prefer

pasteurisation a process by which pathogenic microorganisms are destroyed

pathogenic bacteria cause disease and illness, such as food poisoning

perishable foods spoil rapidly, usually have a high water content and good nutritional content

permitted additives list additives accepted as safe are placed on this list and reviewed by the European Food Safety Authority

pesticides chemicals used to kill pests: e.g. insects, weeds and microbes

pests insects, animals and rodents that destroy or infect food

physical activity level (PAL) the number of kilocalories you use to fuel all of your physical activity

piping hot food that is hotter than 75°C for two minutes, which is checked using a food probe

pin disc rotating plates or balls with rods and pins used in size reduction to break the product

plant oils oils from nuts or the seeds of cereals, fruit or flowers

plant sterols chemicals that help to block the uptake of cholesterol in the digestive system

plate freezing putting food in contact with a refrigerated plate

pleasure foods treats, indulgence and luxury items packaged and sold to aid convenience, e.g. in store delis, patisserie within supermarkets

polysaccharide simple or complex carbohydrate, formed from hundreds of glucose molecules

polyunsaturated fats contain two or more pairs of carbon atoms, and are therefore capable of holding more hydrogen atoms

prebiotics healthy, non-digestible food ingredients containing non-starch polysaccharide

preservation the process of treating food to prevent natural and microbial decay, by modifying the conditions which favour enzyme activity and the growth of microorganisms

preservatives prevent the spoilage of food by the action of microorganisms to improve the storage life of foods

primary food processing basic treatment of raw food materials to make them suitable for further processing or immediate consumption

primary foods used raw or processed only to make them suitable for either immediate consumption or for further processing

probiotics biocultures containing living, helpful bacteria that help to maintain a healthy digestive system and immune system

profiling test where a taster uses a star diagram to plot the attributes of food, which can then be compared to another taster's results or another product

protein a substance built up of chains of amino acids

Q

quality assurance a guarantee to the customer about the quality standards of a food business

quality control checking the quality of a product during or at the end of production

R

radiation where heat energy passes through space from one point (heat source) to another (food)

raising agents make a product rise, therefore improving its texture

rancidity decomposing and going off

ranking test where tasters rank different samples of food according to particular attributes, e.g. sweetness of apples

rating test where tasters rate food according to its sensory qualities

recipe modification changes to the ingredients, processes and techniques to create a variation of a product to fulfill a consumer's real or perceived needs and wants

reference nutrient intakes (RNIs) estimated amounts of protein, vitamins and minerals needed for 97% of the population (this will be far too much for some people)

respiration the chemical reaction that allows cells to release energy from food

rickets poor bone formation in children, caused by a lack of vitamin D or calcium

risk assessment the process of considering what harm could happen and when it might happen, and then taking preventative action to make sure it does not

rotary cutting knife very sharp knife with a mechanical slicing action

run an amount or quantity produced during one production or processing

S

sanitisers remove dirt, grime and bacteria

satiety a feeling of fullness

saturated fat solid at room temperature, mainly found in food that originates from animals, contains high levels of cholesterol

scale of production the method of production - one-off, batch, high-volume or 'just in time'

screen *see sieve*

scurvy disease caused by lack of Vitamin C in the diet

secondary food processing transforms food materials into food components or composite foods

secondary foods combined or processed to make them into new food products

selective breeding where animals are bred to achieve particular characteristics

'sell by' date used by the food retailer to inform stock rotation as a critical control point

sensory descriptors words created to describe the appearance, odour, flavour, mouthfeel and aftertaste of a food product

sensory profiling test that gives detailed, descriptive evaluation of the range of differences between products

setting agents increase the viscosity (thickness) of a mixture

shortening fat used to coat flour particles to create a flaky, tender texture

sieve pass through a mesh to separate large and small particles from the food, depending on the size of the screen

smart food materials raw ingredients that have one or more properties that can be significantly changed in a controlled fashion by external stimuli, such as agitation, temperature, moisture or pH

soluble fibre found in the flesh of fruit and vegetables, oats, beans and lentils; is partially broken down during digestion to form a gel type substance that can coat the digestive tract. This helps to speed up digestion and coats the intestine to help lower blood cholesterol levels, prevent cancer and other digestive problems

specification a detailed description of a product, includes technical and measurable details, collated from the research and consultation stages of the design process

spoilage food 'going off', due to natural decay, microorganisms or enzyme action

spray drying where a fine spray of the product (milk, eggs, dessert mixes and coffee) is sprayed into a chamber with hot air, allowing the moisture to evaporate and the fine particles of food to be collected in powder form

spray washing a common wet method of cleaning - a small volume of water is pressure-sprayed; the force of the spray cleans and washes the food product as the water runs over it

stabilisers bind and absorb large quantities of water to create gels and thickening properties in jams and emulsions

standard components pre-manufactured components used in the manufacture of commercial and domestic food products

staple crops grown in large quantities to provide basic food energy to populations

sterilisation a process by which foods are heated for a long period of time at very high temperatures

sucralose naturally occurring low-calorie substances, many hundred times sweeter than sugar

suet solid, hard fat made from animal fat

sun drying drying in direct sunlight, allowing moisture to slowly evaporate

sustainability ensuring that the world's natural resources are preserved for future generations

synerisis the separation of liquid from a food product

T

tamper-evident seal show if a product has not been opened

tamperproof seal a safety device used to prevent cross-contamination

technical specification detailed list of measurable points to which a product must conform

test kitchen a small-scale kitchen used in product development for the testing and trialling of food products

thickening agents increase the viscosity (thickness) of a mixture

thixotropic becoming thinner when shaken or stirred, but thickening again on standing

tolerances limits set to aspects of a product (e.g. size, shape, consistency, finishing processes, thickness) to ensure consistent quality

traceability where food can be traced or tracked through the supply chain to the point of production and distribution

trans fatty acids (trans fats) produced when manufacturers add hydrogen to vegetable oils by hydrogenation

triangle test where tasters identify the odd one out from a test of three samples (two are the same, one is different)

toxin poison produced by a pathogen, such as moulds and bacteria

24/7 24 hours a day, 7 days a week

U

ultra heat treatment (UHT) a process treating food using very high temperature

unsaturated fat found in foods originating from plants and oily fish, can be polyunsaturated or monounsaturated

'use by' date the date by which high-risk, perishable foods (raw and cooked meats, chilled foods, dairy products) should be used; after this date, the food may not look or taste different, but it will be unsafe to eat

user requirements the qualities that will make the product attractive to the target user group

V

vegan a strict vegetarian who does not eat any dairy products, eggs or honey

vegetarian someone who does not eat meat

W

water soluble vitamins (C and B complex) dissolve in water, cannot be stored in the body and can be destroyed or lost through preparation, processing and cooking techniques

weirs compartments used in the flotation washing process to retain water and force food under the water using paddles, to remove debris

wet cleaning using clean water to free food from contamination and chemicals

X

xanthan gum produced using biotechnology, where it is produced on the outside of cells of the bacterium *Xanthomonas campestris*

Y

yeast microscopic, single-celled fungus that reproduces and gives off CO_2 in the process called fermentation

Index